The Primitive City of
TIMBUCTOO

HORACE MINER is Professor of Anthropology and Sociology at the University of Michigan. He received his Ph.D. degree in 1937 from the University of Chicago. From 1961 to 1962, he was a visiting professor at Makerere University College in Uganda.

He first went to Africa at the age of sixteen and has been back many times since. In 1940, he crossed the Sahara both ways to study Timbuctoo; in 1942, he landed in Algeria with American troops and subsequently received the Legion of Merit for counterintelligence work in Tunisia; in 1950, he returned to Algeria to conduct research among the Arabs of the Casbah and a Saharan oasis; from 1957 to 1958, he studied a development project among the Hausa in northern Nigeria.

A fellow of the American Anthropological Association, the American Sociological Association, and the African Studies Association, he has been a member of the governing body of the International African Institute and a consultant on indigenous labor for the International Labor Office, Geneva, for the past fifteen years.

In addition to articles in the major professional journals in anthropology and sociology, Horace Miner is the author of *St. Denis, A French-Canadian Parish* and *Culture and Agriculture*, co-author of *Principles of Sociology* and *Oasis and Casbah, Algerian Culture and Personality in Change*, and editor of *Social Science in Action in Sub-Saharan Africa*.

The Primitive City of
TIMBUCTOO

Revised Edition

———

Horace Miner

———

ANCHOR BOOKS
Doubleday & Company, Inc.
Garden City, New York
1965

THE PRIMITIVE CITY OF TIMBUCTOO was originally published for the American Philosophical Society by Princeton University Press in 1953. The Anchor Books revised edition is published by arrangement with Princeton University Press.

Anchor Books edition: 1965

TO AGNES

Foreword to the Anchor Edition

Because time-depth provides perspective, an author must look back to bring into relief the meaning which a new edition can give to an earlier work. When this study first appeared, several books had already been published with "Timbuctoo" titles, yet very little was actually known about that city. Most of the then current knowledge was derived from seventeenth-century Arabic manuscripts and from the accounts of explorers and travelers. Of the three ethnic groups present in Timbuctoo, the Songhoi were little known except for their language, and even its affiliations were a mystery. Although the city had once been the center of Moslem learning in the Sudan and had Moroccan elements in the population, modern Islamic scholars had preferred to study the purer traditions of North Africa. As for the Tuareg, only the outlines of the culture of these veiled men of the desert were known and their sedentary slaves, the Bela, had never been studied at all.

My description of Timbuctoo revealed much of the life of the Songhoi, Arabs, and Bela for the first time. Since then there has been progressive enlightenment concerning this corner of the "Dark Continent." In two scholarly works, Trimingham has traced the events and the results of Islamic penetration of West Africa. Greenberg has discovered the linguistic relationships of Songhoi, and Rouch has described the non-Islamic aspects of Songhoi religion and magic. The definitive work on the Tuareg has now been written by Nicolaisen. Thus the perspective I bring to the new edition of *The Primitive City of Timbuctoo* is based on a surge of knowledge about Africa which is quite as dramatic, in its way, as the surge of independence for Africans has been.

This extension of factual knowledge has been accompanied by an active reconsideration of the concepts and theories which add significance to the facts. Bascom has probed the meaning of urbanization with regard to the populous, but predominantly agricultural, "cities" of the Yoruba. To Redfield's Folk and Urban ideal types, Sjoberg has added those of Feudal Society and its constituent part, the Preindustrial City. In a broader context, the requirements of the new nations have stimulated research on the processes of socio-economic development. The need to understand these phenomena has yet to produce a new theory of urbanization, but the interdependence of urban and economic development is now more clearly seen.

Despite all that has transpired between editions, I have not had to rewrite *Timbuctoo*. As a description of the lifeways of that city in 1940, it required little alteration beyond bringing a few terms into conformity with current usage. Appropriate notations now call attention to the more important recent ethnography. When I shift from description to interpretation, however, the accretion of knowledge has led me to new views and insights and occasional revisions. Finally, there is a short addition to the concluding, interpretive chapter which takes cognizance of the theoretical discussions engendered by the original publication. The new edition thus partakes of the best of two worlds, embracing both the thrill of ethnographic discovery and the satisfaction of finding the meaning of these discoveries in terms of our greater current knowledge.

University of Michigan   H. M.
September, 1964

Preface to the Original Edition

The following pages are based on field research conducted during seven months' residence in Timbuctoo in 1940. In normal times the city is fairly inaccessible. During 1940 the obstacles to travel imposed by submarines, French *Sûreté*, and the Axis Control Commission made the double crossing of the Sahara and the navigation of four hundred miles of the Niger seem like minor obstacles. We had originally planned to remain longer in the French Sudan but after the "phony war" ended with the capitulation of France, we were eventually forced to leave.

The material herein presented was derived through observation, intensive interrogation of six French-speaking native informants, and many interviews with natives through the medium of a French-speaking native interpreter. We did achieve some knowledge of Songhoi, the native Negro language and lingua franca of the city. We did not know the totally unrelated Arabic and Temajegh languages which were also native to large segments of the population. Even though participation in the native life of Timbuctoo could not be achieved, contact with the small French colony was studiously avoided. The result was that while we were never considered citizens of the native city, we were more in the confidence of the natives and had greater entrée into their activities than did the French.

I wish to express my appreciation to those agencies and individuals who not only made the work possible but contributed much to what is worthwhile in this volume. The field work in Africa was done on a post-doctoral field fellowship of the Social Science Research Council. The writing of the report was greatly facilitated by a Demobilization Award granted by the same research council. Dr. Donald Young and Miss Laura Barrett, then both with the Social Science Research Council, were of continuous assistance in major ways and through numerous courtesies. Improvements in the manuscript resulted from suggestions offered by Professors Robert Redfield, Joseph Greenberg and Raphael Patai. I am grateful to the American Philosophical Society, for arranging publication of the manuscript, and to Dr. L. P. Eisenhart for the work which this entailed.

My wife, Dr. Agnes Miner, to whom this volume is dedicated, shared in the discomforts of life in Timbuctoo, took an understanding attitude toward her husband in the throes of writing this book, and throughout contributed greatly of her own time, energy, and ability.

I am indebted to the late Dr. B. Maupoil for his assistance in the French Sudan. I wish also to express my gratitude to Mr. Herbert Wolfe and Monsieur Raymond Rougerie and his family for their consideration and kindness in Algeria. Monsieur Dupuis-Yakouba, who gave up the brotherhood of White Fathers to become a recognized member of Timbuctoo native society, gave me assistance. His grammar and dictionary of the Songhoi language were invaluable. Mr. Floyd Bowman not only helped with many linguistic problems, but he and his family showed us many courtesies and aided materially in pulling me through a severe case of black-water fever.

Portions of the material in the chapter on circumcision and age-sets were previously published in "Songhoi Circumcision," *American Anthropologist*, XLIV, 625–631.

University of Michigan   H. M.
June, 1952

Introduction

The fabulous name of Timbuctoo would appear to many as sufficient justification for a book on the people of that city. For the ethnologist the need for such a study is obvious because of the paucity of our knowledge about that part of the world. Others might focus attention on the results of culture contact in this primitive melting-pot, but the genesis of this research rests on still other grounds. Timbuctoo was studied to provide a picture of primitive urban life.

The following monograph may be read, without the last chapter, purely as an account of the life-ways of a primitive city with all of the problems of acculturation and accommodation which the cultural diversity presents. This introduction outlines the theoretical problem which led to the descriptive study. The final chapter draws inferences from the data with regard to this theory, but an attempt has been made to leave the body of the account as free from such considerations as possible. In this way it is hoped that the data will serve a useful purpose whether or not the reader is interested in, or agrees with, the theoretical conclusions.

Sociologists have long concerned themselves with the distinctive characteristics of the city,[1] but the communities which they have analyzed are all outgrowths of West-

[1] For some of the sociological literature on these subjects, see Bogardus, 1929; Burgess, 1925; Cavan, 1928; Faris, 1931; Mowrer, 1927; Park, Burgess, and McKenzie, 1925; Reckless, 1941; Shaw and McKay, 1942; Thrasher, 1927. (See References at the end of the book for bibliographical information on sources referred to throughout footnotes.)

ern civilization. It would appear to be worthwhile to have comparative data, and to see whether such phenomena as crime, secularization, and group conflict are products of city life *per se* or whether they are the products of our particular type of urban civilization.

While the sociologists have studied the rural-urban contrasts within one culture, anthropologists have been engaged in the analysis of a wide range of small primitive communities. The similarity between certain aspects of primitive and rural cultures and the contrast between these and modern urban society has become increasingly obvious. In primitive and peasant communities, indications of conflict and social disorganization are few. In contrast to the non-traditional and diversified character of our urban society, these cultures are traditional and homogeneous. Sacred values and personal relations dominate people's interrelationships.

These contrasting types of cultural organization have been analyzed by various scholars in somewhat differing frames of reference. But through Tönnies' *Gemeinschaft* and *Gesellschaft,* Durkheim's "social segment" and "social organ," and Redfield's "folk culture" and "urban civilization" runs the same theme.[2] Redfield has this to say in characterizing the folk:

Such a society is small, isolated, nonliterate, and homogeneous, with a strong sense of group solidarity. The ways of living are conventionalized into that coherent system which we call "a culture." Behavior is traditional, spontaneous, uncritical, and personal; there is no legislation or habit of experiment and reflection for intellectual ends. Kinship, its relationships and institutions, are the type categories of experience and the familial group is the unit of action. The sacred prevails over the secular; the economy is one of status rather than of the market.[3]

Modern urban civilization is set up as the other polar type of culture, being typified by a greater preponderance of

[2] Tönnies, 1940; Durkheim, 1915, 1933; Redfield, 1941. Becker, 1950, also.
[3] Redfield, 1947:293.

those traits which are diametrically opposite to the folk characters just enumerated.

In a unique comparative study of these two types of cultures, Redfield analyzed the characteristic differences between urban civilization and the native folk culture of Yucatan through the comparison of a series of Yucatecan communities which showed successively increasing amounts of contact with Euro-American civilization. In this series, the communities were successively larger, size and degree of contact with Western civilization corresponding. The conclusions of the study were that loss of isolation and loss of cultural homogeneity which led to social disorganization were sufficient causes for the development of secularization and individualization.[4]

The complex of traits which characterizes folk culture is observable in such a variety of historically unrelated, isolated cultures that it clearly defines a broad type of social organization. The contrasting type of organization, with its opposite traits, has been observed only in modern urban society. The growth of ancient civilizations has been linked with the development of cities like Troy, Thebes, Athens, and Tenochtitlan. Yet there is a strong suggestion that these civilizations and their cities were characterized by strong traditions, powerful religious systems, and forceful familial organization. One might ask if the secular, impersonal man of our cities, therefore, is not so much an urbanite as the epitome of our particular type of civilization.

The same problem may be posed in a more precise way. The sociologist, Louis Wirth, gives as a minimal definition of the city: "a relatively large, dense, and permanent settlement of socially heterogeneous individuals."[5] Dense concentrations of population arise in two ways. Intensive agriculture has produced such communities notably in Java, China, and in the Guinea coast area south of Timbuctoo. More often such density arises under conditions of cultural specialization and loss of isolation, primarily through trade and commerce. The first type of dense pop-

4 Redfield, 1941:369.
5 Wirth, 1938:8.

ulation is culturally homogeneous; the second, heterogeneous and hence urban. Inherent in the basic definition of
the city, then, are the two conditions—loss of isolation and
loss of homogeneity—which Redfield found to be sufficient
causes for the development of social disorganization, secularization, and individualization. Theoretically, therefore,
these three traits should be found wherever we find the
conditions of urban life.

In the Yucatan study the series of Mexican communities
shows a progressive increase in the amount of contact
with Western civilization. This is paralleled by an increase
in preponderance of characteristics of the city, as just
defined, in the several communities. The increasing prevalence of traits of civilization in the more urban communities can therefore be attributed either to the inherent nature of urban communities or to the peculiar nature of the
Euro-American culture with which the more urban communities have had the most experience.

The same sort of difficulty is encountered in testing folk-
urban theory in any series of urban and rural communities
in the United States. American cities show the characteristics of civilization to the most marked degree, but does
this result from the nature of the city or from the special
nature of our culture? To throw light on this question it
would be desirable to have available a series of descriptions of cities which developed independent of contact
with our particular form of civilization. This volume is an
attempt to provide one such study.

We have accepted Wirth's minimal definition of the city
as quoted above. The setting of our investigation, therefore, requires a large, dense, heterogeneous population
living in a permanent community which developed outside of the flow of Euro-American civilization.[6] In this set-

[6] Junek, 1946, has proposed a culture trait list for Western
civilization. One is struck by the frequent inclusion of the
same traits which many sociologists use in characterizing the
city. The only one of Junek's traits present in Timbuctoo, before the French occupation, was "books." Even this trait
similarity is superficial, as manuscript books, used only by a

ting we are interested in discovering if the society is well-organized, sacred, and personal like the folk societies or if it is disorganized, secular, and impersonal like our urban society.

Let us be clear as to the nature of the qualities. The best evidence of social disorganization is the existence of conflict which can be traced to inconsistencies in the culture patterns or lack of adherence to cultural standards. There is also conflict in well-organized societies, but there it tends to result from competition in terms of a single cultural frame of reference. Young men fighting over the attentions of one girl represent this type. Culture may precisely pattern such conflict, as through duels. In contrast there is the conflict which results from the operation of divergent values in the same culture. Religious denominational strife is a typical example. Such conflict may be inter-individual or intra-individual. In the latter case it is evidenced by personality disorganization resulting from the interiorization of conflicting standards.

We shall employ Redfield's concept that a culture trait is sacred to the extent that there is emotionally supported reluctance to call it rationally or practically into question. In these terms, a completely secular society is impossible, for social values are sacred by definition. The degree of sacredness of a society may be judged on the basis of its reluctance to change and the extent to which conformity with cultural norms is considered imperative.

In social relations, an individual can be said to behave in a personal manner to the extent that his actions reflect his recognition of their implications for the person affected. Through animistic beliefs, objects may be endowed with personality and treated in a personal manner. At the other extreme, completely impersonal behavior toward an individual disregards all of his social roles and treats him as an object.

There are several very real problems involved in the use of ethnographic description to throw light on the theory

---

highly select literate group in Timbuctoo, differ markedly from the form and function of books in Western culture.

under consideration. Some of these problems should be made explicit at the outset, both to indicate that the author was aware of them and to point out limitations of the data. Additional methodological problems, which became important in the field, will be discussed in the concluding chapter.

This study partakes of the difficulty present in all studies which attempt to discover the ethos, dominant motif, or other underlying theme of a society. The reader is basically dependent upon the judgment of the field worker, who determines what facts will be recorded and how they will be presented. Some readers may feel that, had another emphasis been adopted, the materials could have been as adequately organized around it and other evidence brought to bear.

Every field worker is faced with the problem of selecting material to record from the stream of events which surround him. If he works with informants, he makes a selection of data in the very questions he asks. If he has a particular theoretical orientation, this will bias him toward the collection of certain sorts of data, to the exclusion of other sorts. It is really only the danger of systematic exclusion of theoretically pertinent data which we fear. The use of independent, parallel studies of the same society can check the objectivity of field reports, but this has rarely been systematically attempted. The reader must be content with the assurance that this author had no proposition to prove—only a hypothesis to test. Negative results are quite as rewarding as positive ones. If the reader finds the data do not support the conclusions, at least this will be an indication of lack of bias in the record. If the reader wishes he had more data, he must know that the author shares his wish.

There is, however, one systematic bias in this report which must be noted. In terms of the theory, all evidence of culture conflict and of secular or impersonal behavior is crucial. These characteristics are, by definition, excluded from the ideal type of folk society. The literature indicates, in fact, that these traits are very rarely in evidence in small, isolated societies. Hence the presence of such traits in Timbuctoo would be indicative of urbanism. Situations and incidents reflecting culture conflict or secular or impersonal behavior were, therefore, sought in the field and are here reported. Because of this selection, such incidents loom larger in this report than they do in the lives of the people of Timbuctoo. The well-integrated, traditional, and personal ways of life are described as the culture of the people. Life in terms of these cultural patterns fills most of the daily activities of the populace. The conflicts reoccur also and, because they are unusual, provide topics of conversation. Because they are indices of urbanism, they are also of unusual interest to the social scientist.

The selection of a research site to meet the specifications set by the problem was not easy. It is more difficult than one might suspect to find cities free from Euro-American influence. The long tentacles of colonial and economic imperialism have sought out every accessible large population of the world. The resultant influence of the western world can be seen from Shanghai to Mexico City.

Certain practical considerations played a part in the final selection of Timbuctoo. Obviously the choice was limited to those communities about which there was sufficient literature to judge in advance whether or not they met the definition of "cities." Among the various possibilities, the ease with which research could be conducted was the deciding factor. City size was a consideration in this connection. It has been found in studies of populous American cities that large staffs, working over long periods, were required. With the research facilities at my disposal, it was apparent that a man and wife could not learn much about a very large city, in less than a year and in a completely foreign tongue.

After searching the libraries for some time, Timbuctoo was finally selected. It possessed the advantage of being an old community, having a very diversified culture, based on three ethnically distinct groups, and having a compact population reported to be in the neighborhood of ten thousand persons. (I later found it to be something over six thousand.) From the point of view of size alone, Timbuctoo might possibly be called a town rather than a city. Towns of this size in America, however, are recognized by both sociologists and the census as being urban. The extreme heterogeneity of culture in Timbuctoo would make it even more urban, according to our definition of the city, than many a community of equivalent size in America.

Timbuctoo possessed the mixed blessing of being in a European colony—French West Africa. This permitted the use of French, which I knew, but introduced a factor of Western contact. The undesirability of the latter feature was mitigated by the fact that Timbuctoo had been captured by the French only forty-five years before. Previously, it had been practically impossible even for European explorers to reach the city because of the fanatic Moslems who inhabited the area. All reports agreed that Timbuctoo had scarcely changed since the French conquest. As this outside influence had been present only within the memory of living men, who could describe any changes which had occurred, it was decided that the French contact would be more of an advantage than a limitation to research—and so it proved.

Contents

ILLUSTRATIONS

Plates

CHARTS AND MAPS

The Primitive City of
TIMBUCTOO

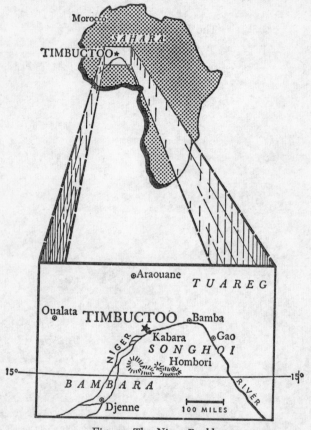

Fig. 1   The Niger Buckle

CHAPTER 1

The Rise and Fall of Timbuctoo

The broad and sluggish Niger River wanders northward out of the jungles, laps at the sands of the Sahara, then twists away southward and ultimately empties into the Gulf of Guinea. Timbuctoo lies where the river and desert meet. For centuries the northbound wealth of the tropics and the southbound products of the Barbary coast flowed through the city. Thus Timbuctoo owes its historical importance to its favorable location as a transshipment point.[1]

The first recorded history for this part of the world consists of Arabic chronicles written around A.D. 1000. At that time the center of dominance of the Sudan was the Ghana Empire to the west of Timbuctoo. This empire was strongly influenced by the Arabs who had invaded North Africa in the early eighth century and then infiltrated the western Sudan. The city of Ghana, which adopted Islam in A.D. 1076, was the focal point of caravan connection with North Africa.

The Birth of the City

Timbuctoo was then only a seasonal camp of the nomadic Tuareg—a predominantly Caucasoid people related to the Berbers of North Africa. In the summer the Tuareg moved out of the desert with their flocks and settled near the river. In the fall they returned to their Saharan oases. An early Arabic manuscript says of this summer camp, "In the beginning it was there that travelers arriving by land and water met. They made it a depot for their utensils

[1] The ecological significance of this location is analyzed in Appendix I.

and their grain. Soon this place became a crossroads of travelers who passed back and forth through it. They entrusted their property to a slave called Timbuctoo. . . ."[2]

Later other people established permanent residence here and the population grew. People came from all directions and soon it became a commercial center. The first traders are reported to have come from the west—the heart of the Ghana area. Later people from other neighboring regions, including the Songhoi[3] Negroes, frequented the town. The Songhoi capital, Gao, lay two hundred miles farther east. The king who resided there was nominally Moslem, as were the residents of his city. The rural Songhoi, however, were pagan and the king's power over them was very limited.

Timbuctoo continued to develop on a three-way cultural margin between the Tuareg to the north, the Songhoi to the east, and the Bambara to the west. The Bambara are one of the numerous Mandingo, Negro tribes of the western Sudan. The growing Mandingo Empire of Mali subjugated Ghana around 1240 and began to push eastward.[4] The Mandingo rulers actively propagated the faith of Mohammed in the areas which were brought under their control. By 1300 the urban Bambara, at the eastern limits of the Empire, had been converted.[5]

Important Islamic influences reached Timbuctoo in

[2] Es-Sadi, 1900:36. His *Tarikh es-Soudan* was completed in 1655, but probably made use of earlier manuscripts. The meaning of "Timbuctoo" is purported to be the "woman of the big navel," but the etymology is not clear. The nodular, umbilical hernia is very common in the area today.
The spelling of Timbuctoo herein employed is that used in major books in English dealing with that city, despite the vagary which has brought the German spelling "Timbuktu" into standard English. Other place names in the French territories follow French orthography, as is the practice in National Geographic Society maps of the area.

[3] There are a number of variant spellings, of which "Songhai" has become most common. The orthography used here reflects the pronunciation around Timbuctoo (Rouch, 1954:3).

[4] Monteil, 1923:33.

[5] *Ibid.*, 38.

1336 when the Songhoi came under Mandingo control. Returning from a pilgrimage to Mecca, the Emperor of Mali, Mousa, stopped at Timbuctoo and had the Great Mosque erected (see Plate 13). The later Moslem scribes of Timbuctoo like to think of the city as having been a center of Islamic learning long before this time but evidence in their own chronicles contradicts them.[6] It is quite apparent that the Emperor, who was responsible for the construction of Timbuctoo's first mosque, also made an earnest effort to bring the indigenous "scholars" of the city into contact with the main stream of Arab learning. It was by his order that many of the local savants went to Morocco to study at Fez.[7] As a result of these efforts, Timbuctoo did begin to acquire the learned character which the scribes later cherished. During the next century and a half, two more major mosques were built and Arab[8] scholars began to frequent the city from as far away as Spain.

It is clear that the fundamental cultural elements observable in Timbuctoo today were already well established at the time of the Mali Empire. Tuareg, Arab, and Songhoi were the major groups of this commercial center which drew a steady stream of people from a scattering of other cultures as well. The Islamic influence was strong, and exemplified not only in the Arabs from North Africa but also to some extent in the native population.

[6] Es-Sadi recounts that a native Arabian scholar accompanied Mousa back from his pilgrimage. "He established himself at Timbuctoo and found this city crowded with Sudanese jurisconsults. As soon as he perceived that they knew more than he in matters of law, he left for Fez; gave himself up to the study of law; then came back and reestablished himself at Timbuctoo." (1900:83–84) There is little doubt that the Arabian scholar who accompanied Mousa went to Fez to familiarize himself with the Malikite school of law which prevailed in North and West Africa and which differed from the system current in Arabia.

[7] Ibid., 92.

[8] Here and subsequently the term "Arab" is used to refer to people whose native language is Arabic. They were not Arabians nor were they entirely Caucasian.

The Songhoi Empire

The Songhoi soon freed themselves from Mandingo domination but Timbuctoo remained under the control of the Empire of Mali for another century. When that authority began to wane, the Tuareg captured the city and held it until the Songhoi began their rise to power. This rise was initiated by Sonni Ali, a monarch whose life indicates the limited effect which almost five hundred years of nominal adherence to Islam had on the Songhoi.

Sonni Ali marched on Timbuctoo in 1468. The Tuareg chief of the city fled, accompanied by a great number of holy men or marabouts[9] who were pursued and killed. Ali burned and looted the city, massacring and imprisoning the relatives of the marabouts who had supported the Tuareg. However, he showed great consideration for other marabouts,[10] apparently favoring the Arabs. A chronicle of the period states that the Great Mosque had its first "white" imam or prayer leader about this time. It is re-

---

[9] The term marabout, derived from the Arabic *morābit*, is used throughout this book as the equivalent of the Songhoi *Alfa*, which is an honorific title used to identify men who have become holy, or have acquired *baraka*, through piety and the study of Moslem law and religion. In North Africa, marabout is used more frequently, in a restricted way, to designate the "saints" of religious orders. Trimingham met this terminological problem by restoring to the word "clerk" the clerical meaning it had during the Middle Ages (1961:68).

Islamic scholars will find the orthography of Arabic words somewhat unorthodox. Words which have become part of the English language are written in their English form, such as marabout, imam, cadi, casbah, couscous. As most of the relevant publications with which the author dealt were in French, the orthography of Arabic names and Arabic words without English equivalents follows the French system of transliteration. Songhoi words derived from Arabic are written as they appear in the Songhoi dictionary of Dupuis (1917). Thus the word "genie" is *djini* in Songhoi, both words being derived from the Arabic *djinni*, as the French would write it, or the Arabic *jinni*, as others might prefer. The context will make the linguistic reference clear.

[10] Es-Sadi, 1900:109.

markable that the Arab scribe should even comment on this change of race of the imam. The Arabs are singularly unconscious of racial differences, so this remark must reflect an antagonism between the native, Negroid, and less well-educated marabouts and the more Caucasoid marabouts for whom Arabic was the native tongue.

As one might judge from these events, the religious aspects of Islam interested Sonni Ali less than the political ones. He chose to align himself with the Arabs, but not from any religious fervor. Another Arab chronicle gives us some insight into the state of Islam among the Songhoi of this epoch.

"The manners of this country are very singular. We find a people here who pretend to know the science of occult things, and base this knowledge upon a study of lines traced upon the sand, on the position of the stars, the cries of birds and their flight, etc. They profess to write charms which will increase profits, excite love, and oppose ruin; which will put their enemies to flight in battle and preserve themselves from the sword and the poison of arrows; and many other things that sorcerers practise in incantations. . . .

At last, neither he [Sonni Ali] nor his companions were ever seen in the cathedral mosque, or in any of the others, and from fear of him the thousands of men and women dwelling in his house neither fasted nor prayed during Ramadan. He did not know the Fatiha by heart, nor any other sûra of the Koran. Habitually careless in his prayers, he neither bowed nor prostrated himself during their recitation. He had relations with women that are unrecognized by marriage, or any other contract permitted by Islamism. If a woman pleased him he took her to his palace regardless of her husband or her family."[11]

Whatever his sins before Allah, Sonni Ali was a remarkable monarch. During his twenty-eight year reign, he extended his conquests some three hundred and fifty miles to the west. The important Bambara city of Djenné was wrested from the Mandingo. He defeated the Mossi in the south and brought the territory inside the Niger bend

11 Dubois, 1897:104-107.

under his sway. His conquests even included the Bedouin tribes north of the river.

Shortly after the death of Sonni Ali, in 1492, one of his generals seized the throne. Where Ali had distrusted the marabouts, this emperor, Askia[12] the Great, gathered them about him as advisers and showed great zeal in strengthening the Moslem community. After making a pilgrimage to Mecca, Askia the Great conducted a holy war against the pagan Mossi. In the following years he pressed over five hundred miles to the east, conquering the Tuareg tribes in that area as well as the Hausa states. His dominance in the west is said to have extended to the Atlantic. The peripheral conquests were never integrated into the empire like the central segments. The core of the Songhoi Empire, stretching east and west for almost a thousand miles, was carefully organized. Askia took a direct hand in the appointment or recognition of officials in all important cities. With the trade routes protected, commerce and learning prospered. Timbuctoo became the dominant focal point of all traffic through the area. The coterie of marabouts centered around each mosque numbered among them savants of real fame in the Moslem world. The cadi or judge of Timbuctoo became the Supreme Justice for the entire Songhoi Empire. Holy men and students from all over the Sudan came to the city, mingling with the merchants from distant lands. Timbuctoo had reached its zenith.

The Moroccan Conquest

Upon the death of Askia the Great, fratricidal wars temporarily weakened the empire but later Askias reasserted the dominance of the Songhoi. An important element of the commerce of the empire was rock salt, slabs of which were mined in the central Sahara and brought by camel caravan to Timbuctoo. Although the mines were under Songhoi control, they were actually closer to Morocco than

[12] *Askia* was the title of the ruling lineage which replaced the *Sonni*.

to the Sudan. The North African Moors, having been driven out of Europe, dreamed of southward expansion. For half a century successive sultans of Morocco tried to foment trouble with the Songhoi over the mines. Finally an expedition of nine thousand Moroccans, renegade Christians, and Andalusians traversed the Sahara and entered the Sudan. In 1591 they defeated a larger Songhoi army and entered Timbuctoo.

The order and prosperity which reigned in the Sudan during the Songhoi Empire came to an abrupt end. All of the vassal peoples revolted and assumed control of their own areas. Remnants of the Songhoi army, led by various remaining members of the royal family, kept the Moroccans occupied in the field for two years. Meanwhile, the population of Timbuctoo, for the only time in the history of the city, took a hand in their own fate. They besieged the local Moroccan garrison for two months in the casbah or fort which they had built. The pasha commanding the Moroccan field forces was informed of the situation by messenger and had to divert three hundred men from his campaign to restore order in Timbuctoo.

The Moroccan pasha, finally tiring of playing cat and mouse with the Songhoi troops, brought his army back to Timbuctoo. The entire wealth of the city was confiscated and distributed to the soldiers. Like Sonni Ali, the pasha recognized the potential threat which lay in the influence of the local judges, jurisconsults, teachers, and learned men. All of the most influential ones were imprisoned and those who were not massacred were eventually exiled to Morocco. With the native leaders and, incidentally, the bearers of the great culture of Timbuctoo, disposed of, the Moroccans settled down to organizing the Sudan.

Timbuctoo was the administrative center of this Moroccan colony and the pashas used the city as a base for their troops. There was also an emir, who was comptroller for the Sultan of Morocco. During the first twenty years, the various pashas of the Sudan were named by the Sultan. In fact, they were sent to the Sudan to replace an incumbent whose authority was being revoked or to fill a vacancy created by the demise of a pasha in battle or by poisoning. As ties with Morocco weakened, subsequent pashas were elected by the Moroccan troops and later by their descendants. Even nominal subservience to the Sultan of Morocco was soon abandoned and bickering among the Moroccan leaders increased. One pasha after another was chosen and deposed, some staying in office but a single day. The final century of control by the descendants of the Moroccans saw no less than a hundred and thirty-two pashas.[13]

One author has seen in the Moroccan conquest a favorable influence on the commerce and the intellectual level of Timbuctoo, at least in the early days of direct control by the Sultan.[14] Such a view is scarcely justified considering the liquidation of many of the intellectuals. As for commerce, the contacts with North Africa became so rare that, as early as 1600, one pasha in Timbuctoo managed to hide the news of the death of the Sultan of Morocco for a whole year. Peace was barely established over the trading area when internecine conflicts among the Moroccans reduced the Sudan to a virtual state of anarchy.

In one way, however, the Moroccan conquest brought Timbuctoo into closer contact with Islam than ever before. The Arab troops intermarried with the local women and their descendants, known as *Arma*,[15] became distinguishable only as a native ruling class, having adopted the Sudanese language and many of the customs of the native Songhoi.

Since the initial foundation of Timbuctoo as a seasonal camp by the Tuareg, these desert nomads had hovered

[13] Molouk es-Soudan, 1901. See pp. 364–373 for chronological list of all pashas.

[14] Introductory comment by Houdas in Es-Sadi, 1900:ix.

[15] Barth (1890:301–302) shows that the term *Arma* is derived from the Arabic word for "sharpshooter" or "musketeer". In Songhoi the plural form of *Arma* is *Arma di yo*, all nouns forming their plurals the same way. For simplification, the singular form of Songhoi words is used throughout for both numbers.

around the city as it waxed and waned in wealth and importance. Whenever organized authority weakened, the Tuareg were on hand to pillage. But the Tuareg never liked to live in the city, as some of their slaves did. The masters desired only to loot it. Yet they were astute enough never to ruin the commerce of the city.

With their declining power, the Arma came to rule Timbuctoo only on sufferance, the Tuareg exacting tribute from the Arma, who, in turn, exploited the rest of the population. The trade of the city had declined from the level it reached in the palmy days of the Askias, but it was still a prize worth capture. The end of the eighteenth century brought the Bambara who defeated the Tuareg. But this distant authority could not maintain itself and the Tuareg again assumed control.[16] Subsequently two more short-lived Sudanese empires successively dominated the city before it fell to the French.[17]

European Conquest

While the peoples of the Sudan were struggling openly for the control of Timbuctoo, the nations of Europe were striving desperately to establish claims to the city. No fewer than eighteen European explorers set out to bring back accounts of the city before the feat was finally accomplished.[18] An Englishman, Mungo Park, reached the location of the city's port on the Niger in 1806 but hostile Tuareg on the river bank forced him to continue his way to his ultimate death in the rapids on the lower Niger.[19] Twenty years later another Englishman got to the city, but was shortly slain in ambush.[20] These were the only ones of the eighteen to get close to the city from which no European returned. In 1828 a French adventurer named René Caillié, after a year's overland trek in Arab

16 Tauxier, 1942:90–107.
17 *Ibid.*, 143, 171, 181.
18 Caillié, 1830:I, iii.
19 Park, 1815.
20 Caillié, 1830:II, 79–84. Dubois and Seabrook are in obvious error as to the date of Laing's arrival at Timbuctoo.

disguise, arrived at Timbuctoo and stayed there for two weeks. He returned to France to claim the ten thousand franc prize offered by the Geographic Society of Paris to the first man to describe the city. The English denounced Caillié as a liar and faker and continued their attempts to explore the area.

In 1853 a Prussian, Barth, was the sole member of an English expedition to reach Timbuctoo. He spoke Arabic and claimed to be Moslem but he was generally believed to be Christian. The only thing which saved his life was that, during his stay, he remained the virtual prisoner of an Arab benefactor. So far no important, direct influence from Europe had affected Timbuctoo. In 1880 a German explorer openly spent sixteen days in the city and lived to tell his tale.[21] Europe was closing in. Seven years later a French gunboat reached the port of the city but was forced back, unable to land, because of the hostile Tuareg. It was in December 1893 that the first members of a French expedition entered the city. A French party sent out against the Tuareg was almost completely wiped out. The next month a column commanded by Joffre, later to be Marshal of France, arrived on the scene and the *paix française* began.[22] The natives who had kept out Europeans with fanatic zeal were subject to a new rule and new cultural influences.

That rule was but one more episode in the sequence of empires which dominated the city. In 1960 French control, like its predecessors, came to an end. Timbuctoo became part of the new nation of Mali, whose territories embrace much of the old Mandingo Empire of the same name. But the Timbuctoo which emerges from the following pages is that of 1940, when Joffre's conquest was still a living memory and independence only a dream.

[21] Lenz, 1884.
[22] For various and conflicting reports of the capture of Timbuctoo, see Dubois, 1897:352–371; Seabrook, 1934:237–239; and Joffre, 1915.

CHAPTER 2

The People of Timbuctoo

The desert warriors of this part of Africa are subjugated but hostile. A white man's life is now in no danger as long as the forts on the northern and southern edges of town are garrisoned by the handful of French officers and their seven hundred native soldiers. On the other hand, an admired resident of the city is the son of an Arab who murdered the French Commander some years ago.

The desert caravans are safe when they are accompanied by the native camel corps of méharistes but in 1940 the last raid on an unprotected caravan bound for Timbuctoo had occurred only seven years earlier. A remaining colonial sore spot is Spanish Mauretania which is civilized at only a few places along the Rio de Oro coast and is absolutely undisciplined in the interior. Operating from this base, which is free from French reprisal, the Moors make sorties into the French-controlled Sahara to prey upon unprotected caravans. When such raids are reported, the méharistes are informed by radio and they trek to the desert wells upon which all desert travelers are dependent. Even then the marauders have been known to pass up a well and escape to Mauretania.

French control over the Tuareg is still precarious. Violence among these nomads and between them and the Negroes is not uncommon. In 1917 the Germans incited the Tuareg to revolt against the French. The uprising spread westward as far as Timbuctoo before it was crushed. In the fall of 1939 the Tuareg chiefs of the Niger area assembled and, believing that the French were fully occupied in Europe, divided the country among themselves and started their raiding and robbing again. The French hastily made a display of force which caused the Tuareg to reconsider, but the méharistes were still paying protracted visits to the nomads' country a year later.

The natives of Timbuctoo react to French rule in varied but readily understandable ways. Those who were the previous overlords of the city resent their loss of position and wealth. Europeans may feel that imperialistic wars of conquest are on a "higher level" than other wars of subjugation, but the natives consider the French simply the most recent exploiters of the city. In addition, the new rulers are despised for their Christian faith. The only opinion in favor of the French springs from an appreciation of the peaceful era which they have maintained. A man who has had a Tuareg threaten to cut off his arm to obtain a tight-fitting bracelet does not quickly forget the incident. The lance scars on house doors are a constant reminder of the old days and the Negro still cowers before the noble Tuareg and is glad of French protection.

Population

Since the early days of the Songhoi Empire, the depredations of Tuareg and Moor upon the far-flung trade routes of the city have reduced its commerce and thereby its population. Judging from the extent of the ruins of the old city, it was probably never much more than double its present size. Commercially, the recent restoration of peace has no more than compensated for the accompanying loss of the slave trade and the infringement of European merchants upon the old trade system. The major shift in commerce has been the elimination of practically all of that part of the river-borne trade which brought products of the Sudan to Timbuctoo to be taken by caravan to Morocco and Algeria. These products which gave Timbuctoo its fabulous reputation—gold, ivory, ostrich plumes, hides, wax, incense, and gum—are now largely bought up by Europeans and withdrawn from the native trade before they even reach Timbuctoo. Local trading posts have completely taken over the distribution of cloth, which used to come by camel from the north. All of these factors have kept the city from regaining its ancient size.

The population of Timbuctoo in 1940 was five thousand persons according to the French census. The officer who compiled the census believed it to be accurate, but it is surely underestimated. The census procedure was to have the heads of households in each quarter of the city register their dependents, including slaves. The native chiefs of the city and of the quarters were responsible for accuracy. As this count is the basis for the yearly head taxes, and as the chiefs are known to be very prone to accept bribes, it seems unlikely that everyone would be registered by this procedure. In fact, when general mobilization was declared in 1939, the French found many young men in the marketplace who had not been registered. The natives all know that the census lists do not include the whole population and consider it a great joke on the French.

Attempting to secure a more accurate figure for this study, a house count was made from a recent aerial photograph and the number of households multiplied by the average number of persons per household.[1] This calculation would place the minimum permanent population at six thousand. It is impossible to give more than a very ap-

[1] The war made it impossible to obtain the photograph for reproduction here. The grass huts surrounding the city were counted in the photograph, using compounds or isolated huts as units—not all huts having a fenced enclosure. In the city, the mud-walled houses are built adjoining one another in such a manner that from the air they are indistinguishable, but the inner court of each is visible. By counting courtyards the minimum number of houses was placed at 1,000 and the minimum number of households in huts and compounds at 500, making 1,500 in all. Taking a hundred known Arab families residing in houses and seventy Bela families living in huts, the average household was found to consist of four persons in each instance. Henry Barth, who visited Timbuctoo in 1853, calculated "about nine hundred and eighty clay houses and a couple of hundred conical huts . . ." (1890:324). There probably has been an increase of huts since that time, due to an influx of Bela slaves.

proximate breakdown of this figure. The Tuareg slaves number about a thousand, the Arabs and their slaves probably close to fifteen hundred, and the remainder are Songhoi. After the short season of rains, nomads camp around the city with their herds and flocks to supply milk and meat to the population. When the *azalai* caravan leaves or arrives, the owners of thousands of camels spend months in the city. Transient traders are almost always part of the life of Timbuctoo so that the city is functionally larger than its permanent population indicates.

There is little likelihood that Timbuctoo will grow unless there is some major economic change. At present the crafts are overcrowded and many natives born in Timbuctoo settle in other Sudanese cities. There is a large group of these emigrants at Gao, the old Songhoi capital to the east. The seat of the French colonial government for the region has been moved from Timbuctoo to Gao, which promises to be a growing colonial city, leaving Timbuctoo dependent upon its native commerce. Even today Gao, with its hotel and wide, straight avenues, is distinctly French, whereas Timbuctoo remains Sudanese in character.[2]

The average size of the households in Timbuctoo is four persons. Both high infant mortality and low birth rate cause families to be small. In a sample of over two hundred families, the maximum number of live births to any woman was six. The vital statistics taken by the French are so incomplete as to be useless but it is well known that many babies are stillborn or die shortly after birth. Heavy infant mortality also occurs after the first year when poor supplementary foods cause severe digestive trouble.

[2] The number of French in Timbuctoo was quite small. There were only five French women in residence and the wife of an American missionary. There were four civil officials: administrator, treasurer, teacher, and director of post and telegraph. Two French traders, three Army officers, including the doctor, complete the clique of the elect. In addition, there were a number of French noncommissioned officers but still the total European population was less than forty persons.

Health and Medicine

While abortion is far from unknown, the small number of births may also be laid to another cause. There are numerous wealthy men who have had several wives but have had only one child or none at all. The cause for this sterility is probably the prevalence of syphilis. The natives consider syphilis as inevitable—just as we think of childhood diseases—and believe that it should be gotten over with as soon as possible. Judging from the scars of old skin lesions, practically the whole population is infected. Aside from known prostitutes, the French doctor treated 141 cases of syphilis in the sample month of May 1940. Considering the native's unconcern over this disease and his dislike for European medicine, this is a large number of cases under treatment. The figure is even more significant when it is compared with the number of other maladies treated during the same month.[3] Only inflammation of the eyes was more prevalent, which is hardly surprising in this country of sand and filth.

In order that this small clinical sample of a population of thousands will not give an incorrect impression of the state of health of the natives, something must be said as to the relations between the natives and the French doctor and his assistants. The Songhoi word which is used to des-

[3] Cases under treatment by the Army doctor among the civil population in May 1940. All under twelve years listed as "children."

	Adults ♂	♀	Children		Adults ♂	♀	Children
Conjunctivitis	35	63	70	Surgical (frequently the result of violence)	12	9	6
Syphilis	54	71	16	Gonorrhea	14	3	0
Respiratory	39	24	38	Guinea worm	3	2	0
Digestive	39	25	20	Mumps	0	0	2
Malaria	22	8	27	Trachoma	1	1	0
Skin Eruptions	23	10	7	Leprosy	1	0	0
Otitis	9	7	14				
Meningitis	4	4	11				

ignate white foreigners is *toubab*, derived from the Arabic word for "doctor." The word was first used in connection with the European explorers who used their medical kits as an introduction to these natives—a common practice throughout the uncivilized world. But now we find a contradictory situation in which the natives resist foreign medical treatment to the utmost.

In initial contact with Europeans, it seems likely that the natives have no real faith or interest in the curative power of the stranger's medicine but ask for treatment out of curiosity. Explorers and missionaries have often commented upon natives who come to be treated, when they are quite well, just in order to see the stranger and his equipment at close hand. The medical kit simply forms a focus for a new social relationship. When the native's curiosity is satisfied, the stranger's medicine will be appealed to only when all native methods fail. Such was the experience of the *toubab* at Timbuctoo.

It must be remembered that it is the stranger who is uncertain of his social relationships—the very reason that the explorer uses the medical device to establish himself. After the Europeans have colonized and come to dominate the aborigines, free medical treatment plays an entirely different social role. It is now the white man who is socially secure and the native who is uncertain. The dispensary becomes the symbol of a foreign overlord who has no respect for local beliefs. In Timbuctoo the doctor and the hospital epitomize for the native the French ridicule of maraboutic powers, witches, and all native tradition. Small wonder that recourse is had to the doctor only after native treatments fail—and after the patient, in many instances, is beyond cure.

The following anecdote well illustrates the native attitude toward the French in matters of medicine. I had tried to dissociate myself, in the natives' minds, from the French and the missionaries. In this role, I expressed a deep interest in local witchcraft. One morning I was informed by the native who lived in the courtyard below that his pregnant wife had been attacked by a witch the

[1]   Ancient Mosque of Sankore

[2]   Tuareg Nobles in Town

[3]   Daga in from the Bush

[4]   Young Bela

previous evening. He explained that his wife had bought some dried fish from a slave boy who had touched her elbow as she ate. Soon afterward she had fallen rigid and unconscious on the bed. My cook had helped diagnose the case as the work of a witch. The boy witch was caught and a marabout summoned. The holy man quickly brought the young woman around. My friend, who knew of my interest in such cases, apologized for not having called me when his wife collapsed, but explained that it had been impossible as I had been talking to the French doctor on my terrace at the time! The doctor's unsolicited and well-intentioned visit, following my inconspicuous call at his dispensary, had cost me a first-hand account of witchcraft.

The treatment of a case of witchcraft by a marabout, a student of the Koranic word which decries belief in such superstition, exemplifies the culture mixture which has occurred in Timbuctoo. A glance at the physiognomy of the marabout with his rather narrow nose, *café au lait* skin and kinky hair tells a similar story of race mixture. While there is extreme variety and blending of both cultural and racial factors, they follow definite patterns reflecting the past history and present social organization of the city.

Culture Divisions

There are three languages commonly spoken in Timbuctoo and linked with the principal culture elements of the region—Songhoi, Arab, and Tuareg. Songhoi is an indigenous language of the Sudan. It shows no relationship to neighboring tongues, but is distantly related to the Central and Eastern Sudanic languages.[4] Songhoi has two distinct but mutually intelligible dialects. That spoken in

[4] The affinities of Songhoi were indicated by Greenberg, 1963. Concerning the dialects, the best discussion of Djerma is to be found in du Picq, 1933. A dictionary is that of Marie, 1914. For the western dialect see the adequate grammar and dictionary of Dupuis (Yakouba), 1917. The phoneme rendered "ngh" in the common spelling of "Songhoi" is a very nasalized "ng."

the eastern part of the Songhoi area, beyond Gao, is called Djerma, while the western dialect of Timbuctoo and the Bend of the Niger is simply called Songhoi. The natives of the city refer to their speech as *koyra tyini* or "town talk." It is this tongue which is used in all commercial relations among different segments of the polyglot population. Songhoi grammar is extremely simple, unlike Temajegh, the language of the Tuareg or, as they call themselves, Kel Tagilmus—"People of the Veil."

The Tuareg are divided into three quasi-castes—nobles, serfs, and slaves.[5] The slaves, who are known to the Songhoi as Bela, live in grass huts around the outskirts of the city. The serf or Daga tribes are nomadic herders who move separately from the nobles. After the rainy season the Daga camp in the bush near the city and come in to trade. The nobles rarely enter Timbuctoo. Even in the past their visits were largely limited to raiding and plundering. They cannot speak Songhoi and must use their Bela slaves as interpreters when the need arises. The Bela are the only permanent residents of Timbuctoo who speak Temajegh.

The third prevalent language is Arabic. The Arabs are sharply divided into two groups—the urban, commercial Arabs and the Berabich who are the desert nomads, often called Moors. While the latter speak nothing but Arabic and have only occasional contact with the Arab population of Timbuctoo, the town Arabs speak Songhoi as well as

---

[5] The Tuareg distinguish the nobles, serfs, and slaves as *Imajeghan, Imghad,* and *Irawellan* (Rodd, 1926:15, 134–142). Rodd implies that the Bela are herders, not agriculturists, in the Air district (pp. 134–136). This is not true at Timbuctoo. The Songhoi use the terms *Surgu* (also for Tuareg in general), *Daga* and *Bela* for the three castes. The Tuareg upper castes do not even consider the *Irawellan* (Bela) to be "People of the Veil," which, strictly speaking, they are not because they do not wear the veil. Culturally, they are Tuareg none the less. As cross-caste marriage is permitted and manumission can raise the status of a slave, these subdivisions are not true castes. However, such mobility is uncommon.

The definitive work on the Tuareg is that of Nicolaisen (1963).

Arabic, due to their numerous contacts with the other residents of the city. The same is true of the Negro slaves of the Arabs. Those of the population whose native tongue is Songhoi distinguish themselves by the term *koyraboro,* meaning "townsman." For them the Arabs and Bela are outsiders in spite of long residence in the city. All of the natives are nominally Moslem and therefore should repeat daily prayers in Arabic. Most *koyraboro* do not understand the prayers which they phonetically desecrate. The native marabouts, however, have been schooled in Arabic and have a fair knowledge of the language, although they use it only for religious purposes. A marabout or *Alfa,* as he is known locally, possesses a very high status position because of his Koranic knowledge.

Other status distinctions among the *koyraboro* are derived from the period of the Moroccan conquest. The free Songhoi fled to the south and those who remained did so as serfs or clients of the Arma.[6] These serfs were called "black bodies"—*Gabibi.* The *koyraboro* are still recognized as either Arma or Gabibi and both speak only Songhoi. Inasmuch as we shall be specifically discussing Timbuctoo, we shall refer to the *koyraboro* as the Songhoi. As their language indicates, Songhoi culture is most marked in this group. However, it should be remembered that the Songhoi in Timbuctoo, particularly the Arma, have been much more influenced by Arab culture than the Songhoi living around Hombori or Niamey.

The subdivisions of the major ethnic elements in and around Timbuctoo and the languages which they speak may be clarified by the following chart (Figure 2).

Whereas French contact has been recent and superficial, the long association between Arab and Songhoi has

[6] According to Yakouba, but this could not be verified. Kâti (1913:198) attributes the origin of the Gabibi to a group of a hundred slaves given the Cadi of Timbuctoo by Askia Daouad (1549–1582). Dupuis (1917) gives Songhoi terminology showing that the descendants of captured slaves had progressively improved status until the fourth generation, who were free clients called *Gabibi.*

Figure 2

CHARACTERISTICS OF THE POPULATION

Culture Base	Sub-group	Origin	Racial Type	Status Level*	City Population	Language Native	Language Second
ARAB	Town Arab	Migrants from North Africa and their descendants. Such contact was strong even in the fifteenth century.	Caucasoid & Mixed types	1	ca. 1,500	Arabic	Songhoi
	Arab slave	Enslaved West African Negroes and their descendants.	Negroid	3		Arabic	Songhoi
	Berabich	Nomads who entered Sahara sometime after A.D. 1000	Caucasoid & Mixed types	1	(nomads)	Arabic	None
SONGHOI	Arma	Descendants of sixteenth century Moroccan Arab invaders and their Sudanese wives.	Mixed types (more Caucasoid)	1		None	Songhoi
	Gabibi (serf)	Indigenous to Sudan.	Mixed types (more Negroid)	2	ca. 3,500	Songhoi	None
TUAREG	Surgu (noble)	Indigenous to Sahara.	Caucasoid	1	(nomads)	Temajegh	None
	Daga (serf)	Probably result from ancient mixture of nobles and slaves.	Mixed type	2	(nomads)	Temajegh	None
	Bela (slave)	Enslaved and acculturated groups of Sudanese natives.	Negroid	3	ca. 1,000	Temajegh	Songhoi

*Numbers indicate status difference and equivalence. Lower numbers equal higher status.

resulted in a great deal of cultural diffusion, including linguistic borrowing.[7] The Moroccan conquest and commercial contacts with North Africa introduced many new social forms. Thus, the chief and the judge of the city are known by terms of Arabic origin, *emir* and *cadi*. Other words have been borrowed along with the religion. Thus, paradise and hell are called *aldyenna* and *aldyhennam*. Likewise, foods, objects of material culture, and techniques, which were brought to Timbuctoo by the Arabs, have carried their Arabic terms along with them. The terms used by the Songhoi for books and writing, guns, wheat, tea, and coffee are Arabic. The names for the days of the week and the months of the year show a like origin. As we shall see later, there has been borrowing in kinship terminology, but in this instance Songhoi has lent more commonly than borrowed.

Racial Types and Race Mixture

The physical anthropology of the people of Timbuctoo was outside the scope of this study, but a few general comments on the racial types will be worth while. The physical strains which have mingled to produce the population of the city are Negroid and Caucasoid. The latter are Mediterranean stocks, most commonly designated as Arab and Berber. Both are light-skinned and have straight or wavy black hair. The Arabs have aquiline noses, while the nose of the pure Berber type around Timbuctoo is straight, long, and thin. The Berbers are tall; their limbs as well as their digits are exceedingly long and thin. While their eye color ranges from dark to light brown, the blue eye of the northern Berber was never observed.

The Tuareg show a complete gradation from Berber to Negro type. The nobles are Caucasoid Berbers. The maintenance of race purity within the noble caste, in spite of

[7] A detailed list of Arabic words used in Songhoi is to be found in du Picq, 1933, for the Djerma dialect. There probably has been even more borrowing from Arabic in Timbuctoo. For borrowing of Arabic by the Hausa under similar conditions, see Greenberg, 1947:85–97.

intercourse with Negro concubines, results from the matrilineal nature of Tuareg society. As caste rules forbid a
man taking a woman of higher status than himself, the
children of noble mothers always have noble fathers. The
children of noble men and their Negro slave women follow the lower caste of the mothers. Rodd indicates that
there is a tendency in the Air district for such slave children to become body servants to the nobles and later to
be manumitted into the Daga serf caste.[8] This would explain the racially mixed type of Daga observed at Timbuctoo, where I was told a similar process operated. The
upper caste Tuareg most often seen in the city belong to
maraboutic tribes. These groups have been greatly influenced by the Arabs. They speak Arabic fluently and trace
their descent from the Prophet. They are strongly patrilineal so that mixed blood children belong to the father's
group, thus introducing Negroid traits.

The Bela slaves of the Tuareg are almost pure Negroids,
showing the characteristic Negro traits to a more marked
degree than any other part of the population. We know
that these slaves were derived from the capture of Sudanese Negroes. The intermediate Daga caste evidences a
mixture of the Berber and Negro traits. The Daga women,
with their straight, black hair, hemispherical breasts and
caramel-colored skin are reminiscent of Hindu women. By
European standards, they are the most beautiful in the
Sudan and are much sought as concubines by unattached
Frenchmen.

The Arabs and Songhoi show all degrees of mixture between Caucasoid and Negroid types. The latter is seen in
its most Negroid form among the Bambidye or "children
of Bamba," a town to the east of Timbuctoo. Miscegena-
tion between Arab and Negro has resulted in racial mixture unlike that among the Tuareg, where race-caste distinctions are discernible. On the basis of physique alone,
one cannot always distinguish between Arab and Gabibi,
to take the two extremes. Caucasoid traits appear most
marked and most frequently among the Arabs, next in

[8] Rodd, 1926:136.

strength and frequency among the Arma, and are least marked in the Gabibi.

A significant deduction can be drawn from the Caucasoid traits seen in the Gabibi. Arabs from Morocco and Negroes from Timbuctoo have intermarried a great deal since the sixteenth century and their first contacts probably go back to the beginning of the millennium. Unlike the matrilineal Tuareg, all children of Arabs belong to their father's group, so that theoretically the Arabs and the Arma, who are descendants of the early Arab conquerors, should show Negro-Caucasian mixture. On the other hand, the Gabibi should be pure Negroid, as Gabibi men never married Arab women. The marked Caucasian strains which exist in the Gabibi can be explained only on the basis of widespread illegitimacy.

Again, reference to Figure 2 may assist in the clarification of the racial components found in the ethnic divisions.

Dress

Out of the kaleidoscopic confusion of peoples which the newcomer sees in the markets and narrow streets of the city, order finally becomes apparent. The different native groups can be distinguished on the basis of dress—clothes, jewelry, haircut, and hair arrangement. Each native knows his own fashions of dress and can recognize the cultural identity of other people. Out of the total picture of what he recognizes as an Arab or a Daga, the native cannot abstract the diagnostic characteristics. This, of course, is not unusual. We ourselves might claim ability to distinguish an upper from a lower class person, yet be at a loss to enumerate the bases of such judgment. In addition, we must always remember that distinctions in dress are not in themselves diagnostic. Clothes are but partial evidence of the total social personality and if they fail to conform to the other indications of social position, the personality becomes ludicrous.

When knowledge of a person's background is lacking, outward expressions of that background are sought in judging his social position. Race, speech, manners, and dress are the most obvious of these overt signs. Caucasian racial traits have some status value in Timbuctoo but, as we have already seen, most culture and class groups in the city are not racially distinct. The population is large and diverse enough that only a few know one's actual economic and status position. The rest of the people can be impressed by a fine show of clothing. If the choice must be made, money may be spent on clothes rather than on the customary platters of food for distribution to relatives on festive occasions.

It is striking that some people prefer to impress those with whom their contacts are the most impersonal and ignore the opinion of their intimates, who know their actual situation. One of my acquaintances, a freed Bela slave, assumed the veil and dress of the nobles. He was naturally the laughing-stock of all who knew him. Although aware of this, he still enjoyed sitting in the market place in all his grandeur, contemplating the fine figure he cut for strangers. When working, he resumed his Bela garb, as he was not in an economic position to dress as a noble all the time.

Emphasis on dress is not always intended for strangers. Even friends may be so unfamiliar with one's actual economic condition that a show of opulence can give increased status. Girl friends and business acquaintances are particularly susceptible to such impressions. Another interesting pattern is found among intimates, all of whom use clothes to create a good impression. While such comrades know one another's true economic position, their mutual resort to the same device of showy dressing lends status to the well-dressed man even among his associates. This is particularly true of young men who are competing for the sexual favors of girls. Women show a similar competitive concern over their appearance even after marriage.

It should be pointed out in passing that the importance of fine clothes has come into its own again since French occupation. The reason for this is that previously, during the epoch of Tuareg dominance, peopoe dared not wear good clothes in the streets for fear of being stripped by Tuareg marauders. Nevertheless, Timbuctoo was famous for the embroidery of fine robes and the making of beautiful slippers and these crafts survived the later turbulent period.

Forms of dress are not only varied but there is general lack of consensus as to the significance of dress customs. Non-Bela continually told me that the various fashions in which Bela women braided their hair were distinctive of family lines. The truth is that the manner of braiding is frequently changed to follow personal taste. There is a similar confusion over the significance in which children's hair is shaved. In spite of the fact that all male children in Timbuctoo have their heads shaved so as to leave tufts of hair in various designs, informants from all groups and ages failed to agree on the meanings of these hair patterns. Some did not even know the significance of the way their own heads had been shaven as children. One man claimed that babies' hair was tufted at birth and that these tufts were kept and the rest of the head shaved. His early recollections doubtless substantiated this belief as the native barber simply continues the design he finds on the young customer's head. The first shaving, however, is done when the baby is only a week old. The significance of the design is of import only to the family. Some of the better substantiated hair designs look like this from the top of the head:

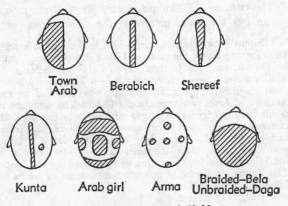

Fig. 3 Hair Patterns of Children

As slaves and Gabibi serfs follow the family hair pattern of the Arab or Arma masters, the manners of head shaving fail to correspond to class lines.[9]

In the name of Christianity the European has covered the breasts and breeched the loins of most of the aboriginal world. The job was done for him in Timbuctoo by Moslems. Perhaps this is slightly unfair to the Moslems as they insisted upon clothing only those natives whom they took in marriage or as household slaves. The diffusion of clothes to other natives went on unaided. The dress of the Arabs, who had superior social status, was widely copied. In fact, during the great period of Moslem conquest, the Arabs had to fight this trend in order to maintain the distinctions between exploiter and exploited.[10]

All adults in Timbuctoo wear clothes but immature children of both sexes run through the streets naked. Girls wear a string of shell beads about their hips until puberty, when they don an ankle-length skirt. Boys put on a loincloth or pantaloons after circumcision, which precedes puberty. As boys and girls grow older, they assume the more complete costumes of their elders but even the very young children may be dressed up in small robes on festive occasions.

Women's Apparel

The costumes of Timbuctoo vary greatly from group to group but the basic pattern is the flowing robe of the

[9] Dupuis (Yakouba), 1914:256–258. Indicating the head patterns for *koyraboro*, the patterns I have depicted are identified by Dupuis, from left to right, as: 1. Gabibi; 2. Alfa; 3. Alfa; 4. Alfa slave; 5. ——; 6. Arma; 7. ——. The overlap is somewhat surprising. Type 1, for example, was identified for me as Arab by an Arab, two Armas, and a Gabibi. The confusion may result from the ignorance of our informants or the duplication of freeman types among their slaves and Gabibi, but Yakouba says the tuft of hair, as in type 4, identifies slaves. It is quite possible that *koyraboro* identified Arabs as marabouts (Alfa) for Yakouba, for they are often so considered by the Negroes. The Kunta are a tribe of nomadic Arabs, some of whom have become sedentarized.

[10] Hell, 1925:44–45.

East. Arab, Arma, and Daga women all wear an outer robe which is draped around the body and over the head, hanging in graceful folds to the ground.[11] Under this robe the Daga woman wears only a skirt wrapped around her waist. When her loose outer garment becomes disarranged, so as to expose her breasts, she feels no shame. Nor is she ashamed to show her face.

The veil is not worn by women in Timbuctoo. When Arab women find it necessary to enter the streets, they draw the end of their robes over their faces. Arma women, who are similarly restricted to their homes, are not so careful about keeping their faces covered in public. The Moslem woman's desire to keep her head covered extends also to the Arabs' Negro slaves. They wear simple, peaked caps or even a hood sewn onto their robes. But the Bela and Gabibi have remained beyond intimate Arab influence to such a degree that they make no attempt to cover their faces or heads. Like the Daga and Arab slaves, they are not restricted to their homes and are the principal vendors in the market.

Bela women, as they work about their house compounds or go about in their quarter of the city, usually wear nothing but a bright, striped, wraparound skirt. For dances and appearances in the market they don Sudanese sandals[12] and poncho-like robes. The Gabibi wear a similar robe but wider than the Bela's. It covers the arms when the extra material is not thrown back on the shoulders. Made of plain or figured white cloth, the robe is distinct

[11] The woman's robe is not sewn but consists of a single, long piece of cloth, wide enough to reach from the shoulders to the ground when wound about the body. Holding a free corner of the cloth at the right shoulder, the robe passes across the front of the body and under the left arm; then across the back, where the edge is pinned over the right shoulder to the corner of the cloth in front. Then the cloth is usually wound loosely once more about the body, under the right arm and over the left shoulder and over the head, the free end falling over the right shoulder and arm.

[12] The Sudanese sandal consists of a single piece of leather which forms the sole and folds up over the front of the foot to cover the toes and instep.

from the usual Guinea blue employed by the Bela and Daga.

Each group has distinctive hairdress. The Daga part their hair in the middle and draw it back in a rather severe manner. The short, kinky hair of the Bela is made into small braids all over the head. On festive occasions, Arma women form long horns with their hair, one curving upward over the front of the head. These horns of hair may be over a foot long and are humorously characterized as "scorpions" because of their similarity to that insect's tail. Two to four large, ball-shaped knots of hair arranged in a line from front to back of the head is everyday hairdress for all Songhoi women. Further variations in hair arrangement distinguish immature from marriageable girls and both from married and old women. Slaves also have a characteristic hair mark.[13]

Jewelry is worn by all women at all times. During holiday festivals the display is dazzlingly rich. Finger rings of silver and stone, necklaces of gold, amber, or shell, heavy "C"-shaped bracelets of silver and ebony or beads, and a great variety of earrings are daily costume. They may not all be worn by any one individual, although it is not unusual. Even nursing babies wear bracelets and anklets. Girl babies have pieces of yarn put through their pierced ear lobes to start the process of beautification. The poorest slave woman can put a peanut through her ear for an earbob. Others may afford a row of small silver rings fastened through perforations all along the edge of the ear, from top to bottom. Even a few nose-rings are worn by the Arma through the nasal septum and by Gabibi through the outer "wing" of the nose. Songhoi girls have tattooed beauty marks—three parallel lines at the outer corner of each eye and often on the brow and chin. Ornaments of stone, shell, and precious metal are fastened in the hair for further decoration. Large hoops, caught in the back hair, often hang down over the napes of Songhoi necks. Timbuctoo has developed a unique jewelry craft for those who

[13] For designs and descriptions of hairdress and clothes, see Dupuis (Yakouba), 1914.

cannot afford golden ornaments. Wheat straw, dyed to a rich, golden yellow, is worked onto a beeswax base to create ornaments which at a distance pass for gold.

Men's Wear

The robe, in various forms, is also the basic costume for men. It is worn over droopy pantaloons, the legs of which fall almost to the ankle. The tunic of the Daga men is narrow and only knee length, exposing the drawers beneath. Among the Tuareg nobles and serfs, it is the men who wear veils. The Daga veils are made of Guinea cloth, like the rest of their clothes. The veil is simply part of a long piece of material, the rest of which is wound about the head. White cloth is often used as a final wrapping of this turbaned head, the crown of which remains uncovered.

Tuareg accoutrements are as characteristic as their clothes. Stone bracelets and, more recently, those of composition brought in by Hausa traders, are worn above the elbow. These are put on in youth and cannot be removed when growth is attained. In town, the Daga usually carry a yard-long, shillalah-like stick with a large knob on the end, which makes it an effective club for use on man or beast. In the bush they usually carry iron-tipped, wooden-shafted lances. The French forbid the carrying of spears in the city. Nevertheless, one sees many of these people of the bush coming thus armed into Timbuctoo, either from ignorance or in spite of the law. In addition, many wear either the Tuareg straight-bladed sword, with its cross-shaped hilt, or a keen-bladed arm dagger, cunningly sheathed along the inside of the left forearm. Both of these weapons, along with an iron-shafted lance and often an oryx-hide shield, are carried by the veiled Tuareg nobles whenever they come to town.

The pantaloons of the Bela slaves fall only to their knees and their tunics are usually ragged and even more scanty than those of the Daga. To restrain this flopping garment, ill adapted to the slave's work, it is usually tied in around the waist. Being slaves, they do not assume the veil or the weapons of the true Tuareg.

Arab, Arma and Gabibi all wear poncho-cut robes extending almost to the ground. Those who can afford it wear robes wide enough to cover their arms. Some of the younger men wear tunics with sleeves and the sons of a Moroccan merchant wear burnouses but these are quite unusual. Open-heeled slippers, made locally, are the usual footgear of the city Arabs and Songhoi, while the Sudanese sandal characterizes the Daga, Berabich, and Bela—when they are not barefoot. The noble Tuareg wears a wide-soled sandal which acts like a snowshoe on the loose sand and keeps the wearer from sinking in.

The hair and headdress of men is not useful for ethnic identification in most cases. An exception, in addition to the Daga veil, is the bushy, long hair of the Berabich or Moor, who wears no head covering. Most other men shave their heads and their hair is to be seen in all stages of growth. The town Arabs are particularly meticulous about keeping their heads shaved. The men of Timbuctoo grow as much beard as they can, although they may have it shaved off the sides of the face. Full beards, however, are not much in evidence because of the marked Negroid racial mixture.

The Songhoi may wear plain, white, cloth skull-caps which come down to their ears. Shallow black or red fez-like *chechias* are worn by many young men of the same group. Gabibi masons wear a broad, woven, fiber hat while working in the sun. With cloth underneath, this makes an excellent sun helmet. The Arabs go bareheaded or wear turbans, a headdress which does not distinguish them from the Songhoi. Part of the turban cloth may be used to cover the nose and mouth to keep out dust and sand. Such practice is not the everyday necessity which modesty demands of the Daga.

Transportation

Modes of transportation are so intimately associated with the economic position of each population element that they too are distinctive. The only men who consider themselves too good to walk are the Tuareg nobles. Their horses and racing camels take them wherever they go— even into the market. Some Arabs also have camels but in the city they usually lead the animals. A few Arma and Arabs own horses. A very familiar scene in the streets is a Bela or Gabibi riding along on the rump of a donkey so small that his back cannot stand a man's weight. The Daga alone have the distinction of riding hump-backed cattle.

Clothes, hair styles, race, and language can be used to identify the social background of the six thousand inhabitants of the city. An individual's family identity is largely unknown to people of other ethnic groups than his own. His duties and prerogatives often do not hinge on familiarity born of acquaintance but upon the historically determined social role of the group with which the individual is identified by his appearance.

CHAPTER 3

The City Quarters

The sprawling, mud-colored city huddles close to the sand from which it is made. Two beam-studded minarets rising above the flat-roofed dwellings are all that elevate the architecture to conform to the visitor's dream-castle images of fabulous Timbuctoo. Great dunes of sand stretch away to the north. The country of scrubby trees to the south is well characterized as the "bush."

The city has always been partially in ruins. The summer rains are of short duration but torrential in nature. After each downpour mud houses collapse throughout the town and prudent natives sleep in the streets or courtyards to avoid being crushed. A score of such storms during August and September bring an average of eight inches of rain.[1] A storm is usually presaged by the appearance on the horizon of a dull orange cloud sharply defined against the sky. The cloud approaches rapidly as the women in the market scurry to get their produce under shelter. A moment later the city is engulfed in a whirling, Stygian cloud of fine sand. The sand storm continues for some twenty minutes and then ends as abruptly as it began. At this juncture the air in the houses, which have been closed against the storm, is so humid that it is a physical effort for the occupants to breathe. Then follows the chill rain and relief. Naked children run shivering through the streets, reveling in the rain and fighting for places

[1] These figures are based on meteorological records kept at Timbuctoo by Dupuis-Yakouba. Perret, 1935:173, gives the range of annual precipitation in the Timbuctoo area as four to ten inches.

under the water spouting from the drains on the houses. Here and there a man will be seen on a roof during the storm, throwing earth on a spot through which water is leaking into the house. The rain falls in such abundance that surface water collects in the streets more rapidly than the sands can absorb it and for a brief moment the market place looks like a lake. Then suddenly all is bright and warm and the city returns to its business and its pleasures. Until the shuffling, sandaled feet of its populace plow up the sand again, the streets are hard packed and children play at building beehive-shaped huts in the damp sand.

Such a rain is a pleasant change from the continuous heat of most of the year. During eight months the temperature varies between 100° and 110° in the shade during the day and falls only to around 90° at night.[2] The intensity of the direct sunlight[3] is such that when metal pails of water are left in the sun for two hours, the pails are too hot to be handled and the water must be cooled before use. Even the natives do not risk going bareheaded for long when the sun is high. The masons, who must ply their craft in the open, wear native-woven, conical straw hats imported from the west. Merchants of blankets and cloth keep their wares on their heads for protection against the sun. The market, which for centuries has been held each day and into the night despite storms, Tuareg raids, and French regulations, is almost empty during the early afternoon hours because of the intense heat.

The period from early June to mid-August is the hottest and also the dullest for the natives. The desert is too hot for caravans, no traveling merchants can journey on the

[2] Perret, 1935:168–169, gives the mean temperature at Timbuctoo in January as 79° F. and the July mean as 102° F. Fortunately for Timbuctoo, the prevailing winds in January are from the desert, which is then cooler than the tropical forests to the south. In July the prevailing winds are from the south, which is by then cooler than the desert to the north. There are, however, desert winds in July.

[3] Timbuctoo lies just south of the 17th parallel above the equator and has an elevation of 277 meters.

sluggish, low waters of the Niger,[4] crops await the rains for planting, and there is no grass for the nomadic herders. The rains revive the plants, make agriculture possible, raise the river, and usher in the cool season, at the beginning and end of which the caravans or *azalais* bring back salt from the Taodeni mines in the central Sahara. The departure and arrival of the great winter caravan of some five thousand camels are the high points of the yearly commercial activity.

The extreme drought during all but two months of the year makes the construction of mud houses practical. The dwellings are rectangular and bear some resemblance to the adobe houses in the American southwest. The bricks are usually made of double handfuls of sandy clay with rubbish thrown in for binding.[5] These rough balls are then dried in the sun. Such "bricks" are cemented together with more clay to form the house walls which are then covered with a smooth, surface coating of clay. One season's rains do no more than wash off part of this outer coat, so that if the house is properly coated every few years, the inner bricks remain intact.[6] To carry off the water from the roof, drains must jut out several feet from the wall. Such drains are made of hollowed, split palm trunks or, more recently, of tile or gasoline cans.[7] Where such a drain is lacking or has fallen into disrepair, the run-off from the roof cuts a great gash in the mud wall.

[4] The Niger rises at Timbuctoo from August to January, when high water may even reach the city, and descends from February to May.

[5] The use of rectangular bricks made in molds is unusual but old in the Sudan.

[6] At Bourem, on the Niger between Timbuctoo and Gao, the natives found that by mixing their clay with a vegetable butter, the house coating was more rain resistant. These clays dried to various pastel shades of orange, mauve, and red and are one of the few beautiful sights of the Sudan. This *terre de Bourem* is used almost exclusively on government buildings, trading houses and the residences of a few rich natives.

[7] While the gasoline can has become the generally accepted article of material culture in most parts of colonized Africa, it is little used in Timbuctoo except as noted, probably because the French there had been using gasoline for about a decade only.

Structures are strengthened by building thick buttresses beside doorways and at intervals around the rest of the walls. These supports are made of sun-dried bricks and some cut stone[8] and are an integral part of the wall. Such buttresses are to be found in their most elaborate form at Djenné, where they dominate the architectural style. We know that masons from the Djenné area introduced mud houses into Timbuctoo.

Doors are made of wood and are studded with iron. Most have large ornamental knocker rings. Windows are few, small, and high. Wooden grills of Moroccan design are fitted into these small apertures and constitute the most obvious evidence of the sixteenth century conquest. The rooms of the houses are narrow, dark, and dirt-floored. The explanation of their narrowness is to be found in the limitations set by the method of roofing. Palm trunks, cut short for strength, are used as beams. Palm fronds and matting are laid over the beams and plastered with mud to form the second story flooring or the roof, as the case may be. The ground floor rooms open into a small, inside courtyard where the cooking and most of the living are done. The native houses are practically devoid of furniture with the exception of a benchlike wicker bed and a thin mattress of rushes which is rolled up when not in use. A few reed mats and leather cushions to sit on are moved about the floor. Kitchen utensils and a store of woven and leather goods complete the household inventory.

The winding streets are bordered by the continuous walls of dwellings, broken only by doorways. The shifting sands have been so redistributed during the ages that the entrances to some houses are half choked. On entering, one must descend several feet to reach the floor level, which once was on a level with the street. Other doorways have been left high above the street, the sands of which have gradually blown elsewhere. A number of the houses

---

[8] Judging from the content of mosque walls, the use of stone in small quantities may be old. The French have constructed many buildings completely of dressed stone. During our stay the small mosque of Sidi Yahya was being reconstructed after the old form, but of stone. This was done on French initiative.

have low, earthen benches jutting out into the street to either side of the doorway.[9] The Songhoi like to spread their mats and lie on these "beds" in the evenings when the houses are stifling. The streets themselves are so narrow and tortuous that none would permit the passage of an automobile until houses were torn down to create some passageways for the half dozen cars that are used by the French.

The Bela and Arab slave compounds on the outskirts of the city are built so as to leave somewhat wider streets, for land is less at a premium here than in the heart of town. These peripheral dwellings consist of beehive-shaped huts. As early as 1325 the Mandingo emperor forbade their con-

[9] The architecture of Timbuctoo houses conforms to great extent with Arab houses in North Africa and, from what we know of their date of introduction from Djenné, could have been Arab-introduced into the Sudan. Also the distribution of such dwellings in Africa corresponds with Moslem influence. Blackman, 1927:32, describes low benches, such as we have just noted, beside doorways in Egypt. She cites (pp. 281–282) A. M. Blackman's evidence that such benches were common in ancient Egypt. This is the only evidence I discovered pertinent to the very poor case for the Egyptian origin of the Songhoi, which has been made by practically all writers on Timbuctoo. The occurrence of such benches in Egypt does not, of course, rule out the possibility of their having been introduced into the Sudan by Arabs.

Monteil, 1932:185–195, states that the architectural type and the molded bricks may have come from the Near East and Africa Minor through early commercial contacts. He disagrees with Dubois' theory of Egyptian origin of the houses and also with the contention that Abou Ishaq, a relatively late Spanish Moor, was the originator. The *Tarikh es-Soudan* states that the Songhoi Askia secured five hundred masons from Dia, west of Timbuctoo and north of Djenné, near the end of the fifteenth century. The *Tedzkiret en-Nisian* comments on the unusual height of the houses of Milad and Mansour, two of the Moroccan conquerors, which may indicate that two-story houses were a direct introduction from the north. The Djenné masons trace their descent from a seventeenth or eighteenth century Moor.

In summation, the present architecture combines older and more recent traits and the original mud architecture should be considered an importation from the north or northeast, which occurred under unknown circumstances.

struction in the central area of the city.[10] The huts are built of grass thatch over a crude framework of gnarled scrub wood. They are six to eight feet high in the center and some ten or fifteen feet in diameter. There are no windows and but a single doorway, so low that one must stoop to enter. Inside these dwellings, the family possessions are fastened onto or stuck into the thatch walls.

As fires cannot be built in these inflammable homes, cooking is always done in the yard. Even so, many old people have been burned to death when sparks ignited the tinder-dry thatch. The fenced-in compound may contain one or two houses. In addition, a work-hut, with thatched roof and open sides, is often built to provide shade in the open air. This lacking, the woman follows the shade outside of her hut. Around the yard runs a head-high fence of tightly bound dry grasses which is stronger than the material might suggest. There is a crude straw gate which can be closed and locked when the owners are away. Honesty is not to be counted on in this community.

The Quarters

The city, including the straw huts, is divided into a number of different "quarters." The four dominant quarters of the central part of the city are called Badyinde, Sankore, Dyingerey Ber, and Sara Keyna, as shown in Figure 4.[11] These are old divisions which the French have

[10] Pefontan, 1922:84.

[11] Barth, who visited the city in 1853, records *Sane Gungu* as being one town quarter. It was peopled by rich merchants from Ghadames and consisted of the mud house section on the southeast edge of town. By the time of Dubois' visit in 1895, the quarter seems to have lost its identity as no mention is made of it. Barth, who was a virtual prisoner in Timbuctoo, had access to the seventeenth century *Tarikh es-Soudan*. The *Tarikh*, p. 222, speaks of the quarter of Sane Gungu and the Ghadames merchants and other details which correspond with Barth. There is thus strong possibility that the quarter was no longer recognized in Barth's time. In 1940 that part of the city was considered as part of Sara Keyna.

The quarters and their names have changed radically since

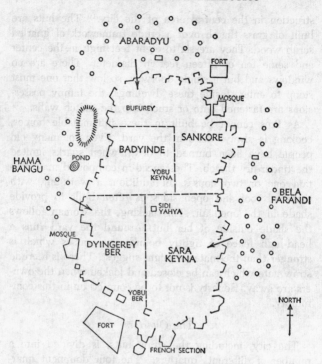

Fig. 4 Schematic Plan of Timbuctoo. (Approximate scale: three inches equal one mile.)

retained but combined administratively with peripheral quarters. The native system of chiefs over the four quar-

the early days as the peoples and landmarks have changed. Pefontan, 1922:83–84, states that the first mud houses were built around 1290 by people from Biru (Oualata) and the quarter was known as *Birouqué Kounda*. The Mali king, Kankan Moussa, built a palace in Timbuctoo shortly after 1325. The quarter around the palace was called *Madougou*. The palace has long since disappeared. A large dune on the west edge of town was indicated to me as its location. This location corresponds with Dubois' location of the palace but not with that indicated by Pefontan, which appears to be in error. Another quarter grew up between the two just mentioned. It was known as *Bissaoutjire*. None of these quarters is now recognized.

ters still functions. Sankore and Dyingerey Ber (Great Mosque) take their names from the mosques which are located in them. Badyinde's name is derived from a large depression which formerly became a pond during high water—a part of the general morass of Niger floodland to the south and west of the city.[12]

A glance at the city plan will show that there are other distinct quarters: Abaradyu, Bela Farandi, and Hama Bangu around the outskirts, and internal subdivisions such as Bufurey in Sankore. Arrows on the diagram indicate with what quarter each suburb is formally identified, but their distinctness is more significant than this French arrangement. The French have constructed their residences and government buildings across the southern edge of town. The only French who reside in the native city are those who run trading houses around the Little Market; the old "White Monk," Yakouba, with his native wife; and an occasional French soldier's household.

The northern hut quarter of Timbuctoo, called Abaradyu in Songhoi, derives its name from the Arabic *abradje*, meaning nonurban habitations. It was in this suburb that caravans were unloaded after their trip from the north. While the camels recuperated in the bush for several months, the Arabs stayed in easily erected huts in Abaradyu. Not being sedentary, they had no use for more permanent houses. In addition there was greater safety in remaining together than in dispersing throughout the city. Depredation was the rule and Tuareg and Arma alike seized every opportunity to rob merchants and their caravans.

The quarter of Abaradyu is still Arab. But in addition to the old population there is a new element composed

---

[12] *Dyinde* certainly refers to this "ditch" or "canal." The old men say that once it was possible to go by boat from Sankore to Dyingerey Ber. The first syllable of Badyinde may be derived from *baña* (hippopotamus) for these beasts are prevalent in the Niger, or it may come from *ba* (to break), in some such sense as "the severed canal," if it did not connect with the branch from the Niger. Barth, 1890:345–346, says the whole quarter was covered in the flood of 1640.

of Arab "slaves" living in independent households no longer under the control of a master. Before the dawn of the *paix française* all slaves were household slaves except the Bela of the Tuareg. A separate household of Arab slaves would certainly have been seized and sold by some Tuareg, Moor, or Arma. Even unimportant freemen and particularly their children were in danger of surreptitious capture. Gabibi were normally protected by the noble families to whom they owed allegiance.

The French have eliminated some aspects of slavery. They have forbidden the use of the French word for "slave" and substituted "captive." The capture of new slaves and sale of slaves, except for concubines, has been stopped. The purchase of concubines is looked upon as marriage and actually frees slaves. Moslem law states that if a concubine bears a child by her master, she becomes free upon his death. A mistreated slave may appeal to the French for freedom or simply run away, for now the danger of being reenslaved is gone. The determining fact in the eyes of the French as to whether a person is freeman or slave is who pays the head tax—the individual or a master. Unlike other large French Sudanese cities, Timbuctoo has no "free quarter" where emancipated slaves reside.

Many aspects of the old system of slavery were not particularly harsh and a household slave was probably in a more favorable position than a poor freeman today. On the other hand, the wealth of even an unimportant freeman is now secure. Yet many slaves still prefer slavery to economically precarious freedom. There are few other roles open to them in the society. Prostitution is one type of service for which a free woman can always find a market and many prostitutes live in Abaradyu. An alternative employment is household work of the type which used to be done by slaves. Arabs who have no slaves speak of "hiring" a household "slave." Such service may be secured in return for poor clothes and food and forty cents a month.[13]

---

[13] The wage paid to native domestic help by the French is approximately three dollars a month and does not include clothing and food.

Probably the most vicious aspect of the old system of slavery was the ruthlessness with which families were broken up. The Tuareg made a practice of separating children from their parents, which may account for the almost complete acculturation of Bela to Tuareg ways of life. Some work, such as that in the salt pits at Taodeni, was literally killing. There men worked all day in terrific heat with their legs in salt water. The only drinking water was also salty. Most of the slave trade of Timbuctoo went to Arabs of the north.

In the straw huts of Abaradyu reside not only emancipated Arab slaves, concentrated in the western part of the quarter, but there is a section on the desert edge of the Abaradyu where the Berabich live. Being men of the bush and desert, they are as peripheral to the city socially as they are physically. There is a separate group of shereef[14] huts and in still another part Arab families of the smith-caste reside. The Arabs live in grass huts identical with those of the Bela, but a married Arab has two huts—one in which his wife can remain out of sight while he entertains his friends in the other. Household slaves of Arabs in Abaradyu have their huts inside or adjoining the master's compound. A few mud houses have been built in the quarter by richer Arabs and even a few Gabibi. An Arma or Alfa would never deign to live there.

In the eastern part of the quarter are concentrated Bela slaves. These Bela are the Alkhali Sidali (the matrilineal relatives of Sidali). This group belongs to a nomadic, maraboutic tribe of Tuareg distinct from the desert-inhabiting Kel Inerkunder, who are masters of the Bela residing in Bela Farandi on the eastern outskirts of the city. The Bela of Abaradyu and their masters are more influenced by Arab culture than are other Tuareg. Rodd[15] supports the existence of "Arab" tribes of Tuareg who fill an ambiguous position of being neither noble nor serf. The Alkhali Sidali slaves speak both Temajegh and Arabic.

Arab slaves and Sidali slaves intermarry a great deal and

[14] The shereef are the descendants of Fatimah, the daughter of Mohammed.
[15] Rodd, 1926:138–139.

feel a close bond with one another. The Kel Inerkunder Bela regard the Alkhali Sidali population as part of the Arab slave group. It is the Arabs who distinguish them as Bela, but the Sidali Bela very rarely intermarry with the Tuareg slaves of Bela Farandi. Alkhali Sidali slaves are not enough like the Tuareg to be so identified by the true Bela, yet their Temajegh speech and matrilineal organization distinguish them as Bela in the eyes of the Arabs.

In addition to Bela Farandi, whose residents have already been identified, there is still another quarter of huts. These are built to the west of town around the large pond which is the source of water for most of the city. The pond is owned by the emir or native chief of Timbuctoo. It is visited daily by water-carriers who scoop its green water into goatskin bags with the aid of gourds. Then they jog off with the hundred pound skins of water on their heads. Water is thus delivered to regular patrons who pay the carrier for the service. The young daughters of the lower classes carry home water in tins and jugs. Most of the professional carriers are Bambidye, originally from the Songhoi town down the river. Although the work is considered very degrading, I had the service of a holy-blooded shereef, who brought three skins of water a day in return for a dollar and a half a month. While he was really a deeply religious Arab, whose faith did not conflict with menial work, the fact he was doing such labor led my Songhoi cook to comment that my water-carrier must be from the bush, where men born on Friday are said to take the title of shereef.

A servant of the emir is overseer of the pool and keeps cattle out of this source of drinking water. Such care does not extend to preventing the water-carriers from wading into the pool to fill their water bags. The water is the source of the Guinea worms that afflict the population.[16]

---

[16] The eggs of this worm enter the digestive tract where they hatch into parasitic worms which make their way through the intestinal walls and along the bones until they emerge, usually between the knee and the ankle. By this time they are about the size of a pencil lead but are several feet long. The process

Every Tuesday and Friday, the guardian exacts ten centimes (about one-quarter of a cent in 1940) from householders who habitually get water at the pond and fifty centimes from the professional water-carriers. In the old days, the slaves and Gabibi of the emir lived in huts around the pool and the section was known as Hama Bangu (Hama's Pond), after the name of the caretaker. The quarter has now been increased by the settlement of other Gabibi and occasional Bela.

In the city of mud houses one can recognize a certain preponderance of one class or ethnic group in each quarter of the town. No one group, however, is present to the exclusion of all others, as the Bela are in Bela Farandi. The accompanying chart (Figure 5), based on observation and the statements of informants, expresses these concentrations.

Figure 5

ETHNIC CONCENTRATIONS IN CITY QUARTERS

Quarters	Arab	Bela	Arma	Gabibi
Dyingerey Ber			*	**
Badyinde	*			*
Sara Keyna	**			*
E. Sankore	*		*	
W. Sankore (Bufurey)	**			
Abaradyu	**			
Bela Farandi		***		
Hama Bangu		*		**

(Degree of prevalence: *presence marked; **dominant group; ***sole residents)

Arabs and Gabibi are to be found in all quarters and it is probable that a few Arma are likewise sprinkled throughout the "house" sections but not in the huts. However,

---

of removal consists of pulling the worm out a few inches each day. The worm is wound up on a small stick, which is bandaged in place until more can be reeled up. The process is painful but nothing compared to the resulting ulceration if the worm is broken off.

public opinion identifies each group with the quarter where it is the most numerous. Popular attitudes regarding the various quarters are colored by these identifications. Many of the marabouts live in Sankore, to which they are still attracted by the mosque which was once the greatest center of learning in the Sudan. The residents of this quarter are supposed to be fine-featured, and to be honest and upright to the extent of being almost holy.

The western section of Sankore, called Bufurey, is probably at least two-thirds Arab. It will be noted that the Arabs, being the latest comers and not arriving as a unit, are the most dispersed of all the groups. However, Arabs consider Bufurey "more attractive" than the rest of the city, converting their preference for the place into an aesthetic judgment. Actually, it looks just like other parts of the city and non-Arabs do not consider it attractive. But one sees more Arabs in its streets, it is close to Abaradyu with its Arab populations, and it is near to both the mosque of Sankore and the arrival point of the camel caravans. If camels have to pass through the narrow city streets, they often become frightened and break their precious loads of salt. Hence it is advantageous to caravan traders to be near the arrival point of their caravans. Such facts, plus familiarity, are the things which make Bufurey attractive to the Arab.

Dyingerey Ber is considered to be a center for the feared use of fetishes because here the Gabibi live in great numbers. Although the Koran forbids the use of such heretical powers, the Gabibi are well known for their sorcery. A century ago Dyingerey Ber was an Arma and Gabibi quarter. Many Arma still reside here and even those who live in Badyinde are said to participate more in Dyingerey Ber life. One finds other people who live in one quarter but are said to belong to a different one. The reason for this lack of conformity lies in a system of age-graded societies which are organized on the basis of the quarters of the city. Even though a person might change his place of residence, he would continue his social activities with the age-group in his original quarter.

The quarter of Badyinde contains many of the non-Songhoi elements of the population. Moroccan, Syrian, and Arab merchants, in addition to the only non-Bela Tuareg families in the city, live in Badyinde. For the Songhoi, this quarter reeks of the impersonal greed of the market which it surrounds. Before leaving the question of attitudes toward the various residence areas, it should be added that Bela Farandi has the reputation of being a nest of thieves.

A résumé of the residential plan of Timbuctoo shows a central city of houses built of bricks and peripheral suburbs of straw huts. The inhabitants of the suburbs are poor and of low status. In it reside slaves and recently emancipated slaves, serfs, low class Arabs, and mobile bush folk who know and care so little about the city that they are willing to live here. The permanent residents follow the low status professions of farmers, smiths, donkey-owners, water-carriers, leather-tanners. The outskirts have earned their reputation as centers of prostitution and thievery. The people are poor and dress poorly. But even among themselves there are class and culture divisions, both geographical and social. The Bela and Arab slaves will have none of each other and the poorest Gabibi is better than either, while the poor Arabs are aloof and superior. Within the city of houses, the natives recognize the social superiority of Sankore, the Arab ethnic quality of Bufurey, the Arma and Gabibi dominance in Dyingerey Ber, and the disunited, commercial nature of Badyinde.

As has been pointed out, the commercial importance of the city is waning and with it the population. This has led to the evacuation of residences which have been allowed to fall into disrepair. Significantly, there are more of the tumbled-down, clay houses on the edge of the city, adjoining the huts on the outskirts. Such ruined houses are sometimes occupied by poor households, particularly Arma families, many of which are almost destitute since the French have replaced them as masters of the city. Occasionally a straw hut is built in the courtyard of a rain-eroded house which is in too bad condition for habitation.

One finds a few mud houses built on the inner edge of the straw hut sections. These are the houses of the more prosperous lower status groups who still cling to the neighborhood in spite of the status display of a real house. In addition to having personal attachments to the area, the owners of these houses are probably unable to escape their tradition-marked social position which is evidenced in race, speech, clothes, and means of livelihood.

The Market

The location of the market place has an interesting history. In the days before the French, there was a Big Market and a Little Market—Yobu Ber and Yobu Keyna. The great open expanse of the Big Market lay in the southwestern edge of the city, while the Little Market was tucked into the passageways of the heart of the town.[17] When the Moroccans occupied Timbuctoo, they built their fort in the southeastern quarter of the city. Faced with continuous incidents between Moroccans and the Songhoi, the pasha had the main market moved to a spot just outside the entrance to the fort, where his troops would always be on hand in case of trouble.[18] In relating this incident, the Arab chronicle bears witness to the fact that even in the sixteenth century the market was the focal point of impersonal contact between the peoples of the city—a breeding spot of strife.

With the decline of the power of the pashas, the principal market seems to have reverted to its old location. When the French took over, their main fort, first trading-post, and mission were placed beside the Big Market, where a pavilion was erected for the native merchants. In a short while, the dissatisfaction of residents of the northern part of the city with the extreme southern location of 'the market caused the French to expand the more central Little Market. The European traders followed the shift and now the Big Market is a bare and sandy area around

[17] Barth, 1890:324. Yobu Keyna is designated as being principally a butchers' market in 1853.
[18] Es-Sadi, 1900:265.

which rise the French administrative buildings, constructed in a sophisticated "native" style. Perhaps a score of women display their wares in the Big Market. The bulk of the retail selling is now done in the Little Market which, confusingly, is now really the big market.

This shift in the location of the market place evidences a fundamental change in the focal point of communication and trade. French influence, while providing the capital and initiative for the expansion of the Little Market, was not the sole cause of its growth. A more fundamental explanation of the shift lies in the fact that when Timbuctoo was larger, the Big Market was more centrally located with respect to the whole city. Midden refuse indicates that the city used to extend farther south than at present.[19] The growth of the southern part of the city probably occurred during the prosperous period of the Songhoi Empire and its decline was ushered in by the Moroccan conquest and the troubled days which almost ruined the city's commerce.[20]

The change in the nature of the wholesale trade of Timbuctoo during the last two centuries also appears to have influenced the city's internal pattern. There was a decline of incoming, river-borne goods, which are now dominantly agricultural. European commercial interests drew off the richer produce which formerly reached the city. As a result, the salt trade, coming in from the north, has gained in relative importance.

We must recognize that the market functions in a retail rather than a wholesale capacity. As such, its central location to the city is important. However, there is an advantage for wholesalers to be close to the terminal point of incoming shipment. The wholesalers control much of the retail market and are hence interested in market location.

[19] Pefontan, 1922:82–83, gives the limits of the city at successive epochs. The source of his data is not stated. The southern extension of the city he indicates as existent in the late seventeenth century.

[20] It is possible that this southeastern extension of the city was the quarter of Sane Gungu. See note 11 above.

The shift of dominance from the Big Market, near the end of the Niger canal, to the Little Market, closer to the arrival point of caravans, may also reflect the increased importance of the salt trade.

The forces which brought about the shift in market location had been physically restrained by the mud walls which delimited the Little Market until the arrival of the French. There was a lag because no political or economic machinery existed to handle such a problem of city-wide significance. Timbuctoo never evolved any answer to most of its municipal problems. Sanitation was not considered a problem. Excretae dried rapidly in the streets and no one minded the smells. Robbery was part of the pattern of life. While more homogeneous towns defended their integrity against invaders, Timbuctoo capitulated without defense to one conqueror after another. The Arma and Arab residents had guns, but still individual Tuareg armed with spears entered the city and plundered the unprotected at will. Unlike other Sudanese cities, Timbuctoo never seems to have been walled, although the Mandingo and later the Moroccan conquerors did throw up breastworks to protect their interests there. No vestige of these works remains.

CHAPTER 4

Elementary Economics

Currency and Exchange

Diminutive cowrie shells, originating in the Indian Ocean, were long ago introduced into West Africa and became a recognized medium of exchange.[1] Like gold, these shells were also widely used for adornment. While cowries were employed as currency for most transactions, gold was the medium of exchange when large values were involved, particularly in the payment of tribute. The use of both gold and cowries was limited to the larger communities where there were markets.[2] In the bush and desert, barter is still necessary and the traveler must carry salt, cloth, or kola nuts to trade for food. A medium of exchange implies more than recognition of exchange value, for the bush people knew the value of cowries as they know that of francs today. The acceptance of a medium of exchange which cannot be consumed itself—cowries as against salt— necessitates easily available stocks of commodities for which the currency is exchangeable.

Like any commercial center, Timbuctoo has had its economic fluctuations. In times of dearth and famine, prices soared. Such conditions brought out the gold hoards, which normally did not circulate, and the value of cowrie shells increased relative to gold. The value of both, of course, declined relative to food and cloth, but gold showed the most marked decrease. Another factor involved in the cowrie-gold ratio was the greater practicability of cowries for small market transactions and hence the

[1] Rattray, 1923:234. Monteil, 1932:279.
[2] Caillié, 1830:II, 30.

greater demand for them under conditions of famine-inflated prices. On the one known occasion when the cowrie value of gold did not decline during a famine—that of 1738 —the evidence is positive that it was the shortage of gold which kept its value up.[3]

As European interests established a foothold on the coasts of West Africa, they drew off appreciable amounts of the gold supplies of the interior. Gold increased in value, doubling its cowrie value by the end of the nineteenth century. As the amount of gold decreased, another medium of exchange appeared—French francs. This currency had a recognized exchange value in Timbuctoo even before the city was captured by the French. As francs became more current than cowries, they declined in value relative to cowries. But by 1940 cowries had been entirely replaced by the official French currency.[4]

[3] The exchange in the year of 1735 was 2,000 cowries to a *mitsqâl* (about 4.5 grams) of gold. (Molouk es-Soudan, 1901: 101. Translator's footnote in error.) This rate may still have reflected the depressed conditions resulting from the great famine of 1711–1716, during which the gold exchange fell to 700 cowries (*ibid.*, 63), and the subsequent famine of 1721– 1722. By early 1738 the rate was 3,000 cowries to the *mitsqâl* of gold (*ibid.*, 190). During the famine which struck that summer, the value of gold relative to cowries remained constant, much to the wonderment of the native economists of that day (*loc. cit.*). Not even the oldest men had ever heard of such a phenomenon. As early as 1617, the chroniclers had recorded the fall of the gold exchange to 500 cowries during a famine in that year (Es-Sadi, 1900:338).

There is good reason to believe that the exchange remained stable during the 1738 famine because of a shortage of gold in circulation. It is recorded that in July the pasha collected a heavy tribute of 1,000 *mitsqâl* of gold from traders of the city, thus removing it from the market (Molouk es-Soudan, 1901: 190). The famine had passed its peak by the end of August when the pasha was deposed and succeeded by another. In November yet another pasha took power and imposed a new duty of 1,500 *mitsqâl* of gold on the merchants. The amount *was paid in cowries*, showing that gold was not available. The rate by then was 2,000 to the *mitsqâl* (*ibid.*, 107).

[4] During the first half of the nineteenth century the exchange seems to have held around 4,000 cowries to the *mitsqâl* of gold

French pieces are now known by Songhoi terms. This is an unusual acculturation pattern with respect to currency, which most frequently carries the nomenclature of its country of origin. There is no longer any hesitance in accepting French currency,[5] although market vendors still often refuse to accept paper money which has been torn and mended. Everyone knows that such bills are redeemable at the French *poste* and they are singled out for transactions with the big merchants who have dealings at the *poste* through postal and telegraphic money orders or savings accounts.

Price

In the commerce of the city, the profit-minded natives run the gamut of practices which uncontrolled, laissez-faire economy makes possible. They even have a trick or two to teach the French traders. These latter run little hole-in-the-wall stores for native trade. Their retailing methods are distinctly French—cloth sold by the meter, sugar by the kilogram, and everything for a fixed price. For centuries the natives have bought cloth by the "elbow," measured on the purchaser's arm from fingertips to elbow. Sugar is purchased by the unweighed chunk, and for most transactions there is a fine argument over the price. Such are the methods in the market place today.

The residents of Timbuctoo buy at the store when the goods are lacking or higher priced in the market.[6] They

(Barth, 1890:351. Monteil, 1932:280). In 1880 the explorer Lenz says it was about 8,000 cowries (1884:151), but by the end of the century it was 6,200 (Monteil, 1932:280). In 1880, a *mitsqâl* of gold was worth ten to twelve francs in the desert oasis of Araouan. At St. Louis, adjacent to Dakar, the rate was fourteen or fifteen francs (Lenz, 1884:150). The cowrie-franc ratio was around 1,000 to 1 from 1830 to 1900. By 1928 it had fallen to 160 to 1 (Monteil, 1932:267).

[5] Dupuis (Yakouba) says that there were doubts about the whole currency at first—presumably the non-precious metal and paper currency, as French silver coin had long had recognized exchange value locally.

[6] In this connection, a *koyraboro* marabout and women who were questioned did not know the names of the French trading

are less governed by traditional forms than by the consideration of cost. However, when bush natives come to town, they prefer to buy in the market. Several natives of Timbuctoo make a living by buying at the French trading houses and then reselling the same goods to the bush natives the way the latter like to buy. The success of these middlemen is entirely dependent upon the bush folk's dislike of French retail methods.

The small stores of the non-French, most of them run by Arabs, employ a "one price" system in the sense that prices are not subject to haggling. Yet prices are varied as occasion permits, according to the amount the store owner thinks each buyer will pay. There are functional limitations to bargaining in a store. Haggling over price is an individual proposition and inherent in this system is secrecy. Successive buyers must be unaware of the prices paid by their predecessors. In a store there are often many prospective buyers all listening to the prices being quoted to the person who is buying at the moment. Secrecy is lost and some sort of one price system becomes necessary.

The most important factor in a one price system is the standardization of the units of sale. When the unit is an "elbow," which varies with each customer, or an unweighed "chunk," a one price system is meaningless. Thus in the market place there tends to be, at any one time, consensus as to prices of common commodities which have recognized units. These prices are not usually subject to bargaining except over questions of quality. The price of kola nuts and recognized basket measures of common grains thus tends to be set by consensus. The general adoption of old, liter wine bottles as milk containers has had the same effect on milk prices. The supply and demand for such commodities influences the consensus as to price on successive days and even during a single day.[7]

_____

houses located on the market place. They were not landmarks. The reason is that some marabouts are not commercially minded and that women's buying is largely limited to produce sold by market vendors.

[7] Herskovits, 1938:61, states that the price of foodstuffs is set

Unstandardized units and products which are not in wide demand constitute the bulk of the market trade. Prices for these are set by bargaining.

The process of haggling is somewhat formalized. The vendor must state an "asking" price; the purchaser does not make an introductory offer. The vendor, knowing that his price will be beaten down, quotes an initial price at least double that which he hopes to receive. The prospective purchaser then offers about a third of the price asked and the bargaining continues until a price satisfactory to both is reached. In addition to the price setting function of bargaining, it provides very real psychological satisfactions. Even when the happy vendor receives more than the lowest price he had decided to take, the purchaser has the satisfaction of having beaten the price far below the original quotation.

Commerce is conducted on a basis of mutual suspicion. This attitude antedates French influence. Caillié writes that in 1828 it was customary practice in the market for the buyer to place his cowries in the basket containing the goods being sold. The vendor could not touch the cowries until the purchaser took the goods.[8] *Caveat emptor* is the rule of the market.[9]

Guilds

The most formalized division of labor in Timbuctoo is a sort of guild system of hereditary crafts. Slipper-makers, tailors, masons, butchers, barbers, and smiths were once all hereditary tradesmen. Among the different trades there was considerable variation in the form and significance of the hereditary pattern. Recent changes have also affected them unequally.

The Arma dominated the trade of slipper-making, a craft which they introduced from Morocco. Arma boys

---

by the first woman to arrive in the Abomey market and that the price is held all day.

[8] Caillié, 1830:II, 46.

[9] For a discussion of the commercial dishonesty, see Chapter 13.

were apprenticed in this craft for the discipline it provided, but they were not forced to practice the trade as adults. However, no one else could make slippers, for only the sons of Arma could be apprenticed. Most of the Arma received enough income from plunder, trade, and the work of their slaves and serfs to exempt them from physical effort. Even the master slipper-makers left most of the labor to their young apprentices. After a long period of training, these helpers could start on their own if they passed the necessary tests before the master slipper-makers of the city.

The craft of tailoring also had its masters but no formal organization. The making and embroidering of beautiful robes was limited to the Alfa or marabouts. This was not a class-limited craft but one restricted to a professional group. Theoretically, anyone might, with the proper Koranic training, become an Alfa. Actually the training tended to be given only to sons of Arabs and Songhoi marabouts. Not all marabouts made clothes but some thus augmented their income from teaching, healing, making charms, copying books, and even from commerce. Robe-making and embroidery were introduced by North African Arabs along with Islam. The craft may well have been that of local Arab marabouts even before the Moroccan conquest. Like the Arma, the descendants of these Alfa are now as Negroid as they are Caucasoid and quite distinct from more recent Arab arrivals from Morocco. Alfa and Arma are considered to be of equal social status and constitute the only two entirely free groups in the Songhoi population of the city. The tailoring and slipper-making guilds have changed radically in recent times. We shall return to a consideration of these changes after discussing the less altered guilds.

The butchers, barbers, and masons are Gabibi—definitely lower in status and owing some allegiance to the Arma and Alfa families who sponsor them. The Gabibi give presents to their patrons, assist at their life crisis ceremonies, and undertake commercial tasks for them. In return, they receive protection and sometimes even financial assistance. The crafts of the butchers, barbers, and masons are held strictly in family lines.[10] These guilds have hereditary chiefs, and the butchers and masons have distinctive ceremonial dances. The barbers perform important ritual functions during circumcision ceremonies. The dance of the butchers is given on such occasions as a marriage or circumcision in one of their families. They are reported to wear old clothes, hang bones all over their body, paint their faces, and allow free rein to grotesque contortions to amuse the onlookers. The masons' dance costume is characterized only by the conical straw hats which they wear to work.

The Arab and Songhoi smiths are distinct from one another, yet they show definite similarities. Both are considered to be slaves. Each tends strongly toward endogamy, only the men being permitted to marry outside of the group and such marriages are rare. Arab smiths are subservient to whole tribal groups and belong to particular families within the tribes. Songhoi smiths are considered to be the slaves of certain families. Smiths from different Arab tribes intermarry freely but Songhoi and Arab smiths do not. While the Songhoi smiths are renowned for their magical powers, the Arab smiths profess no such supernatural knowledge. They have, however, certain ritual

[10] In 1940 there were fifteen butchers, all Gabibi except for two outsiders, one a Fulani. There were four Gabibi barbers and a larger, indeterminate number of Gabibi masons. The masons belong to two *dyammus* or family groups: the *Woduntye*, descended from Haman and his first cousin and wife Tandu, and the *Dorintye*, descended from Mama and his spouse Samina. The masons in Djenné are known by the Songhoi term *bari*, the family claiming descent from master-craftsmen, Idriss. The guild there is definitely like that of Timbuctoo. The Bambara, who have been the dominant influence in Djenné, have no masons, nor have the Fulani. The craft may have originated with the Da, who were older in the area than the Songhoi. The Bambara do, however, have very low status, leather-working and woodworking castes, and a higher caste of metal-workers, whose wives make pottery (Monteil, 1932:194–195, 237–257). The butchers' guild is not mentioned and apparently the barbers are not so organized in Djenné.

functions to perform in connection with all Arab marriage ceremonies.

The work of a smith includes the making of locks, weapons, pipes, trappings for horses, studding and knockers for doors, and general repair on imported vessels, trays, and the like. In addition to working iron, brass, and copper, the smith is also the jeweler. The making of gold, silver, copper, and brass ornaments, and the inlaying of these metals on wood is all done by the smith.[11] There are various sorts of craftsmen specializing in the different metals. Thus, some who work gold will not touch silver, while others work both precious metals. The wives of smiths do leatherwork which is often closely associated with the metalwork in the finished product, as in weapons and sheaths or bits and bridles.[12]

Decline of the Guild

The craft organization of pre-French days was supported by supernatural sanctions, physical force, popular consensus, and the right to select apprentices. The relative importance of these factors in maintaining the craft system can be judged from the nature of recent changes.

The French did not directly suppress many customs in Timbuctoo except for the selling of slaves, but they did assume for themselves the right to administer all major corporal punishment. They set up their own tribunal for native crimes and limited the powers of the native judge or cadi. In addition to every case involving Frenchmen, all criminal cases must be tried by the French administrator. Natives can appeal the cadi's decisions in civil cases to the French. In practice the administrator supports the cadi in such instances. If the parties in a case before the

[11] In this connection there are to be found today collections of baked clay jeweler's models in some Arma homes, presumably the onetime masters of smiths. These models present the shape and design of various ornaments and were apparently brought to Timbuctoo from Morocco. The jewelry craftsmanship has declined, judging from the relative superiority of old ornaments.

[12] This is true of the Tuareg smith also. De Gironcourt, 1914:43.

cadi refuse to accept his decision, all he can do is threaten to turn them over to the French.

The French administration has declared a democratic regime and states that a man can follow any profession he chooses and marry any woman who will have him. This means that the sanction of physical force no longer supports the class-craft organization. Yet the hereditary crafts are protected by generally recognized supernatural forces. If anyone but an apprenticed Arma tries to sew leather slippers, it is believed that the needle will turn against him and prick his hand. If a person who is not from a family of masons tries to build a house, he will topple from the wall to his death. None but the actual builder of a house or his descendants can repair that house on pain of the same fate. No house owner would have his house repaired by a mason who was not from the builder's family because the owner would not want his house to collapse. The same sort of craft-supporting powers have even developed around the new profession of cooking for the French. While there is no hereditary aspect to this craft, there is a sort of apprenticeship as scullion boy and domestic servant before becoming a cook. If an underling fails to obey the commands of an experienced master, the master turns the objects of the craft—in this case boiling water—against the novice. It is not unusual in all of the crafts for the master to give useless orders, simply to show his superiority. If the apprentice fails to obey, the master will curse his work.

The relative importance of such belief in guild-supporting powers is to be seen in the degree of alteration which has occurred since physical force can no longer be used against those who infringe upon guild prerogatives. There has been a great influx of Gabibi into the trades of slipper-making and tailoring. The other crafts have not been invaded. There is no reason to believe that the supernatural sanctions supporting the Arma and Alfa crafts were less potent; they are simply not strong enough to keep outsiders away.

There are three factors which seem to be responsible

for singling out these particular trades for democratic freedom: differences in the nature of the organization of these crafts from those not broken down, French schools, and the status attached to the crafts. This final factor is in large part responsible for the desire of Gabibi to learn these trades. Slipper-making and tailoring are the only guild crafts which were not traditionally practiced by serfs or slaves. Gabibi who have learned to make slippers or robes almost invariably claim to be noble, a claim which is not easily disputed where genealogies are not widely known.

The French have been teaching slipper-making and tailoring in one of their schools for natives. There are two French schools in addition to the tutoring of pupils done by marabouts. The Madersa is a French-stimulated revival of the old Sankore school. It concentrates on Arabic literature but teaches also some Temajegh and French. The children of rich, noble, or particularly religious families are to be found in this school. The introduction of French language training has to be done very gradually and almost surreptitiously because the best families realize that most of the French-speaking natives are servants for the French. The élite do not want their children to acquire the status or character of these marginal natives. The French trade school was a later introduction and concentrates on the French language and technical training. Its small student body is secured through the city quarter chiefs, who fill the required quotas by taking the children of families who cannot afford to bribe the chiefs not to take their offspring. This means that the lower classes and poorest children go to the French trade school. The families of the children selected have some satisfaction in seeing their boys learn lucrative, upper class crafts.[13]

We have seen that slipper-making and tailoring differed from the other crafts in that they were collateral activities

---

[13] In addition to the sewing of slippers and clothes, some metalwork is also taught but it is not the same sort of work as that of the local smiths. This is training to serve the French, not the natives.

of social groups defined on other bases. While their apprenticeship system was more formalized than the more strictly hereditary crafts, they lacked the formal organization of the other guilds with their chiefs, dances, and special social functions of a non-craft nature. Today, these latter trades continue their exclusive training along the old lines.

There is another good reason for the change in the slipper trade in addition to desire for status and the introduction of French training. Not all Gabibi slipper-makers learn their craft in the French school. In fact, more seem to learn from legitimate Arma masters. Recall that all Arma were apprenticed but not all practiced what they learned. When the French destroyed the economy of the Arma rulers, based on taxation and extortion, many Arma turned to the only non-degrading means they knew of making a living—that of making slippers. They needed apprentices to do the work and the Arma who were inexperienced leather-workers could not get Arma apprentices because they were sent to the best masters for training. In the social flux brought about by French rule, Arma, who were losing status, took Gabibi apprentices, who began to rise in prestige.

The collapse of the system of control over selection of novices and the suppression of violent outbursts resulting from crossing of class lines can be laid to French interference. The informal sanctions of ridicule, gossip, and ostracism were no more effective checks than the supernatural controls. With respect to these latter, it should be added that Gabibi who complete their apprenticeship under Arma masters have nothing to fear, as the final part of the instruction is magical. Slipper-makers trained in the French school and novices who start work on their own before their apprenticeship is completed simply ignore these sacred sanctions.

Arma public sentiment was naturally against this change, but could only express itself through refusal to buy from Gabibi craftsmen. The Arma could deride the upstart Gabibi, but who cared? Gabibi were willing to buy from Gabibi, particularly if the price was lower. Whereas, under the old system, the customer had his slippers made to order, as the upper classes continue to do, the lack of orders caused some craftsmen to prefabricate slippers and display them for sale in the market place. Prefabrication had always been done for export trade, but even good slippers decline in value when they appear in the Timbuctoo market place because of the culture pattern of made-to-order shoes. Slipper vendors in the market are Gabibi, very old Arma, and apprentices who never finished training—all obviously marginal craftsmen.

The economic implications of the craft breakdown are significant. The old system controlled quality and limited the quantity of production. Both quality and quantity are now out of control. Even before the French regime, there was free competition among the Arma so that prices remained reasonable from the consumer's point of view. Those who could not pay the price could always get the Sudanese sandals made by the Bela. Now the price of slippers made by half-trained men is lower but at the expense of quality and beauty; also at the expense of the craft, which is now so overcrowded that slipper-makers are continually emigrating to other cities, an exodus which cannot go on forever and which destroys the export trade of Timbuctoo.

Production and Trade

The crafts make up but a small part of the economic life of Timbuctoo. Almost the entire male population and many of the women are engaged in trade. Even farmers carry on commerce in their off-season. The chart of economic activities gives a schematic idea of the place of the various groups in the commerce and production of the city. The Arabs are the leading men in commerce and some are the richest men in the city. They held this position long before French occupation and controlled even more of the river trade before the French wood-burning, stern-wheelers started plying the Niger.[14] The Berabich have some wealth in camels but the city Arabs are the most affluent. Even in Caillié's time, Moroccans came here to make their fortunes and return home. Some children of those who stayed still cling to this desire to return to Morocco.

Figure 6

THE DIVISION OF LABOR IN TIMBUCTOO

Production, Crafts, and Professions

Arab	Arma	Alfa	Gabibi	Bela
Smiths (slaves)	Slipper-makers	Tailors	Slipper-makers	Sandal-makers
Troubadours (slaves)*		Teachers	Tailors	Basket-weavers*
Camel-breeders		Healers	Barbers	Tanners
		Charm-makers	Masons	Farmers
			Butchers	Donkey-breeders
			Bakers*	
			Farmers	
			Donkey-breeders	
			Basket-weavers*	

Commerce and Transport

Caravaneers	Wholesalers	Wholesalers	Market retailers*	Market retailers*
Wholesalers	Landlords	(limited)	Donkey-drivers	Donkey-drivers
Retailers	Money-lenders		Wholesalers	
Shop-keepers			Money-lenders	
Tabliers				
Landlords				
Money-lenders				
Shippers				

* Female.

Figure 6 not only illustrates the Arab position in commerce but shows the Gabibi and Bela to be the real

[14] Caillié, 1830:II, 27. Also on p. 54 he says, "The Moors occupy the finest houses in the city," and on p. 53, "They have considerable influence on the native king."

producers. They also provide the bulk of the services, exclusive of camel transportation. Since the restriction of extortion from serfs, this group has prospered. They are not limited in their economic activity by upper class restrictions. The Arma does not want to work in the first place, and further he feels it is less degrading to live on charity than to do menial physical tasks. The Gabibi have always worked and now not only can they retain the product of their efforts but they can invade hitherto forbidden pursuits. As a group, the Gabibi are now probably richer than the Arma—a reversal which has come about in the last forty-five years. The Arabs maintain their position through their ownership and knowledge of camels and the advantage their wealth gives them over small buyers and lenders. The Gabibi have always been in commerce but are now gaining a stronger position.

Most of the farming in this area is done in the small Songhoi villages which lie along the river. They produce rice, millet, and the sorghum called Guinea corn. These grains are imported wholesale to Timbuctoo. The small traders retail grain daily in the market. The richer dealers hold their grain for the inevitable price rise before the next harvest. Sometimes these wealthy men succeed in cornering all or large parts of the available grain and force the price to exorbitant levels during virtual famine conditions. Even the small vendors play at the same game.

In 1940 the rains refused to fall in spite of all supplication. With a drought and crop shortage in prospect, practically none of the stored grain was brought to market. Then the rains came and the age-old nature of the practice of withholding grain was evidenced by the familiar chant of the children all over the market place, *"Ibere hawi, hayni farta, saba farta, mo'idye farta!"* (Enemies are ashamed, millet comes out, Guinea corn comes out, rice grain comes out!). The rains had assured a new crop and the grain hoarders had to abandon their hope of the high prices which a shortage would have caused. Grain wholesalers would let their own relatives go hungry if they knew that their kin were able but unwilling to pay the high price demanded. Poor relations would be provided for, but what happens to neighbors and others is nobody's worry.

The Bela, the Arab slaves of Abaradyu, and the Gabibi do some farming. The Bela are the only ones to cultivate watermelons. They and the others raise grain on owned or rented Niger floodlands, including islands. The land around the water holes about the city is also irrigated, largely by the Gabibi. Some vegetables are raised here, mostly for French consumption.[15] Caillié reports that only poor tobacco was grown around the ponds.[16] Tobacco is no longer cultivated. That which is not brought by caravan from the north is raised at Bamba on the Niger.

The agricultural imports most important to the natives consist of rice, millet, Guinea corn, wheat, shea butter, and kola nuts.[17] They are all relatively imperishable which explains their importance over vegetables which cannot be stored because of spoilage. Condiments like peppers, garlic, and pimentos are imported for wide native use in sauces. Songhoi fare, in addition to milk, poultry, and meat,[18] consists largely of wheat bread, boiled rice, rice or millet flour gruel, and couscous. This last dish is made of small pellets of rice, millet or wheat flour. Meat, condiments, and vegetables in season are cooked with the

15 Carrots and beets and a little poor celery are French introductions. Onions, corn, and radishes, along with cantaloupes, pepper, and wheat are known by their Arab names, indicating their origin.

16 Caillié, 1830:II, 58.

17 The administrator estimates that three thousand tons of rice and wheat enter the *Cercle* of Timbuctoo yearly from the nearby *Cercles* of Goundam, Niafunké, and Mopti. (A *cercle* is a territorial, administrative unit. That of Timbuctoo includes fifteen villages in addition to the city.) This is in addition to the rice grown in the Timbuctoo *Cercle* itself. Shea butter for cooking, and even for oiling the skin, and kola nuts, which are chewed by men and women alike, must be brought from the Gold and Ivory Coasts or the Senegal. Wheat was formerly brought from North Africa by caravan, according to Caillié, 1830:II, 69.

18 Chickens, pigeons (a Moroccan introduction), beef, and mutton are usual.

rice or used as a sauce with the couscous.[19] The Arabs depend a great deal upon heavily sugared tea, the ingredients of which must be brought by caravan or secured at the French trading houses. Dates are also a luxury which must be imported from the north. Like the Songhoi, the Bela depend on rice, millet, and Guinea corn.

The only vegetable products which come from the villages near Timbuctoo, in addition to the cereals which are grown in sufficient quantities for the city, are gum arabic, peanuts, and gourds to be used as vessels. Gum has always been an important export. It used to be part of the caravan trade but now is largely absorbed by the French trading houses.[20] In addition to these companies there were six non-French shop owners whose stocks were worth over 50,000 francs (about $1200) apiece. One of these was a Syrian, two others Moroccans, one an Arma, and two Sudanese Arabs. Eight other Arabs and Moroccans each had stocks worth less than 20,000 francs apiece. The native traders buy raw materials and resell them to trading houses as far away as Bamako for eventual export to Europe. They also sell a variety of European trade goods to the local natives. The keeping of shops is a pre-French introduction of the Arabs. Caillié comments on seeing three such stores containing cloth, guns, salt, and ivory.[21] An early eighteenth century manuscript likewise mentions the proprietors of shops.[22] It is striking to note that the present Syrian merchant, who is despised by all the natives as a Christian, makes a comfortable living selling to these selfsame natives in competition with Moslem traders.

[19] For the names and preparation of various dishes, see Dupuis (Yakouba), 1914:261.

[20] Around three hundred tons of gum a year are exported. In 1940 there were three trading houses operating—Maurel & Prom, Société Commerciale du Soudan Français, and Buhan et Teisseire. The largest export house, Cie. Française A.O.F., was closed because of the war, and the private export house of Ober was closed due to his recent suicide when he was caught in a fraud.

[21] Caillié, 1830:II, 51.

[22] Molouk es-Soudan, 1901:45.

The other major exports are animal products—hides and wool.[23] The sources of both are the Tuareg herds and flocks which range the bush country and supply the city with both meat and milk. Hides and wool represent a newly developed export trade. Hides still have, as they used to, some direct native sale to the Bela for tanning and sandals, to Arma for slippers, and to smiths for making other leather goods. Wool is not woven locally but some raw cotton is imported from around Diré, to the west, and is woven on a narrow loom. Native woven blankets from Hausa and Fulani tribes, Goundam and Hombori Songhoi, and even the Arabs of Touat find their way into the market. These are both cotton and wool fabrics woven on six to eight inch looms. The narrow bands are then sewn together to form wide pieces. Some Bela men and Songhoi women do weaving in Timbuctoo but this has never been important. The Touat Arabs make the only wide loom blankets which reach Timbuctoo. An occasional camel's hair blanket enters the commerce from this source. Most of the cloth used for clothing in Timbuctoo comes from the French trading houses or the stores of the native merchants. Cloth used to be a principal import from Kano in Nigeria. The trade in animals on the hoof is largely in the hands of itinerant Hausa merchants who yearly take an estimated two or three thousand head of cattle and ten thousand sheep to Mopti or on to the Gold and Ivory Coasts. These traders bring into Timbuctoo kola nuts, cloth, and other European trade goods, particularly glass beads and composition bracelets. These latter objects have almost entirely replaced the old stone and shell equivalents in the market. The Hausa merchants now usually come by automobile bringing herders to drive the livestock back.

When outsiders come to Timbuctoo—Arabs with dates and tobacco from Touat, Hausa with kola and trade goods, bush Bela with hides and gum—they lodge with residents of the city with whom they may or may not have been

[23] Thirty tons of hides and forty of wool are exported annually, according to the French administrator.

previously acquainted. Strangers can apply to the city chief for lodging and he will direct them to one of these hostels. A system of accommodation for strangers is an urban product of the fluidity of part of the commercial population. The owners of the lodgings often fulfill a directly commercial function, acting as middlemen in the sale of the transients' goods.

The economic role of some of the groups which are peripheral to the city has been seen for the herding Daga and the farming Songhoi and Bela. It should be added that all the native pottery is imported from Kabara, Diré, and other towns. The river folk, both Bozo and Songhoi, supply fish which forms an important element of diet. Boats for hauling produce, particularly grain, are also provided by those who depend upon the floodland for crops or the river for fish.

The increasing importance of French trading houses in the local economy has had a marked effect on the native cost of living. Between 1902 and 1928 the price, in francs, of all commodities increased from five to twenty times. In the same period, the collapse of the franc on the international exchange and the replacement of the shell money by European currency caused cowries to increase their franc value sevenfold. However, the general conversion to a franc exchange gave the native little advantage from the stability of the cowrie. Native products for which there was no European market rose the least in franc value. These included kola nuts, native hoes, bars of iron, blankets, slippers, soap, pipes, and salt bars. Competition among French traders caused agricultural products to show the greatest price rise and European materials—cloth, paper, needles, thread—to show less increase.[24]

Government estimates of native income and cost of living, made in 1932, show that farmers and traders are the only groups which earned the twenty-four dollars a year necessary to feed a single individual adequately.[25] The slave and serf farmers are in a better economic position

24 Monteil, 1932:267, 293.
25 *Ibid.*, 295–296.

than those slipper-making, noble Arma who have no capital for commercial enterprise. The traders, particularly the Arabs, are in the most favored position, earning up to sixty times more than small craftsmen. The serf Gabibi had a traditional place in retail market trade which many have been able to expand and capitalize upon.

The Market

The market place provides a good picture of the division of labor based on class and sex. While the French have segregated some vendors according to type, there is a great deal of informal grouping of those fulfilling the same function. Notably the Bela and Arab-slave woodsellers have been placed at one end of the market and the Daga milk vendors at the other end, as these products are quickly sold, leaving the space free for the movement of the population. Likewise, the construction of masonry stalls has located the butchers in a building especially designed for them. In other booths are tailors, merchants of cloth and trade goods, and numerous young Arab *tabliers*.

The last-named type of merchant has a single, small table before him covered with little items of trade, all of European manufacture: matches, needles, bluing, mirrors, penknives, etc. Of course, tables, as well as the produce thereon, are foreign introductions. The remaining vendors either set up matting shelters in the center of the market or have two traditional places to squat with their merchandise—one position in the morning shade of the buildings and another in the afternoon shade. The diagram of the market place pictures the situation on a day just before the onset of the hot season which stifles commerce. As will be noted, milk is still available as the Daga have not yet left with their herds, but vegetables and melons are lacking. While there were 176 vendors and craftsmen in the market at this particular moment, the number could easily reach 250 during a busier season. These numbers do not include the numerous irregular vendors who have no fixed place in the market but who

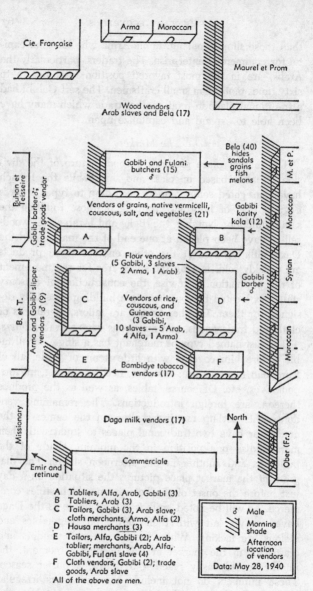

Fig. 7 The Market

The market diagram contains the following labels:

Cie. Française

Arma | Moroccan

Maurel et Prom

Wood vendors
Arab slaves and Bela (17)

Gabibi and Fulani butchers (15) ♂

Bela (40) hides sandals grains fish melons

M. et P.

Vendors of grains, native vermicelli, couscous, salt, and vegetables (21)

Buhan et Teisseire

Gabibi barber; trade goods vendor

Moroccan

Gabibi karity kola (12)

A

B

Syrian

Flour vendors (5 Gabibi, 3 slaves 2 Arma, 1 Arab)

Gabibi barber ♂

B. et T.

Arma and Gabibi slipper vendors ♂ (9)

C

D

Vendors of rice, couscous, and Guinea corn (3 Gabibi, 10 slaves — 5 Arab, 4 Alfa, 1 Arma)

Moroccan

E

F

Bambidye tobacco vendors (17)

Daga milk vendors (17)

North

Missionary

Emir and retinue

Commerciale

Ober (Fr.)

A   Tabliers, Alfa, Arab, Gabibi (3)
B   Tabliers, Arab (3)
C   Tailors, Gabibi (3), Arab slave; cloth merchants, Arma, Alfa (2)
D   Hausa merchants (3)
E   Tailors, Alfa, Gabibi (2); Arab tablier; merchants, Arab, Alfa, Gabibi, Fulani slave (4)
F   Cloth vendors, Gabibi (2); trade goods, Arab slave
All of the above are men.

♂   Male
///   Morning shade
←   Afternoon location of vendors
Data: May 28, 1940

carry a few pieces of goods or a blanket on their heads while they look for a buyer.

It is noteworthy that the only male vendors are either craftsmen or sellers of cloth and other trade goods, largely of European manufacture. The women, who are the principal sellers in the market, are all slaves or serfs. Alfa and Arab women not only do not sell in the market, they may not even buy there. Their slaves or husbands do the shopping. It is obvious, therefore, that the retail trade remains in the hands of lower class groups and that the upper class families who have no serfs or slaves to handle retail selling are entirely eliminated from this part of the commercial life. The *tablier* represents a sort of store owner on a small scale. The Arabs dominate this position as they do the larger merchandising ventures. The slipper-makers and tailors in the market are marginal, as has been indicated, the better craftsmen remaining at home and working on order.

A glance at the identity of the occupants of the buildings surrounding the market will show the extent to which foreign influences cluster about it. There is not a purely Songhoi function represented. The Arma, a Moroccan-Songhoi mixture, are present in one store and the emir's office. Other structures are stores, four belonging to Moroccans, five to Frenchmen, one to a Christian Syrian. The remaining building is the residence of the missionary. It is significant that the groupings in and around the market place are based on the commercial functions and not the ethnic origins of the vendors.

The market does not begin to fill until well after sunrise. Around six o'clock it is swept by native convicts under the very informal supervision of native police guards, who frequently lend a hand in the sweeping. The population does not arise early, for it retires late. The nomadic Daga arrive about seven with their skins of butter, gourds, and bottles of milk. During the next hour the *wey fefere* (basket women) arrive with their four or five small baskets of produce neatly stacked and balanced on their heads. A native woman never carries anything in her hands unless her head is "full." Even an empty bottle or a stick of firewood is carried on the head and only a young girl would show her lack of skill by steadying the load with her hand. The carriage of the women is exceedingly straight and their movement smooth and graceful as a result of this continual balancing of objects on their heads.

Until noon the buyers wander through the market, treading gingerly between the vendors to avoid stepping on the wares spread out on the ground. The air is usually full of the harsh-voiced ejaculations of shrewish women as they berate a customer who refuses to buy from them or as they belabor another vendor who has stolen a customer. These squabbles often end in violence which has to be broken up by onlookers and friends. No vendor saves her produce for regular clients but sells to the first comer. No credit is given except occasionally by a man who sells more expensive goods, and then only to an intimate friend.

As the day grows hot, the women set up poles in the sand to support matting shades. By noon the heat has driven all customers home and the vendors seek the deep recesses of the shadows to sleep. The market seems deserted and its usual hubbub dims to a silence broken only by the occasional high-pitched chanting of a prayer. Trading does not recommence until mid-afternoon. In the old days the activity in the market continued well into the night in order to supply the people who worked until sundown and had no opportunity to buy during the day. Now, because French traders live next to the market place and want quiet, the vendors are driven out by the police at sunset. A score or more sellers of food products assemble in an open place in Sankore quarter to continue serving the late workers. Nothing epitomizes the heavy-handed rule of the foreign minority as well as these French regulations which forbid commerce and even dancing to tom-toms after certain hours, because a handful of French dislike the noise. A city under a burning sun, Timbuctoo found its principal pleasures at night, as it still does, but it seeks them more quietly than formerly.

After the dissolution of the market, one hears the cries of merchants hawking their products through the streets, the bush folk simply naming their wares but the townsmen using traditional calls: *"Takula-koy!"* (Baker!) or *"Kara bakoy di yo!"* (The yellow girl friends!—meaning the yellow loaves of bread), *"Kosam koy!"* (Milk seller!) or *"Bomo bakoy di yo!"* (People who indulge themselves! —meaning that people who like milk should buy some).[26] The hawkers are dependent upon an unknown and varying clientele.

The Salt Trade

The principal commercial life of Timbuctoo is now largely dependent upon the salt trade from the Taodeni mines in the Central Sahara. There are two large *azalais* or salt caravans a year, one leaving at the beginning of the "cold" season and the less important one departing at the end of the season.[27] The trip to Taodeni requires three weeks each way and the only oasis passed en route is Araouan, a week's trek north of Timbuctoo. In recent years the larger caravan has included some four thousand camels while the old trade may have demanded more.[28]

[26] Caillié comments on street vendors of kola nuts crying their wares during the day (1830:II, 50). Yakouba does the same for sellers of butter (1914:249), though these were not recorded during my stay.

[27] Leaving Timbuctoo around early November and late March. Es-Sadi, 1900:89, mentions the arrival of a large *azalai* salt caravan in the Arab month and year corresponding to mid-April-mid-May, 1730.

[28] Unfortunately Caillié and Barth give no figures. Dubois seems to recognize the periods of the present *azalais* as those of market caravan activity but says the largest caravans had a thousand camels. He states that 50,000 to 60,000 camels, carrying salt and other goods, entered the city each year. However, the official and only actual count up to 1895 was 14,000 in that year, which may have been unusual, as it immediately followed the French conquest (Dubois, 1897:257). Barrows, in 1926, says 3 or 4,000 in the *azalai* but refers to Dupuis Yakouba's statement that there were 15,000 in 1907 (1927: 152). Monod puts the figure at 3,000 in 1934 (1937:235). My

Smaller commercial caravans to Morocco and Algeria depart when enough people can gather to protect themselves. Caillié reports 1,400 camels in the group he accompanied to Morocco in 1828.[29] Now, with French protection, the groups can be smaller.

The salt mines of Taodeni are controlled by Arabs and worked largely by Negro slaves. The chief of Taodeni exacts from mine owners and workers a fixed tribute, in which the French now share. Some young Arabs choose to go on their own and work in the mines for limited periods in order to make enough money to buy camels. The miners cut the rock salt, out of stratified beds, into tombstone-like slabs weighing over fifty pounds apiece. Nine or ten bars can be worked out a day. At the mines such a block was worth ten francs (twenty-five cents) in 1940. Each bar is worth about fifty francs in Timbuctoo so the buyer of salt works on a comfortable margin. However, one has to be a camel owner to buy salt profitably at the mines, for the carrying charge to Timbuctoo is four-fifths of the number of bars carried.[30] It is obvious that an independent miner does as well by selling his salt bars at Taodeni as by having them transported to Timbuctoo.

The profit in the salt traffic is not limited to the camel owners or even to those who work the mines. The credit and interest system in Timbuctoo is highly developed and plays an important part in the trade with Taodeni. Moslems are forbidden to take usury but by interpreting usury as the making of money on loans of money, they keep a

---

own figure is derived from the known salt import of the two *azalais* of 1939–1940 (35,000 bars) which would necessitate some 7,000 camels in all. A camel can carry about five bars.

[29] Caillié, 1830:II, 422.

[30] This is not exorbitant. The caravaneer makes the same profit which he would make if he transported salt which he had purchased at the mines. The values given are not fixed but approximate the average and are used by the Arabs in planning their commerce. Bars actually sell for forty to fifty francs on arrival in Timbuctoo, but increase in value if held or shipped farther.

clear conscience by dealing in cloth instead of money.[31] If a camel owner needs capital to buy salt, he can borrow it from the rich men of the city. The wealthy man will give him bolts of Guinea cloth (valued at fifty francs in 1940) upon the signature of a promissory note to pay in cash seventy-five francs per bolt at the end of six months, or a note for one hundred francs per bolt to be paid in a year. These promissory notes are written in Arabic before witnesses and may be extended through mutual agreement or forcibly collected by appeal to the cadi. The borrower uses the cloth to pay for the goods which he will take to Taodeni to exchange for salt. When the salt reaches the Sudan, it is sold for cash, permitting the caravaneer to pay his debt. The creditor exacts one hundred per cent interest but rationalizes the transaction as a sale of cloth on a deferred payment plan. The cadi would have nothing to do with an agreement to repay a money loan with interest.

In this connection the French are again put at a disadvantage because of lack of understanding of native commercial methods. The credit of the wealthy native merchants is good at the French trading posts. Such natives secure Guinea cloth from the French, put it out at interest, and pay the French the original cost when their loan is returned. Thus they manage to exact interest on capital lent by the French without interest. Usury is also common among small merchants. They may lend to men who are buying staples to eat while mining at Taodeni. In these arrangements the miner promises to repay each twenty francs loaned with the delivery of a bar of salt in Timbuctoo. This means that he must send five bars for each one owed in order to cover the cost of transportation. The merchant receives at least one hundred per cent interest on his loan.

It has already been intimated that the caravans carry produce to Taodeni to barter for salt. The commodities include tobacco, sugar, shea butter, grain, dried meats,

[31] Barth reports that the actual buying of salt in Timbuctoo was formerly done entirely with cloth woven in Kano (1890: 352).

but no cloth, as food is the prime interest in this desert settlement. Mutton and beef are specially prepared for this trade by cutting and drying the meat in large slabs one half to two inches thick. Some of the salt must obviously be purchased for cash at the mines but the increased value of the produce which is bartered for salt provides an added opportunity for profit to the caravaneer.

The salt of Taodeni is particularly white and dense. More accessible mines, such as those of Tichit, have offered some competition, but the pure Taodeni product is preferred even as far away as Dakar. The solid nature of the bars[32] and their ability to shed water makes their transport particularly easy. While salt from other sources, including Europe, is never seen in Timbuctoo, it competes farther away from the mines where the price of Taodeni salt is higher. This is doubtless responsible for some loss of trade. In addition, some of the salt no longer passes through Timbuctoo but is taken directly to Diré, Bourem, and Gao, because the way is now safe. The shipment of salt by boat from Timbuctoo is a profitable trade in itself.[33] Some bars eventually reach the Atlantic port of Konakry in Guinea.

The commercial life of Timbuctoo is based upon a hinterland extending a thousand miles to the north and the west and half that distance in other directions. Not only is the city dependent upon this hinterland but within the city the various population elements are economically interdependent.

[32] When a bar is broken, although the halves are lashed back in place, there is immediate loss of value because of the eventual loss of salt through friction between the broken edges and because the bars are less easily handled.

[33] Barth in 1854 (1890:353), before the French conquest, and Dubois in 1895 (1897:255), after the conquest, both note that salt rises to two and a half times its value in Timbuctoo when taken to Sansanding in the west.

CHAPTER 5

Islam

Dogma and Non-Dogma

The organized religions of literate cultures classify supernatural phenomena so as to distinguish between beliefs and practices which are part of their dogma and those which are not. But such classification means little to a nonliterate population. In our discussion of the supernatural in Timbuctoo we shall look at the distinctions through native eyes, a view necessitated by the differences of belief within the population. The dogma of Islam will be our point of departure, for in these beliefs we would expect the greatest homogeneity.

Islam draws a sharp line between believers and nonbelievers. The Koran is quite explicit on this point. Friendship with Jews and Christians is forbidden and Hebrew and Christian teaching refuted.[1] All of the religions which stem from the Near East are mutually exclusive. Each feels every one should profess its particular beliefs, and struggles to keep its monopoly in every community or group of believers. Within these social units, the common sacred belief is the core of in-group feeling and a powerful unifying force. The Koran explicitly tries to create political unity through common religion. Mohammed unified his converts, theretofore broken into small tribal units, by uniting them against the non-Moslem world.[2]

Islam requires a monopoly on belief for it provides the civil and criminal law of the society as well as its religion. While it is possible for community life to continue in spite of divergent religions, all members of the community must

[1] See Sura 5 of the Koran, for example.
[2] Hell, 1925:23–24.

be subject to one body of law. Where Moslems have lost their governmental dominance, they have had to submit to forms of law other than their own. At the same time they have continued permissible forms of the Islamic legal system for their own religious group. Thus, they not only have religious antagonism to the superimposed and conflicting law but they are held together more than before by common recognition of their distinctive law.

In the development of religions, each, at some time, has supported with its sacred sanctions the approved ways of life of the society in which it evolved. The religious injunctions go hand in hand with a particular way of life. As religions spread to foreign cultures, this correspondence breaks down. Likewise, once a religious system becomes codified and formalized, subsequent changes in the parent culture itself may diverge from the original religious tenets. Finally, the separation of church and state is a revolutionary step making possible the complete separation of religion and law, each to go its own way.

In Timbuctoo, Moslem law prevailed for hundreds of years before the French conquest. It followed the writing of the jurist, Malik Ibn Anas,[3] whose teachings are based on the orthodox practices of the first Arab Caliphs. Moslems admire force, and the law was enforced by the most powerful. During the late period of the Songhoi Empire and the early period of Moroccan dominance, the law was administered by the viceroys and pashas. As the spheres of dominance of the leaders shrank, so did the application of justice suffer. Even in the later days of virtual anarchy, the law was the same but was enforced only within families and by the strong upon the weak. It is important to recognize the fact that without a powerful government, the various peoples of the Sudan, both in the cities and in the bush, did not have enough in common

---

[3] Among the features of this Sunnite school is the taboo on the eating of horse-flesh. Certain of the prayer movements, as those during the lavation and upon initiating the prayer, are also distinctive.

to create an orderly form of life, acceptable to all, in spite of their common religion. Within each homogeneous, local culture group, however, the sacred laws were enforced and binding. Beginning with the advent of the first Christian explorers in the Sudan and culminating in the period of French dominance, Moslems were drawn closer to one another through their mutual dislike of Christians.

Islamic belief and practice in Timbuctoo today present a core of custom which is common to the entire native population. This basic Moslem doctrine affects the religious behavior of different individuals to varying degrees. Some are good Moslems, others are bad; but common to all are certain mutual understandings. The greater part of the culture which is common to all the people of Timbuctoo consists of this religious core, the common knowledge of the physical aspects of Timbuctoo, the mutual recognition of commercial custom, and the recent general recognition of French dominance. The universally shared core of Islamic belief constitutes the broad outline of the dogma of the religion. The details of the religion—its history, philosophy, and ideals—are known only to the marabouts and some Arabs. These men can read the Koran and have grown conversant with it through study. The rest of the populace has had no formal religious training. They have learned from others whose knowledge and example have often varied greatly from the precepts of the Prophet.

Becoming a marabout is not like working for a D.D. degree. There are no fixed standards, no examinations, no symbols of attainment of office. A marabout, like a rabbi, is simply a learned man. The more he studies and learns, the more respected he is. In a society where the great majority of the population have no education, the man who has studied a little stands out. Koranic study emphasizes rote learning. The student learns Arabic while he learns Koranic passages. In this process he is indoctrinated with the teachings of Mohammed. A real student progresses to the critical study of the Commentaries on the Koran and the history of the religion. Some Alfa of Timbuctoo have only a smattering of Arabic and a sketchy knowledge of the Koran. They are looked down upon by the better informed marabouts and the Arabs. They are looked up to by the rest of the population.

The marabouts write magical Koranic charms, prognosticate the future, and work supernatural cures. Some of the forces of evil which they combat, such as devils and genii, are recognized in the Koran. The religion provides media for combating non-religious supernatural powers. In the dogma, it is a sin to appeal to, or utilize, these other supernaturals. But the fact that the religion plays an active role in protecting the faithful against infidel forces actually strengthens belief in their potency.

The supernatural world is thus a unitary frame of reference. Within the logics of that world, those people with the strongest Songhoi background and the weakest Islamic training appeal to marabouts but also to non-maraboutic sorcerers and diviners. Those with the least Songhoi cultural background and the most training in the religious dogma, depend entirely on the marabouts and consider resort to sorcerers as wrong. Between the Songhoi and the Arab there is no difference of opinion as to the existence of supernatural powers which do not stem from the religion. There is agreement as to the efficacy of the religious powers. Here is part of the unifying core of religious custom. The hatred of idolatry is not part of this core.

Faith

The belief in Allah and his prophet Mohammed is the greatest unifying force in Timbuctoo. It is the one value shared by all natives. The mere confession of such belief was sometimes all that was required to become part of the in-group. Such was the case when the fanatic Moslems brutally tried to exact statements of belief from the first Christians who entered the Sudan. The most important thing is to believe. The power of the community to make all believe in Mohammed is strong even now when Christians cannot be killed outright. The Catholic missionary, Yakouba, made "ten or twenty converts" among bush natives who came to Timbuctoo. They all lived at the mission. When Yakouba became the consort of a Song-hoi woman, the mission closed and a half-dozen natives went to another mission elsewhere. All of those who returned to their homes reverted to Islam. A Protestant mission has been maintained in Timbuctoo for sixteen years without making a single convert in the city. A half-dozen natives come in to the mission occasionally from the surrounding area.

One of these was converted when he acted as a boatman for some missionaries on a trip up the Niger. They went into the non-Moslem area and there the boatman heard a Christian Negro preach the doctrine which he had always thought was French. He requested more instruction and was converted by the man of his own race. Now, for the past six years, he has been preaching his belief, much to the anger of the marabouts. A missionary recently visited the village of this man, to encourage him, and found him in a crude set of stocks being fed on unground grain and water. The local chiefs explained this treatment by saying that the man was crazy. "He has been crazy ever since the time of his conversion." Since that time, not even his own family had been willing to share their food bowl with him.

The Common Belief

Along with faith in Mohammed is the practice of the faith. Some of this practice is also part of the common core of custom. The fundamental duties of praying, giving alms, and fasting are recognized by all. The fourth fundamental duty of making a pilgrimage to Mecca is recognized—as impossible. It is only expected of the very holy, the great marabouts, and the saints. The dogma on this point does not weigh heavily on many a rich merchant, who could make the pilgrimage, no matter how much the Arabs may mutter that hell awaits him. Among the residents of Timbuctoo, only six men are known to have made the year's camel trip to Mecca. Two of these were marabouts and one rich Arab took his three sons.

Distinctive *rites de passage* also characterize the community of Islam. Religious ritual is expected at birth, circumcision, marriage, and death. The content of the ceremonies varies somewhat among the different population groups, yet the rites are all similar. The annual religious ceremonies likewise constitute a unifying culture pattern. The core of religious belief includes faith in the supernatural powers of the Koran, the marabouts, and the saints. Allied to this is the concept which the Arabs call *baraka*. This is a supernatural power which is similar to Polynesian *mana*. One can secure *baraka* through contact with holy things. This power can also be brought into being by ritual words and acts. It is fundamental to the ceremonies and explicitly associated with faith in charms and talismans.

There is common acceptance of Koranic law, which is concerned particularly with criminal and "family" law. This latter code expresses the rules of marriage and divorce, the rights and duties of marriage partners, and inheritance regulations. The recognition of the cadi as the arbiter in such matters is implicit in this belief. Thus, prohibitions of murder, adultery, and robbery are commonly accepted values, even though they are not infrequently breached. No one questions their validity or the right of the cadi to punish offenders. This is in contrast to the religious prohibitions against prostitution, usury, and divining by casting cowries. Nonobservance of these regulations goes unpunished. The prohibition of swineflesh as a food is so strongly associated with the religious faith that even to come voluntarily in contact with it would not only be disgusting but would be generally interpreted as renunciation of the faith itself. Prohibitions against drinking intoxicants and gambling are generally observed, although no secular punishment marks divergence from the pattern.

Some knowledge of the basic system of supernatural beliefs of the religion is general to all the population. Thus, different people's ideas of God and Satan, heaven and hell, sin, judgment, angels, and devils, and predestination all show a basic similarity. I was told by one Songhoi that two angels stand at the shoulders of every man. One records the good deeds; the other, the bad. When a Moslem goes to sleep, he says, *"Bismillahi"* (In the name of God) to honor these angels. While he sleeps, the angels weigh up the day's sins and good works in a pair of balances. Each good deed equals ten sins. All sins are of equal weight except murder. For this sin, the murdered person gains credit for all of the murderer's benevolent acts. If there are any left over, God may give them back to the murderer. Commenting on his own lack of religious fervor in not going beyond the minimum requirements in the performance of his religious duties, the native stated that he simply was not marked at birth by the finger of fate to be a religious sort of man.

The above account is not unusual in character, nor is it typical except as exemplifying divergence from the norm of the Koran. The belief of this individual elaborates upon the dogma and is in direct conflict with the Prophet on important points. If one accepts the Moslem school of thought which considers only one type of sin unforgiven by God, that sin is idolatry, not murder. Others consider murder one of the seven deadly sins. Predestination involves the worldly fortunes of men, not their acts of faith. Nevertheless, the bare outline of the beliefs of this individual would correspond with that of others—recording angels, the weighing of sins, murder as a serious sin, predestination. The core of common belief derived from the dogma is not elaborate.

The question of free will and predestination has worried Arab scholars but not the average Moslem. The idea of predestination would appear to be in obvious logical conflict with the wide use of religious protective charms in Africa. Religion provides supernatural power to protect one from mundane dangers. But belief in predestination is also a form of protection. It reduces the chances that harm will befall one in any particular circumstances which would appear to bode ill. When a native is confronted with ills which have befallen him or with his own weaknesses of character, predetermination is his inevitable explanation. Successes are interpreted in terms of his own qualities, the power of his Koranic charms, and an overall aura of predestined divine favor. There is little to indicate that the Moslem belief in predetermination inclines Moslems toward lack of initiative. The reference to predetermination, made by all who lack initiative, is the chief evidence to the contrary. Combined with the positive use of religious power, belief in predetermination leads to a feeling of security which is amazing to non-Moslems.

Prayer

The daily prayers are overt acts by which men demonstrate to others their unity of faith and equality as individuals before Allah. The public prayers in the mosques symbolically focus this religious unity on the sacred buildings and their imams. The exclusion of women from prayers at the mosques is symbolic evidence of the superiority of men as explicitly outlined in the Koran. Women pray at home. They were admitted to the mosques "in the old days," but are now forbidden to enter "because they are so sinful." It is common belief that women have a bad effect on *baraka*. The fact that pre-adolescent girls are still allowed in the mosques clearly links the impurity of women to their sexual functions. In North Africa, women are not so excluded except during menstruation and shortly after childbirth.[4] Similar restriction is placed on anyone following sexual intercourse, until he has bathed.

The prayer ritual should be performed five times a day —before sunrise, after high noon, in the afternoon before sunset, at sunset, and before retiring. The times for these prayers are announced by the wailing cry of the muezzin from the minaret of each mosque. Some go to the mosque but most of the men pray wherever they happen to be— at home, in the market, or in the street. The Friday past-noon prayer is the principal community worship. The faithful assemble at the Great Mosque and are led in prayer by the imam. For the Friday evening prayers, men go to

[4] Westermarck, 1926:I, 230–231.

the mosques of their various quarters. The Bela, from their suburban *farandi*, tend to prefer Sankore, which is their closest mosque. The Arabs of Badyinde, which has no mosque in the quarter, assemble at a traditional locale in their section of town.

The daily prayers consist of a ritual lavation with water or sand, prayers repeated in Arabic, and a sequence of formal positions including the characteristic prostration toward the east and touching the forehead to the ground. No one may interrupt a person at his prayers, for if the ritual sequence is broken, it must be entirely repeated. The form of the prayer is one of the most consistent culture traits throughout the city. Strict performance of the duty of prayer is less uniform. The Songhoi elements of the population may omit the prayers usually performed at home. When in company with others at the hour of prayer, they will pray. This means that their prayers may be limited to the three offered during daylight hours. The use of the prayer to demonstrate to others one's participation in the religious community again illustrates the all-pervasive quality of religion in the city. This does not imply that the native is insincere and prays simply as a gesture. He simply feels his religious duty more keenly in situations in which non-performance of his prayers would bring his faith into question. Yakouba reports that he was visited by a group of Tuareg, including both nobles and members of maraboutic tribes. At the hour of prayer, the marabouts drew to one side and commenced their ritual. Yakouba offered to absent himself to let the others pray but the nobles maintained that they did not have to pray as the prayers of the marabouts would cover them as well.

The members of Islamic religious orders[5] spend more time in prayer. Among the obligations of these orders is the long and repetitious chanting of certain orisons after one or more of the daily prayers. Members are easily recognized by the resultant prolongation of their prayers, which they frequently tell off on a hundred-bead rosary.

[5] Montet, 1902, and Rinn, 1884, discuss various of these orders in North Africa. See also Marty, 1920:4.

Those who undertake this added religious duty learn its details through apprenticeship to a member of the order. The *Tijani* is a well-known fraternity of this sort, named after the patron saint in Fez. The additional *Tijani* prayers efface sins and "make one very successful in business." It is usual for those assuming the responsibilities of this order to double the required number of prayers during the first year so as to "catch up" with those who already have all of the accrued benefits. The first year may be one of relative penury as one has to spend his time praying during those periods of the day best for commerce. But the business benefits eventually accrue. The *Tijani* order in Timbuctoo includes two wealthy Arab shopkeepers and a rich Arma merchant who are all reported to have been poor when they began the *Tijani* prayers. The recent addition of an aspiring Gabibi tailor to the order is a significant illustration of the social mobility now possible. In the ante-French epoch, a Gabibi could never have become a tailor. It is very doubtful if he would have been instructed by any follower of the *Tijani,* for the orders are fraternal bodies committed to mutual aid. This fraternal aspect is little emphasized, the religious aspect of the order being the consciously important thing about it. It is obvious that it is used, however, as a means of secular advancement.

Community prayers for special purposes are said in times of crisis. An eclipse of the moon is interpreted as a struggle between the sun and moon. This fight of the celestial bodies may presage the end of the world. There is public prayer in the mosques in addition to the "grinding" of water with pestle and mortar in each house "to separate the sun and moon."

The city is close enough to the agricultural life of the Niger basin to be concerned when the rains fail to fall during the so-called rainy season. After prolonged drought, some marabouts pray continuously in the mosques and others, with their students, chant prayers as they go though the sandy streets and visit the tombs of the saints. Prayer is continued until the rain comes but usually three days or less suffice. Sometimes the power of various leading marabouts is tested during such a period. One after another will lead the prayers, on successive days, until the most powerful brings the rain. In the rare instances in which such prayers fail after three days, another technique may also be employed. Some small children of shereef families are caught, tied, thrown in the blazing sun near the tomb of a saint, where they are left until the rain comes. My informant and his brother were so treated in their youth and rain fell "in a few minutes." Small children are selected because they are still sinless. When God sees the plight of these holy children, he sends the rain so they will be released. There is some hesitancy about thus putting pressure on Allah, for the rains which he sends under coercion are so heavy that the mud houses collapse all over town. Nevertheless, shereef families tend to protect their children by keeping them at home after the prayers of the marabouts have failed to bring rain for three successive days.

Alms

It is a fundamental duty of a Moslem not only to pray but to give alms as well. The giving of part of one's income is required. Other alms are voluntary. The amount of the first type of gift is explicit in the dogma,[6] but, as in the case of sins and benevolent acts, there is little terrestrial bookkeeping. Alms are thought of expressly as gifts to the poor and to holy men. The religion forbids a marabout to charge for his services. He is supposed to be recompensed by donations from the party benefited. Almsgifts may also be made to holy men, simply out of religiously inspired generosity. Alms may be given to the students of the Koran to assist them to live while they study. These youngsters roam in groups through the market and streets every Friday, swarming around donors to collect alms. The students, in turn, make donations to their teachers. Some marabouts move from town to town with their indigent scholars, living on alms. All marabouts live by what they

[6] Two and one half per cent, with certain specifications and limitations.

receive for their religious and legal services and by such commerce as they may engage in—tailoring, for example.

The faith teaches that the giving of alms not only leads to religious blessings but to economic ones as well. The efficacy of almsgiving has been exemplified over and over in local events.

Two merchants of the city shipped salt bars on the Niger by canoe. One merchant had always given to the poor; the other had never done so. The latter received word that the boats had capsized during a storm and their cargoes were lost. He rushed to tell his friend, who replied to his news, "Maybe your canoe capsized but mine did not. I am right with Allah and owe him nothing." Later, word was received that the boat of the almsgiver had not capsized.[7]

This story illustrates two basic concepts concerning alms. It is good business to give them. Almsgiving is largely the concern of the wealthy.

Like prayer, alms may be used as a means to an end. The marabouts of Sara Keyna announced that everyone who could do so should give a sheep to the poor in order to bring to an end the heavy mortality which had marked the recent months. Another case in point is that of two wealthy merchants who were giving daily alms to the poor in 1940 to end the European war which was disrupting their commerce. Alms may also be *post facto* donations. In individual prayers to the saints, for specific worldly benefits, alms of a certain amount may be promised if the request of the prayer is granted.[8] This dickering with the saints resembles the dealings with living marabouts. We might say that Islam admonishes alms and promises economic rewards therefor. The weight of the gift shall influence the importance of the benefits. Timbuctoo is inclined to consider that the importance of the benefit

[7] Here and subsequently all quoted sections not otherwise annotated are drawn from interview material in the author's field notes.

[8] This conditional gift is not unlike the conditional curse ('ār) placed on a saint in Morocco. Such practices are not limited to urban groups. The point here is that they do not conform to the dogma of Islam.

actually derived shall influence the amount of alms owed
to God.

The lack of hospitality for strangers shows a similar deficiency in generosity. The Koran admonishes the Faithful
to extend hospitality to strangers of the same nation or
faith. The Arabs are well known for this quality. The
speaking of Arabic is apt to be sufficient to identify a person as one worthy to receive hospitality. The explorer
Barth owed his life to his ability to speak Arabic and the
protection he received from Arabs as a result, in spite of
the fact that he was thought to be an infidel. During our
stay in Timbuctoo, a young, cultured Arab from Arabia
visited the city during the course of his travels. He was
regarded with general suspicion by the natives, who considered him "too white to be an Arab." He was housed,
however, by two Arab families of relatively recent Moroccan origin. Hospitality for the stranger is confined to
the Arabs and is not a prevalent trait in Timbuctoo.

Marabouts

It was pointed out earlier that marabouts differ in the
amount of training they have received. They differ as well
in their class and ethnic origins. Any child, theoretically,
can become a marabout. Any Songhoi who is literate in
Arabic is considered to be an Alfa by the Songhoi. Even
among the Arabs, a man who is proficient in reading and
writing Arabic is likely to be a marabout.[9] There is no
instruction in these arts, other than religious instruction,
but some Arab children are briefly exposed to this basic
training. Except for merchants with contacts in North
Africa and the Sudan, literacy has no other utility in Timbuctoo. For the student aspiring to be a marabout, the
learning of Arabic is important. It is the language of supernatural power, written and read by all marabouts. The
books of sacred writing and the written charms are all in
Arabic. An interesting example of the sacred character of
the script is seen in the experience of a Christian missionary who was paying a Tuareg marabout to write Biblical

[9] There appear to be some fifty professional Songhoi and
Arab marabouts in Timbuctoo.

passages in Arabic. When the marabout was asked to write certain passages which conflicted with Moslem belief, he refused to commit them to writing. One could not hope to find a better example of a written language being considered as a sacred ritual rather than a secular tool.

There are certain social factors which influence the background from which marabouts come. The Bela speak Temajegh, which the marabouts of Timbuctoo do not speak. The Tuareg marabouts are separate, self-perpetuating nomadic tribes, so it never occurs to a Bela to become a marabout. The sons of Arabs and Alfa are most likely to become marabouts. Their parents know Arabic and are the most thoroughly indoctrinated in Islamic dogma. They also tend to be wealthier and can afford to pay for the requisite training. The Arma no longer speak Arabic and feel no compulsion to train their sons with the marabouts, preferring the discipline of the master slipper-makers. There is a local saying that one must beg while studying or one will never learn to read the Koran. Before the French conquest, the Gabibi were poor enough but, being less touched by Moslem culture and being serfs, they were neither inclined nor free to become marabouts.

The marabouts of each quarter tend to identify themselves with the mosque of their section of the city. The Arabs have no mosque in the city quarter which they dominate. The Arab marabouts keenly resent their lack of control of any mosque, inasmuch as they feel superior to the Songhoi Alfa. There is a strong rivalry and competition among all marabouts. Each tends to deprecate the learning and power of others, particularly of another ethnic group.

There is no religious hierarchy, only the recognized office of imam, the prayer-leader at each mosque. This position is held for life and kept in certain Songhoi families. If a successor is not named by the previous incumbent, the other marabouts select one of his relatives for the position. Upon the recent death of the imam of the Great Mosque, the marabouts chose his brother to fill the post as his son was too young. The muezzin, or mosque crier, is not a marabout but a Gabibi appointed by the imam. The imam lives from gifts made to the mosque. These gifts provide a large income as wealthy Moslems, who wish to give money or produce as acts of faith or as thanks for divine aid, usually give it to the mosque.

The Great Mosque is considered to be the "city" mosque. Its imam is charged with foretelling and averting evils about to befall the city. The giving of alms to the poor or to the muezzin is usually admonished to avert the foretold catastrophe.

Saints

Moslems recognize some persons as living saints. Lacking a hierarchy, public opinion makes a saint. The opinion of the marabouts is, of course, important in forming public belief. Men may become known as saints because of their extraordinary devotion or demonstration of power. Usually saints withdraw from normal social life. They are said to have a singular sign which they make when they do not wish to talk. The left palm is slapped with the back of the right hand or the first two fingers of the right hand. The natives say that all saints are at least partially crazy and can be recognized by their peculiar behavior. As one man expressed it:

Sometimes signs from Allah show us who the saints are, as in the case of Mohammed Banon. As a child he used to go into the bush by himself. To discipline him, his mother hid his food and told him that there was none for him. The youngster toddled off and found and ate the food. When the marabouts were told of this, they said that he was a saint. Saints rarely speak to people, do not sit with others, and eat little. Almoustafa Konate, who was a saint here, read the Koran to himself in the bush. He fell sick; the next two days the sun was covered over, and the fourth day he died.

Some saints are said to possess the ability to fly:[10]

Hassani is a local saint whose paternal kin are all shereef. Every Friday he goes to Mecca and is back the next day. This is

[10] For comparable data see, Westermarck, 1926:1, 148–149, 160; Goldziher, 1890:294.

known because letters have been received from Mecca which say he was there. A different local saint, who was crazy, went alone into the bush one morning. When he failed to return, his relatives made a search and many rode out into the desert on horseback but he was not to be found. That day they received a telegram from his brother in Gao, five hundred kilometers away, stating that he had arrived there at eleven o'clock in the morning.

The reference to modern technical facilities to prove miracles is noteworthy. It would appear that such reference is used to strengthen the rational argument of proof. This rational criticism is not carried far, however. It seems likely that confusion over names and dates, in correspondence between marginally literate individuals, is involved in these cases. When such discrepancies involve a person recognized as a saint, they become evidence of saintliness.

The *baraka* of the saints is great. Their insults are as benedictions upon those who receive them. Their power continues after death and their tombs become shrines through which their *baraka* can be acquired. All Timbuctoo "knows" that there are three hundred and thirty-three saints buried around the city. Many believe the Koran mentions this fact and states that these holy men protect the city from capture.[11] A saint is often laid to rest on an eminence or even in the city itself. He is laid on a bed and covered with fine blankets. A small house-like tomb is built over the body, leaving an entrance only large enough to crawl through. After the funeral, a son of the saint sits outside the sepulcher. Those who visit the tomb give the son a donation, enter the shrine and stroke the body three times and, upon emerging, receive the saint's benediction from the lips of his son.

The *baraka* of a saint may be secured by prayer or by invoking his name. The Songhoi phrase, *"Ya sheku al walidye Albu Kader Dyedani"* (Oh chief, the saint Albu Kader Dyedani) is repeated to cause a woman to start

---

[11] This is, of course, belied by the Koran and history.

labor in childbirth. The phrase may be said as a supplication to the saint along with any request and the promise of an almsgift *if* the favor is accorded.

Charms

The saints possess *baraka* in and of themselves. But more important to the natives is the *baraka* which a marabout controls through his knowledge of Arabic, the Koran, and the techniques for using this power. A fundamental part of these techniques is the writing of charms known as *tira* by the Songhoi. A *tira* is a slip of paper upon which is written a particular Koranic passage having specific magical properties. Every native possesses such charms, preserved in flat, leather packets, a few inches square. Metal packets, decorated with leather, adorn the necks of particularly valuable Tuareg horses and camels.

While everyone recognizes the efficacy of charms, there is a marked ethnic gradient regarding their importance. The Arabs possess a few and often leave them at home. They rarely wear more than one, suspended by a cord around the neck in the common manner. The other peoples of the city are more apt to wear several charms. But even they consider that the Tuareg nobles overdo it. These warriors wear scores of charms hung around their necks. Their chests are often covered six inches deep in magical packets.

Tira to protect the wearer from evil genii and sorcerers are common. As one informant put it, "All Gabibi have charms against devils, the police, and other evil people." A marabout reported that most of the *tira* he was asked to write were to gain commercial advantage and to secure wealth, often in a particular enterprise. If they proved efficacious in that venture, however, they would be worn thereafter. Other charms he writes are to protect the wearer from sorcery, from the blows of enemies, from illness and diseases. Beside providing protection, *tira* are used to secure the love of women, the good opinion of

men, and to make the wearer mentally astute. A single
charm may combine several of these qualities.

The manner in which the charm is to be worn is pre-
scribed by the marabout. Worn in their leather packets
or in leather bracelets or belts (*baka*), the charms protect
the wearer against all manner of ills. *Bakawel,* worn by
women around the abdomen, are used for or against conception and to protect against stomach ailments and witchcraft. Charms for maladies of the head are worn in the
head covering; those for the body and limbs around the
neck or member concerned; those to sustain one in combat
or in business, on the right arm. The marabouts learn some
details of their supernatural trade while they are students.
Other elements of their practice are original revelations
to the particular marabout.

The Arabian traveler mentioned earlier was accosted in
the desert by a Tuareg who tried to rob him. The Arab
hit the Tuareg with his walking stick and the robber ran
away. When I told this story to a Songhoi native, I was
informed that all such travelers have charms to protect
them on their way. Often the charm consists of a certain
Koranic passage which is read every morning three or
seven times.[12] By so doing, the traveler becomes invisible
to malefactors or else people do not think of evil deeds
when they see him. This explanation of the episode is in
marked contrast to the beliefs of the Arabian himself. He
was sophisticated enough to recognize the influence of native magic on the Sudanese practice of Islam.

Ritual Cures and Charms

The *baraka* of Arabic words and phrases may be transmitted by other means than repeating them or wearing
them in *tira*. Marabouts often accomplish this by reciting
the potent passage and then spitting on the object to which
the *baraka* is to be transferred. This is a basic Arabic
technique. A family patriarch gives his blessing by mum-

[12] This is not a true *tira,* in which the *baraka* of the written
word is sufficient.

bling a benediction into his open hands, then spitting on them and rubbing the saliva on the face of the fortunate recipient. Marabouts thus transfer *baraka* to myrrh to protect the owner from sorcerers or to assist him commercially. The recipient burns the myrrh daily and smells the sweet incense, thus acquiring the *baraka*.

In cases of wounds or sickness, the marabout usually treats the case by spitting on the patient. The wife of the native living below us was in an advanced stage of pregnancy. One night I was awakened by her fearful screams. I descended quickly and discovered that she had stepped on a scorpion. I dressed the sting but had barely finished when the marabout arrived and after an appropriate incantation, spat on the wound.

The Bela are the suburban farmers of the city. Before sowing their fields, the farmers decide on a marabout to protect the fields from grasshoppers and mice. This marabout reads from the Koran and then spits into sand, which he distributes to the various Bela. This sand is mixed with the first grain sown. When the crop is ripe, the marabout is called again to provide a charm to protect the grain from birds. If the power of the marabout is not demonstrated by the end results of his charms, another one is employed the ensuing season. If crops are good, he will be reemployed and alms will be given to the muezzin and imam of Sankore.

Still another means of securing the benefit of the sacred word is commonly used in cases of illness from either natural or supernatural causes. The marabout writes the Arabic passages with charcoal on a wooden writing board like that used by the students. The words are washed off with water into a calabash. The patient drinks thrice of this water and his body is washed with the remainder. It has been recorded that to cure a sickness some marabouts follow a custom of inducing a state of ecstasy by music and then telling, on the authority of a saint, what animal must be sacrificed and eaten to effect a cure.[13]

[13] Shabeeny, 1820:33.

Prognostication

Marabouts can also foretell the future for individuals, just as the imam of the Great Mosque is supposed to do for the city as a whole. A marabout is consulted before arranging a marriage, buying a house or a horse, entering upon a large commercial venture, or any other serious undertaking. As a sample of the advice and prognostication in one such case, the marabout told the young prospective groom that he must secure capital before marriage, that he would acquire a four-legged animal, that after marriage he would be poor in two or three months, that he would regain his fortunes, that he would have children and eventually divorce his wife. The marabout simply recited the normal expectation of events associated with the marriage of every youth who lacks wealth. In this particular case, the youth's poor clothes and the two francs which he paid in advance to the marabout were sufficient evidence of lack of means.

The methods employed by the marabouts vary but are all associated with books. In this there is a certain consistency with the statement of belief in predestination—"It is written." The philosophy of predestination is distorted by the further belief that if you can get a look at *what* is written, you can avoid the consequences. Thus, some marabouts insert a piece of blank paper in the "Fortune Book" and close it. After appropriate ritual the book is reopened and the prognostication is found written on the paper.[14] In another type of book, called "Clear Eyes," the supplicant places his finger at random on a chart. His finger thus indicates the effective passage in the book which is read to him by the marabout. Charlatans who resort to trickery are roundly denounced by the marabouts of a purer Islamic training. Considering the compe-

[14] Obviously a different sheet of paper. This type of divination requires a twenty-four hour delay on the part of the marabout, after he is approached for aid, so that he can prepare his script for the book trick.

tition among holy men, such deprecation of the power of others is lost in the general maligning. The Songhoi believe that Arab marabouts do not have as much power as Songhoi holy men. Yet faith in divination is elaborated in the belief that if one consulted three marabouts in different parts of the city on any matter, the same prospects would be indicated by each. The French are likewise "known" to consult the marabouts a great deal, putting on white robes and visiting them at night to avoid detection.

The Family Marabout

The selection of one's marabout is like the selection of a family doctor. Everyone wants a marabout whose ability can be trusted, who has proven himself from past performance to be capable, and who is of one's own ethnic or class group. It is well known that people do not like innovations at critical times in their lives. They prefer to depend upon those procedures which are familiar to them and, if possible, those individuals who are familiar to them. The Arabs use Arab marabouts exclusively, in spite of the fact that many of the Arab families which have been in Timbuctoo for generations speak adequate Songhoi. The Bela marabouts are from the nomadic Tuareg tribe of Red Marabouts, so called because of their light, Caucasian skin. In cases of emergency, when these holy men are not in the vicinity, any other marabout will be called in, usually from Sankore. The Songhoi prefer to patronize the marabouts of their own group.

The family marabout is selected through trial and error and consulting one's friends. In cases of serious illness, one marabout after another will be called if none cures the patient. Everyone recognizes the fact that marabouts vary in ability to produce results. In addition, the amount of money given to any marabout for his services affects the results which he produces. When a marabout was asked if the efficacy of a charm was affected by what Koranic passage was used, the excellence of the Arabic script in the *tira* or the state of holiness of the recipient, he replied that the amount paid for the charm was the sole factor determining its potency. This was, of course, a personal opinion. The failure of a marabout to produce results is most apt to be interpreted as lack of knowledge on his part, but underpayment also may be considered a cause. Some marabouts explain failures by saying, "Allah did not grant the thing desired." This explanation, while closer to the dogma, is not acceptable to the public.

Bargaining with the Marabout

In spite of dogma, which forbids a marabout to charge for his services, the price for making *tira* is set in advance. When such a charm is sought, the marabout is asked how much payment he expects. He usually asks from one hundred to two hundred francs ($2.50–$5.00). Then the bargaining starts, as in any commercial transaction, until both agree on a price which is usually a third or fourth of the original quotation. A small down payment may be made and the remainder paid, not upon delivery of the charm, but when the desired results are secured. Some unsatisfied customers even try to get their initial payment refunded. Delayed payment is only used if a charm is requested for a specific and immediate purpose, particularly connected with commercial ventures. Satisfied customers never default on their payment, both because one pays to Allah what is his and because of the fear of supernatural retaliation by the marabout, whose power has just been demonstrated. Payments for the treatment of illness are made whether the patient lives or dies, although the amount may be haggled over in advance.

The Songhoi have a saying which takes amused cognizance of the marabouts' attempts to get special prices in their ordinary purchases. "*Alfa fedyi; a ma nasu; a hay di ma dao,*" means "A sheep for the marabout; it should be fat; its price should be thin." The marabouts are parsimonious by reputation but no one feels that they should receive special prices.

[5]   Bebe, a Gabibi Mason

[6]   Gabibi Girl

[7]   Mulai, an Arab Shereef

[8]   Old Bela Woman

[9]   Gabibi Market Women

[10]   Poor Shereef Water-Carrier

[11]   Moors from the Desert

[12]   Barbering in the Street

Departure from the Dogma

Before discussing the supernatural beliefs which do not stem from the teachings of Mohammed, a word should be added concerning the obvious nonadherence to the dogma of Islam. This behavior which is not in conformity with the Koran falls roughly into two general categories: (1) customary practices which are approved by at least large segments of the population and (2) behavior which diverges from the standards of all portions of the society.

The first type of behavior stems from supernatural practices native to the Sudan, innovations introduced into the religion by the Berbers of North Africa, and local developments. They evidence incomplete indoctrination in the dogma of Islam, but they constitute a body of supernatural belief just as sacred to its adherents as the Word of the Prophet. The following chapter deals largely with such beliefs. The maraboutic charms, cures, and tricks of prognostication fall into this category. Even usury might be so considered. There is conflicting opinion on the validity of such beliefs, particularly between Arabs and Gabibi, but this simply reflects the lack of cultural homogeneity in the city.

Behavior which is generally disapproved is quite a different matter. It represents nonconformity with accepted values. Cheating, robbery, prostitution, and omission of prayers are examples. All are fairly common in spite of the consensus that they are wrong. In the case of men's adultery, its prevalence is accepted but there is general knowledge that the religion does not allow it. However, the rule against it is an academic thing, not an emotionally supported value such as those against murder and robbery. Hospitality, alms, and the pilgrimage to Mecca are positive prescriptions which would fall in this same marginal position.

Finally, we note that some of the customary patterns which do not conform to the dogma diverge in the direction of introducing the philosophy of the market into dealings with the supernatural. Marabouts charge for their services and their price is bargained over. Their customers may pay only on delivery of results. Almsgiving may be contingent upon the receipt of benefits asked of Allah and the saints.

CHAPTER 6

Genii and Witches

Genii

The darkness of night and the darkness of ignorance of science are peopled with weird and terrible spirits. Genii roam at large or do the bidding of their human masters. Over the centuries the Arabs have added the concept of genii to the preexisting supernatural world of Timbuctoo.[1] The *dyini,* as the Songhoi call them, take horrible forms. Some have the form of Negro forest spirits and are as tall as the sky, with hair to their waists and long fingers and nails.[2] Most genii are dangerous and unusual deaths are attributed to them. They shun daylight, the light of the full moon, and artificial light, but one must continually be on guard against them in the dark. Whistling or wearing

[1] Indigenous spirits and gods come to be regarded as genii during the process of acculturation of Moslem and Kaffir. As the existence of genii is recognized by the Koran, they provide a device for bringing Islam into harmony with pagan religions. Greenberg has shown this to be true among the Hausa and cites evidence of other occurrences (1946:60). Herskovits, 1937, has demonstrated that Christian saints perform a similar role in the acculturation of Negroes in the New World.

Unlike other West African Negro groups, the Songhoi of Timbuctoo do not become possessed by the gods nor are the gods ancestral. I saw only one person possessed by a god during my stay. In this instance, the girl possessed as well as the drummer and most of the observers were strangers to the city. Possession is, however, found among the rural Songhoi (Rouch, 1960).

Rouch, 1945, has further material on Songhoi genii.

[2] This description of a Songhoi *dyini* compares closely with that of the Ashanti *Sasabonsam* (Rattray, 1927:28 and Fig. 19). Their extreme height and ability to materialize and change form have Arabian parallels.

a steel dagger or sword at night will keep them away. The saying of *"Bismillahi"* (In the name of Allah) is frequently used to exorcise them. Genii dislike tobacco and aloes, which is often included in the local smoking blend, and they have been known to snatch a pipe from the mouth of a nocturnal smoker.[3]

There are two sorts of genii—the black and the white.[4] The Songhoi distinguish them as the Gabibi and Arma of the genii. The Arma do not rule the Gabibi, but the latter, as in real life, are believed to have greater supernatural power. This is generally consistent with the Arab belief in good and evil genii and the greater danger from the latter. It is agreed by all that an encounter with evil genii is fatal if you are unprotected.

Sabane, a Songhoi, told me:

Genii are frequently seen and heard around here at night. A genie will appear as a small black spot on the ground and will grow until he is as tall as the houses. He will change into a cat or dog or sheep and then disappear. Once when I was coming into an open place at Kabara, I found the place surrounded by immense figures in great white turbans. They all made a sucking noise at me. Another time I had been to Kabara to lie with a girl and had left the house without bathing. This act particularly offends the genii and many men who have done this have been found lying on the ground, frothing at the mouth, to die a short time later.[5] I passed through Sidi Yahya, on the way to my home which is in another quarter of Timbuctoo. As I was going down a long, narrow street, I heard a dog making a clanking sound in his throat. From this I recognized the dog as one of the good genii of Sidi Yahya, so I let the local genie lead me through his quarter. All at once I found myself beside a great black shape ten meters tall. I stopped stock-still and the dog ran away. I said "Bismillahi" and waited without moving. The dog returned and led me home. While I waited

---

[3] Similar occurrences are sometimes interpreted as the liking of genii for these substances.

[4] The white genii would appear to be derived from the Moslem dogma that some genii were converted to Islam (*Koran*, LXXII). In this connection see also Greenberg, 1946.

[5] The sex act makes one ritually unclean until proper ablutions are performed.

for my grandmother to open the door, the dog ascended into the air.

The experience of living men is like those in the folk tales, which is not surprising as they too are the "true" accounts of past events.

A man from Timbuctoo used to ride to Kabara every night at midnight, with an axe over his shoulder. A genie, who had seen him do this, was talking with a lion and told him that he feared the man. The lion said that he was not afraid, so they waited for the rider. When he came along, the lion crouched and sprang on the man, who cut him down with a blow of the axe. The genie said, "See, I knew he was too strong." The man heard him and looked to see who spoke. The genie, in fright, turned into the trunk of a scrub tree. The man looked for the owner of the voice and then noted the tree. Although he knew the road well, he had never seen a tree there before. Suspecting that it was a genie, he cut it down with a blow of his axe.

Less fearless men, knowing that genii take the forms of dogs and cats at night,[6] never make a hostile move toward these stray beasts. Before I was aware of this I foolishly hurled stones at some howling dogs which were making sleep impossible. My native friends, greatly perturbed, put me straight on the matter the next morning and thereafter I restricted myself to Christian curses.

There is a certain species of genii known as *lantar* or *unkurmi*,[7] believed to be particularly numerous around the towns of Kutakura and Gao.

They are less than two feet high but are exceedingly strong. They have big turbans, black skin, long beards, big bellies, and their feet are turned backward. *Unkurmi* love peanuts

---

[6] The same belief is held in Morocco (Westermarck, 1926:I, 268). Two of the pagan Hausa spirits take dog forms (Greenberg, 1946:31–32).

[7] *Lamtar, lewtar* and *lohar* occur as variants of *lantar*. The *unkurmi* are clearly related to the Ashanti *mmoatia*. These latter spirits are about a foot in stature, their feet point backwards and they do mischief about the house, such as stealing palm wine. They also can tell humans how to make *suman* or fetishes (Rattray, 1927:25–27, Fig. 19). The *aziză* is the counterpart in Dahomey (Herskovits, 1938:II, 262).

and sometimes are seen in the peanut fields at night. If you stop them from eating the peanuts, they will say, "We were not doing any harm; just taking a little bit." When annoyed thus, or just for sport, they will throw you to the ground and kill or craze you. A Frenchman was tripped up and beaten by *unkurmi* near Kutakura one night. He went insane and gibbered about little men with long beards. One of their favorite tricks, when they come out at midnight, is to call people by their names and then attack them. If the intended victim can vanquish an *unkurmi* by catching and beating him severely, the genii will do his every bidding. Many natives have been able to go into business with the merchandise such *unkurmi* brought them.

The Gabibi also know that some foreign tribesmen who have visited Timbuctoo have had genii which spoke through wooden masks. It is believed that these men secured their power by vanquishing *unkurmi* and cutting off their heads, which are the masks. A severely beaten *unkurmi* will also tell his captor *tyini bibi* (black talk) or secret words of sorcery. Whether free or as prisoners, these are the most talkative of the genii. The others apparently subscribe to the idea that actions speak louder than words, for one never hears of their talking. This fact may be what has linked the *unkurmi* genii with the talking mask. At any rate, the *unkurmi* have talked with so many different sorts of people that they are known to be multilingual.

Genii sometimes settle down in a house.

They make their presence known through great flashes of light or through the disappearance and return of property within the house. No surprise must be evidenced at such phenomena but a marabout is asked to ascertain the nature of the genie. The marabout sleeps on his *fisa tyitab* (fortune book). Next morning he will inform the head of the house whether his genie is good or bad. If it is bad, it can be chased from the house by having ten or fifteen Koranic students chant there for several days. Similarly, the burning of aloes will rid the house of its unwanted guest. *Kankarey* are earthenware pots, covered with protective formulas, which are often built into the foundations of houses to protect the future occupants from such visitations of genii.

Usually one's own house is the safest place from genii. They are most common in unfamiliar places—in other quarters of the city or in other towns. Within Timbuctoo the Songhoi consider Abaradyu to be particularly infested with genii. The grass huts of this northern outskirt of the city are inhabited by Arab slaves and transients. It is the area in which the caravaneers stay when they are in town. It is true that the blacksmiths of this suburb are thought to have potent supernatural power, but the Songhoi usually think of the Gabibi and Bela as being the strongest in the "black arts." The most marked characteristic of Abaradyu is its social disorganization. It is the residence of transient strangers, the center of prostitution. Thievery is common, fights not infrequent. From all points of view, it is a dangerous quarter to visit at night.

A few very powerful marabouts are believed by the Songhoi to have white genii to do their bidding. The marabouts deny this but the fact is demonstrated by their works. One Songhoi Alfa has cured insanity, made it rain, and caused cloth to be transmitted magically over great distances through the medium of his genii. The genii impose certain restrictions on the Alfa. He must arise early in the morning or they will kill him. They will also retaliate if he overworks them. The ability of great marabouts to cause things to be transported through the air is obviously similar to the saints' ability to fly.

There is a well-known story in Timbuctoo concerning a marabout and his genii in the epoch shortly following the Moroccan conquest.

The Sultan of Morocco used to come to Timbuctoo each year and carry off two Arma women as slaves. This became so unbearable for the noble Arma that they were ready to go to war. As a last resort, however, they all made donations to a great marabout after the Sultan had returned to Morocco with two more women. The marabouts assembled all the Arma in a big circle and had them all close their eyes. While their eyes were closed, his genii brought the Sultan back to Timbuctoo. The Sultan was packed in straw in a large box which the genii set down in the middle of the circle. The Arma opened their eyes and saw the box. It was opened and the Sultan got out. He said, "Where am I?" They told him he was in Timbuctoo, to which he responded, "It is impossible! I was in my palace surrounded by three hundred guards." Thereupon the Arma threatened to kill him unless he promised to stop taking Arma women as tribute. The Sultan, having no choice but to accede to their demand, gave his word. He was returned to Morocco by the genii and there was no more trouble.

The Songhoi also believe that some Gabibi can control genii. These are black genii who do their master's bidding when he conjures them with magical phrases. These words are a mixture of Arabic and Songhoi or other African tongues. Like the marabouts, the Gabibi deny such control of genii even when they are professional makers of charms. But one sees the work of the genii.

A beggar was seen to ask alms of a Gabibi. The Gabibi was ashamed to admit his poverty so he flourished his empty hand in the air and then opened it to give the beggar the kola nut that his genii had placed there.[8] On another occasion, a group of Gabibi, including a sorcerer, were at Kabara one evening. They had nothing to eat. The Gabibi sorcerer lifted a calabash full of water over his head, called his genie, Yay Wadu. When he lowered the calabash, it was full of couscous and sugar.

The masons, smiths, and butchers are the Gabibi who wield the greatest supernatural power. As these crafts are confined to hereditary guilds, the techniques for controlling the supernatural are secured from one's father or some other older relative. A Gabibi tells me:

Supernatural power increases with age so that older men are more powerful. A young mason would not think of working without previously securing the magic lore of the craft from an older mason. This can be secured only after three or four months' apprenticeship. The masons are particularly fond of using their power. If one of them is doing exceedingly well in

---

[8] The gesture of raising the arm is a common method of throwing the full sleeves of the robe back on the shoulder. The witness may have read this whole story into such a gesture. The oft recurrent economic motive is noteworthy.

his craft, a jealous competitor may have his genie catch the other man at work and throw him from the top of the house. One does not see the genie and one would think that the worker just fell off the house.

Sorcery and Magic

Kambu and *gulli* are fetishes and charms which are more African than Arab in character. The local Arabs are aware of Songhoi supernatural practices but do not consider them to be effective. Thus, the Arabs believe in genii and their control through marabouts, but deny supernatural powers not based on the Koran. Non-Arab Alfa, however, often have faith in non-Moslem powers of sorcery and magic and are called upon to combat their effects, even though such marabouts are not sorcerers themselves. Most sorcerers are said to be strangers in Timbuctoo, such as Bambara, Mossi, and Fulani, all of whom are recognized as being "masters of evil" (*dabarey futu koy*).[9] Although sorcery is damned by the better trained marabouts and now outlawed by the French, there are also Bela and Gabibi sorcerers resident and practicing in the city.

A magician is called a *tyinibibi koy* or "master of black talk." He does his supernatural work through secret incantations. These spells may impart supernatural power to non-Koranic charms (*gulli*), may control genii, or the words themselves may work the desired effect. The incantation of the *tyinibibi koy* and the ritual of the sor-

[9] A Fulani visitor in Timbuctoo was regarded as a sorcerer because of ethnic origin. While he denied this, he describes some of the sorcery of his vllage. The materials with which the sorcerer works are chicken, carp, and crocodile eggs, carp heads, and fresh butter. Butter or egg white is eaten as part of the ritual of becoming a sorcerer. If ever forced to desist from sorcery, he vomits up these original substances. (Similar beliefs are associated with witches in Timbuctoo.) A victim may be driven insane by introducing carp eggs into his food or drink, burying a carp head in an ant hill or by filling a hole with crocodile eggs which have been opened and left in water for seven days. This last procedure may also kill or drive insane the close kin of the victim.

cerer mix Arabic words and script with the African elements of the sorcery and magic.

The Gabibi have the reputation of being the greatest *tyinibibi koy* in Timbuctoo. Their cultural cousins, the Songhoi of Bamba and Hombori, are known to be even stronger "black talkers." The following account of Mulai, an Arab, of his experiences among the Songhoi of Hombori sheds light on their customs. Mulai professes the usual Arab disbelief in the power of the snake head and dried frog charms which he saw being sold in the village markets of Hombori. He does not like the idea of having to take the vendor's word for the properties of these charms. He smells fraud. An Arab can read the charm written by a marabout and see for himself if the text is pertinent to the supernatural property claimed for it. Arabs have been known to refuse charms if not satisfied with the content of the text.

He also suspected trickery in the scheme regularly perpetrated on strangers by the *tyinibibi koy* of Hombori. These magicians claim to have charms with which they can change dirt into kola nuts, mud bricks into gold, wrapping paper into paper money. These local alchemists demonstrate their power for the benefit of strangers. They can, however, be prevailed upon to sell their charms. Such a *tyinibibi koy* joined a group of travelers which included Mulai. He recalls:

A French franc piece was requested from each of us. The magician then took some of the blue wrapping paper which comes around sugar loaves and tore it in pieces. He rolled up the pieces of paper, rubbed them over the back of his neck and head and then opened his hands. The scraps of paper had turned into French five franc notes, which he distributed among us. I said I would rather have back the one franc piece than keep the bill. The magician assured me that the paper money was all right. He explained that he had to use this device to get the one franc pieces because associated with his charm was a taboo against drinking or eating anything bought with the wealth created by the talisman. I did not want to purchase his charm, but, having heard that these five franc notes changed back to paper, I spent the money in the market as soon as possible.

The incident is a good example of the continual balance which secular evidence and sacred beliefs struggle to maintain. The Songhoi did not believe in the charm because overtrustful local natives had proven it a fraud. On the other hand, the Songhoi did not give up their faith in all charms, only in this one. An item of sacred faith can be maintained only in the absence of incontestable evidence contrary to that item of faith, except when the cultural content of the faith can explain the discrepancy. The practical proof of efficacy witnessed by Mulai, whose faith said that what he saw was impossible, left him in an ambivalent situation to which he responded ambivalently. The single objective demonstration made inroads on his faith.

The *tyinibibi koy* of Timbuctoo include the guild artisans. With the exception of the slipper-makers and tailors, they are Gabibi. In addition to these craftsmen, other Gabibi make supernatural charms which they sell. Many-colored string and thong charms are the most common. These cord charms (*gulli*) have much the same properties and are worn in much the same way as the *tira* written by the marabouts. A common element of the cord charms is the presence of various colored strands usually including yellow, black, and red. The cords may be braided or knotted, the words of magic being spoken into each knot until the cord is about half its original length. The string may be wrapped around an animal tooth in some charms. The power of these *gulli* is such that it is said that a Gabibi never tries to borrow money from another Gabibi but broaches the loan to an Arab or Arma who is not so apt to have powerful counter-loan charms. The fact that the Arma and Arabs are richer may also be important. In actuality, a Gabibi will borrow from anyone.

The native confidence in charms is great. Their power is reputed to be recognized even by Christians.

All important people wear them, even though they may not admit it. The French commandant wears them in secret. Even Christian missionaries have been seen buying many of them.[10] The Bela get out of many difficulties through their talismans. At Goundam a Bela was tied before a wall to be shot. As the soldiers raised their rifles, he disappeared, leaving only the pile of ropes. Many have been known to walk right out of jail in Timbuctoo. One man was sent to jail under guard by the French commandant. A short while later the commandant saw the man in front of his office and reviled the guard. This time the commandant himself went with the guard and saw the man locked up. The Bela was soon seen again lounging in front of the office.

Stealing, while in a state of invisibility induced by magical charms, is so common that successful robbery is usually explained in these terms. The belief finds corroboration in the fact that it is the Bela who steal the most frequently.

A man entered a house, in which a number of salt merchants of Timbuctoo sat, and stole salt bars without being seen. He was later observed selling them in the market. There are also charms to make people sleep so that you can steal from them without awaking them.

Other charms are also known in Timbuctoo. A stone ring with a point on it is commonly worn by men on their little or ring finger of either hand. Women wear them in their hair. They are sold like kola nuts in the open market. The wearer is protected against the "evil mouths" of others. This danger stems from the belief that compliments from non-intimates bring evil upon those praised. People therefore tend to avoid direct compliments and fear those directed to them. If two charm rings are broken accidentally, while being worn, the wearer is protected forever from

[10] The French administrators and missionaries, of course, have bought native charms as souvenirs and evidence of idolatry. Their denial of the virtues of these charms seems to be belied by these purchases. My own apparently credulous interest in the supernatural in Timbuctoo probably further fortified the natives' belief that Christians recognize native supernatural powers. The French attempts to suppress sorcery have the same effect.

this danger. The silversmiths make silver rings for the little finger, which are love charms. When given by a girl to an admirer, they are an invitation to the bed.

The tools of trade of the Gabibi sorcerer are his *kambu* and the knowledge of how to create and use such fetishes. *Kambu* means "tweezers" or "tongs," the body of the fetishes made in Timbuctoo consisting of a short pair of metal tweezers. The smith who makes the tweezers may be the sorcerer, but other Gabibi also know and practice the ritual creation of *kambu*. Once created, the *kambu* can be controlled by anyone who possesses it and knows the associated lore. It can be used for divination, to cause enemies to sicken or die, or to duplicate the powers of the genii.[11]

Some of the mysteries of the *kambu* are not secret but a sorcerer will not divulge this knowledge to a white man for fear of imprisonment.[12] The mystic words the creation of which go into a *kambu* are kept secret even from other natives. The following account was secured by Mulai from a Gabibi smith who made a *kambu* for Mulai at my instigation and eventually for my possession. The description was checked with the finished product and with the accounts of a Gabibi and a Bela who had seen *kambu* made and used. Mulai described it thus:

The tongs employed as the body of the fetish are made of either copper, silver, or iron, differing with individual sorcerers. Between the ends of the tongs is put a written charm. The writing is in a mystic Arabic script in which the letters are written upside down. A piece of cloth from a saint's tomb is wrapped around the *kambu* and sewn onto it.[13] Further charms

---

[11] See Appendix II for traits similar to *kambu* and *gulli* in North Africa and on the Guinea Coast.

[12] The illegality of sorcery was a handicap in obtaining first hand ethnographic material on this subject. However, the natives showed no reticence about discussing the subject and describing what they knew of it, as long as they were not asked to identify themselves with the practice.

[13] In Morocco, cloth is hung near the tomb of saints to gain the *baraka* of the saint and to leave the ills of the devotee with the cloth. The cloths are felt to be contagious and capable of

are written on this cloth. Then four cords, red, white, black, and yellow in color, are tied about the *kambu*. A long section of each string is left free. Secret words are spoken over each cord as the Gabibi spits on it and ties it in a knot. Five cowries are then sewn on either side of the *kambu*.

A white cock, known as *bono dyongu*,[14] is secured and taken into the bush. The throat of the bird is cut and the blood is smeared over the *kambu*. Then the cock is cut open and cleaned and the *kambu* placed in its open belly. The bird is then put in some hidden place, either in the bush or in the house. While chanting a secret incantation, spikes are driven through the wings so as to spreadeagle the bird on the ground. The *kambu* is oriented so that its head is to the north, opposite that of a buried person.

Every morning and evening the sorcerer chews red and white kola nuts together and spits the chewed kola all over the *kambu*. At these times he faces to the west and addresses the *kambu*, chanting the Moslem *fātihah*. Every ten days a sheep is killed and the blood put on the fetish. A black sheep is preferred but it may be of any sex or age. When forty days have gone by, the *kambu* is taken out of the chicken. The free ends of the cords are wrapped around it and pulled tight. The *kambu* speaks, making a sound like a cat, "Nyow." The words of the *kambu* can be interpreted by the sorcerer. The fetish, having spoken, has proved its power and is put away in a leather sack. On every recurrence of the day of the week on which the *kambu* first spoke, it must be given kola and the blood of a white cock. The fetish may be put into service at any time after this.[15]

---

transferring the ill which they bear (Westermarck, 1926:1, 553–556). In another description of the *kambu* ritual, the skin of a jackal was used instead of cloth. Others described the cloth as coming from a shroud.

[14] *Bono dyongu* means literally, "Hundred head." It refers to a kind of cock that has "100" small protuberances on the skin of its head. In another account, a black *bono dyongu* was used. Other than the ritual killing of this bird is supposed to bring ill fortune. If one's wife is pregnant and he kills a *bono dyongu*, the baby's head will be crushed in birth.

[15] Variations from this description are reported by another informant. The types of metal used are iron, copper, and brass. Three cowries are used instead of the double-five. The cords

When the owner desires to use the properties of the *kambu*, he takes one of its cords and winds it tightly about the body of the fetish. At the same time he tells the *kambu* what is desired of it. As the cord is wrapped around the fetish, it speaks again. The fetish is then put in the sun. The *kambu* gets out of the sun and into the shade. The owner then puts it back in the sun. This is repeated three times and then the desired end will be achieved, although it may take some time to come about.

The *kambu* "moves out of the sun" through the movement of the shade. The native knows that the shade moves but this does not preclude the possibility of the *kambu* moving also. This is not as startling as it might seem. I can sit in one spot and watch the sun move over me, from one horizon to the other. People in whom I have implicit faith tell me that it was really I who moved while the sun stood still. It did not look that way to me, but in the frame of reference in which it is explained, I not only believe but "understand." The sorcerer has faith in other people than those whom I revere. Within their frames of reference he too "understands" that squeaking strings and changing shadows are really the *kambu* speaking and moving.

Shadows are not just natural phenomena for the native. At night they have been seen to grow into genii. The *kambu* is not inanimate. It must be "fed" with ritual kola nut every week or it will die. It can speak. The ends accomplished with it are observable. Natives fear it and pay handsomely to obtain its help. The native frame of reference is as consistent and as much in accord with reality as my own. The reality of human life and death, of acts and ideas is dominant for the native. The reality of science and the laboratory dominates my thought. The native actually has more personal experience with his type of reality than I with mine. If the *kambu* fails to kill a human victim, it is because of the protective power of the charms

___

are black, red, and yellow only. The *bono dyongu* is killed to the west of the city. The regular "feeding" of the completed *kambu* is on Friday and consists of the chewed-up red and white kola nuts but no chicken sacrifice.

which the victim wears. If my doctor treats a patient but he dies nevertheless, it is because the bacteria were stronger than the drugs. While I have not seen the bacteria, in which I believe, every native has seen the charms which protected the intended victim of the *kambu*.

The difference between the native and myself is not in our manner of thought or in what we observe. We differ in the nature of the techniques in which we place our faith. The technique of the doctor is no more rational than that of the sorcerer. Rationality operates within a set of logics—a frame of reference. The techniques of the doctor, however, are more practical. It is this secular factor of efficiency, recognized by every man, which leads to the ultimate dominance of the doctor's techniques in my cultural order.

To return to the realm of logic of the smith whose ritual was just described, he affirms that he would use the *kambu* against anyone who worked in a metal other than that which his forebears used. It will be recalled that the smiths are family guilds specializing in particular metals or combinations of metals. It is said by some that *kambu* made of iron are considered all-powerful. Those made of copper are only effective in witchcraft against children or in their protection. *Kambu* of brass can only protect health and wealth. The colors of the *kambu* cords have special significance. When the fetish is to be used to make a victim sicken or die, the particular colored cord selected to tighten around the *kambu* depends upon the skin color of the victim. Thus, the black strand is used against Negro Bela and Gabibi, the red against Arabs, and the yellow against the French.

The practice of sorcery as described by a Bela indicates divergent but related ritual and concepts:

The sorcerer starts his work against a victim by using a wooden figurine. A cock's throat is cut in the dark of night and the blood poured on the figure and rubbed all over it. Then a small bundle of thorns, about four inches long, is bound together with red, yellow, green, blue, and black yarn. Sometimes hair strands or other exuviae of the victim are included in the bundle. The sorcerer chants his secret charms over his creation and spits on it several times. This ritual identifies the fetish with the victim. The fetish is buried in the sand an arm's length deep. Some fragments of the yarn are put into the victim's house, food, or water. He will then sicken and remain ill as long as the fetish remains buried unless counter-sorcery is employed.

The Bela who had witnessed this ritual also witnessed the cure. The surest sign that illness is caused by sorcery is the inability of the traditional remedies to effect a cure. The symptoms are characterized by the way the pain moves from one part of the body to another, frequently causing swelling. The victim, in this case, called another sorcerer when he became deathly ill. The sorcerer found the yarn in his house and removed it. He also made an incision in the patient's back and extracted a thorn—"one that had been in the buried fetish."

A Frenchman, who ran a successful private trading house in Timbuctoo until his recent suicide, is believed by the natives to have possessed a powerful fetish. Ober was a small man but powerful and greatly feared by the natives whom he beat mercilessly. A competing trading house finally caught him changing the trade marks on bolts of cloth in order to sell them as better goods than they were. Faced with trial and prison, Ober shot himself. His long success and power in Timbuctoo are attributed to a fetish which is still supposed to be in the wall of his closed establishment. He was often heard in conversation with his fetish, which told him how to get out of trouble. During his last episode, he had lain in bed for three days talking to the fetish, which refused to help him, saying he would be caught this time and put in prison.

Cowrie Readers

The supernatural practitioners we have mentioned thus far are almost always men, the exception being occasional women "black talkers." In one kind of fortune telling, however, the seers are women. These are the cowrie readers. The past, present, and future are told by these women by casting cowrie shells and reading the events from the positions in which the cowries fall. For example, one cowrie coming to rest upon another indicates intercourse and hence a child to be born. The cowrie sets consist of twelve to fourteen shells, the dorsal sides of which have been cut off. Some readers murmur secret incantations over the shells before casting them. The reading of cowries is always most satisfactory when performed on Friday.

The Arabs do not frequent the cowrie readers, preferring the marabouts and their books of divination. They are non-committal as to the efficacy of the cowries. The Songhoi recognize individual variation among readers. Some are better than others and some are rank frauds. A cowrie reader told a young man that his best friend had gone to a sorcerer to bring harm upon him. He refused to believe this and deemed the woman a charlatan.

Witches

The supernatural world of Timbuctoo has yet another class of beings—the witches.[16] They are called *tyerkow* or referred to in circumlocution so as not to attract them by calling their name. Unlike genii, witches are thought to be human beings with special supernatural powers. Unlike sorcerers, who actually practice sorcery, there are no people who actually practice witchcraft. Thus witches exist only for the people who fear them, see the results of witchcraft, protect themselves from them, identify people as witches, and occasionally even force such a person to "confess" to being a witch.

It is believed that witchcraft runs in families. The children or spouses of witches are encouraged to become *tyerkow*, which they can do through the agency of those who are already witches. The *tyerkow* gives the neophyte cowrie shells and goat butter which must be swallowed

[16] Beings similar to the *tyerkow* are referred to in the African literature as "witches," although many attributes of these creatures appear to be comparable to those covered by the European concept of "vampire."

together in one gulp. The cowries and butter form small stones called "eggs" which remain in the stomach of the witch. If he is ever caught, he is forced to regurgitate the "eggs." The breaking of a witch's eggs breaks his spell.

Witches leave their skins at night and go forth in search of their victims. While in this state, they are entirely red in color. They may travel on the backs of devils. The swish of bat wings which one hears about a house at night is really a witch trying to gain entrance. If it gains entry, all the residents who are not already asleep will fall asleep immediately. The witch selects its victim and sits on his chest and drinks blood from his neck. The victim cries out but no one can hear. The *tyerkow* returns home and gets into his skin before dawn. Witches return midnightly to the same victim and he becomes thin and weak and his eyes grow dim. The victim is sick and has a fever in the early morning and evening.[17]

Witches also attack people during the daytime and it is then that they are most likely to be caught. During the day a witch has his normal human form, but he can attack victims by merely touching them. Analysis of some such instances of witchcraft indicates that the witch usually sells the victim something which he eats or puts in his mouth, although the natives do not recognize this as important. The symptoms are violent gastric upset, with loss of consciousness usual. As with sorcerers, the Bela, Gabibi, and particularly strangers from the bush are suspected of being witches. The normal contact of the Songhoi with such strangers is commercial, which explains why the purchase of food and witchcraft are associated.

Witches are supposed to hold midnight meetings at a pond to the south of Timbuctoo, beside which stands a tree which, symbolically, is half white and half red. Another assembly point is at *Koyma hondu*, the great dune covering the ruins of the Askia palace near Gao. At these places, under the direction of their chief, the witches select their victims. Some say that each must provide one of his own male relatives for the others to feast upon.

[17] Malaria seems to be the disease diagnosed as the result of nocturnal attack by a witch.

Tira provide the most common protection against witch-craft. A powerful charm keeps the nocturnal witch from drinking the blood he sucks and forces him to spit it out on the robes of his victim. Another prophylactic device is the Moslem prayer for protection against all infidel pow-ers, *'llah al kafir 'llah kulu sein kadir.* It is repeated as a charm by the *koyraboro* who then spits in the four cardinal directions. This will keep witches out of the house or will keep them from leaving, if they get in, so that their identity will be revealed. The unmasking of a witch is the best way to stop his activities.

A person who believes he is being bled dry by a witch may appeal to a marabout for aid. Otherwise a Gabibi *tyinibibi koy* is called. The Gabibi presses the fingernail of the patient and if the nail is white under pressure, in-stead of the normal pink, a witch is responsible.[18] The Gabibi speaks his "black words" into goat or sheep butter. The patient eats some of this and the remainder is rubbed over his body. If the witch is to be apprehended, a dag-ger is stuck in the sand before the door of the house, with the proper incantation.[19] The witch is thereby forced to come to the house in his human form.

Once a *tyerkow* is apprehended, he can be exorcised by forcing him to drink water until he regurgitates his "eggs." It is said that the witch is forced to give the names of his victims, who can then secure charms against him. The most common practice, if the victim is sick and the witch is discovered, is to bring the *tyerkow* before the cadi. The cadi orders the witch to carry his victim on his back. This process restores to the victim the blood which the witch has drunk. The exposed witch is then threatened with death, if he does not desist from his attacks.

Witchcraft is a serious charge. Numerous cases have been brought before the French administrator who always refers them to the cadi. The bringing of *tyerkow* before

[18] A test for anemia which is associated with malaria.
[19] The Gabibi treatment is strikingly like that used by mara-bouts, from which it may be derived. The element of butter and alternative dagger treatment appear to be Sudanese.

French authority places them on a level with sorcerers, thieves, and murderers. The following native accounts are characteristic.

A Gabibi woman of Sankore, who sells tobacco and kola in the market, "took" a girl of Bela Farandi. The girl experienced the usual signs of general malaise through the whole body. She was brought on a donkey to the cadi, where witnesses attested that the Gabibi woman had touched the girl and was a witch. There was a great crowd of people—everyone from the market, the native police and soldiers. The cadi told the Gabibi that she would either have to carry the Bela girl across the market or she would be taken to the French and put in prison. The witch carried the Bela through the market and by the time she had reached the other side, the girl was quite well and could walk of her own accord. The brother of this Gabibi woman was also known to be a witch. He was turned over to the French doctor who kept him interned for forty days and gave him something special to drink. But it is known that this did not break his power and that he is still a witch.

In another instance, an old woman from the bush sold a tomato to a Bela woman. She had no sooner eaten it than she became very sick at her stomach. She went home and told her daughter, "If I die, it was that bush woman who took me." The suspect was brought before the commandant, who sent her to the cadi with instructions that if she were found to be a witch, she was to be sent out of town. The cadi called in a diviner who could recognize witches and he confirmed the belief that she was one. The afflicted woman died before she reached the cadi. The crowd beat the old woman and sent her out of town with the threat that the commandant would have her shot if she ever returned.

The literate Arabs of Timbuctoo are skeptical, as usual. They deny the existence of witches and the Arab marabouts substantiate this disbelief. The illiterate Arabs, particularly the Berabich of the bush, and the rest of the population believe that witches do exist.

Everyday Wonders

Supernatural events are not confined to the doings of supernatural beings and special people with supernatural powers. Many everyday occurrences have their supernatural aspect as well as their natural one. We have seen that compliments from strangers cause harm to fall upon the object of the compliments. Praise should therefore be expressed by some circumlocution such as "God should see it." The "hurt from peoples' mouths" is so strong that natives may feel weak at their stomachs if they overhear direct compliments about themselves. One Songhoi told me that he always feels ill the day after a holiday, for which he dresses in his best clothes, because he is so much admired.

This belief in evil effects from people's mouths is closely associated with Arab concepts concerning the evil eye.[20] The glance of a person with the evil eye may cause innumerable misfortunes. Fear of the evil eye is not highly important among the non-Arabs, although evil eye symbolism in designs is found in all the groups. The "hurt from peoples' mouths" is recognized as damage for which the aggressor is liable under native law. If a person or animal is admired by a stranger and dies accidentally or mysteriously the same day, it is said that the cadi will force the malefactor to indemnify the injured parties.

Unusual weather phenomena have supernatural meanings. A cloudy sky all day, such as we observed in Timbuctoo in May 1940, bodes some great catastrophe, such as that which befell France in 1940. It did not "rain blood" for World War II as it sometimes does to indicate impending battles. Lightning is a fearsome sight to all the natives. They cover their eyes, believing that the sight of it will make them go blind,[21] or crazy, or that they will die. They know that Frenchmen can look at "Michael's sword striking sparks" without ill effects, but Frenchmen are just different. In other regards the native is the stronger. The French must drink filtered water because of their susceptibility to disease, while the natives need not filter theirs!

[20] The evil eye and the evil mouth are found in Morocco (Westermarck, 1926:I, 414–478).
[21] For similar belief about lightning in Morocco, *ibid.*, I, 118.

Like the signs of war and bloodshed, many supernatural beliefs are just additional facts about natural objects and phenomena. Dreams often indicate future events. Owls and vultures are evil birds. Storks on one's house bring good luck. There are men in the bush—some say they are Tuareg smiths—who can change into hyenas. Various mysteries are connected by the *koyraboro* with the Great Mosque. The muezzin, after death, never decays. If you fall down the dark shaft inside the minaret, you will land in the town of Diere. There is a dove in a cage in the mosque on whose life the world depends. When it dies, the world will end.

The Songhoi must observe certain taboos and rites to avoid ill fortune. Friends should never pour water over one another's hands to wash or use the same wooden toothbrush. If they do their friendship will end. If burning coals are secured from a hearth on a black potsherd, the owner of the hearth will have bad luck all day. If he is a merchant, he will be unable to sell a thing. The person desiring the embers, therefore, carries them in a handful of sand or in a pottery incense burner. The great lake Debo, near the Niger, must give a fish to everyone who traverses it.[22] If passengers have any cologne water, some must be spilled into the lake to avoid bad winds and storms.

Kabi

The general taboos just mentioned are somewhat similar to the *kabi* or inherited taboo. Particular peoples or tribes have distinctive *kabi*.[23] Such a group also has a

---

[22] As many as fifty fish have actually been known to jump into a canoe.

[23] *Kabi* not included in the text are:
The Fulani (Peredyo) cannot sweep or wash milk vessels on Tuesday or the cattle will die.
Dupuis (Yakouba), 1917, under "kabi" in dictionary:
Arma—monitor lizard (*dyammu karinso*); orange agaric.
Sorko—cannot travel on Tuesday.
Shereef—elephant.
Songhoi—dove.
Tuareg—*hayga* grass.

characteristic name (*dyammu*)[24] which indicates its common descent from a single group of people. Thus, the Da were the predecessors of the Songhoi in this area. Their *dyammu* is *dyitey*. Their *kabi* is the *desi* or catfish, which they are forbidden to eat. A common *dyammu* does not necessarily imply descent from a single common ancestor. There are *dyammu* for the descendants of the Moroccan conquerors from particular towns in Morocco. The ancestors of the *almarkasin* come from Marrakech, those of the *alfasin* from Fez.

The Arabs and Arma also follow the Arab system of recognition of patrilineal descent from a single common ancestor. This results in the recognition of various distinctive lineages within a group having the same *dyammu*. The *Ouled Nasser* are such a particular kin group within the *almarkasin*. A *kabi* may be limited to a family group or extend to all of the same *dyammu*. Indigo cloth dyed by the Mossi or Hausa is the *kabi* of all *almarkasin* and cannot be touched by them. The *Alfa Moyhanma* of Sankore are the lineal descendants of a famous marabout named Moy, who was killed in combat with the invading Moroccans on a Wednesday. The *kabi* of this family prohibits washing of clothes, bathing, and hairdressing on Wednesday.

The idea of family and tribal taboos is so universal among Negroes, Berbers, and Arabs all over Africa that its origin must be considered lost in antiquity. The ethnic origin of particular taboos may be traced, however. The *kabi* of *Alfa Moyhanma* is a case in point. The origin of

---

[24] *Dyammu* of Timbuctoo not included in text but given by Dupuis (Yakouba), 1917, under *dyammu*.

Meyga—Songhoi.
Ture—Arma.
Taraore—Chorfa serfs.
Sise—All Alfa.
Zaouyakoy—Kunta.
Tendeni—Arma.
Addrawi—from Dara, Oued Drâa region.
Alhâa—Arma.
Laludyi—Arma.

the taboo is associated with the incident of Alfa Moy's death. The marabout was a Songhoi but the idea of taboo days is also found among Arabs in Morocco.[25] Even though this specific type of taboo antedates the Moroccan conquest, it must have been introduced through the earlier Arab contacts with the Songhoi, which introduced the seven-day week with its Arab day names.

The taboo against eating catfish is obviously of local origin. The Arabs of Morocco show their desert origin in a general reverence for fish, which are considered as having good *baraka.* They have no fish-eating taboos. On the other hand, the *desi* is *kabi* of the most Negroid groups around Timbuctoo—not only of the Da but of Gabibi and one tribe of Bela as well. The Gabibi say that in the old books of the early scribes it is written that the flesh of the *desi* is like that of man and should be avoided. A Gabibi origin myth for the taboo associates the fish with human flesh in another way.

In ancient times a man and wife and their small daughter set out in a boat with a Sorko fisherman. En route, the boat stopped stockstill. The Sorko said that a spirit was holding up the boat[26] and that they would have to throw in the little girl to the spirit if they were to be released. The father left it up to the mother whether they should do so or whether they should all stay there and die together. The mother decided to throw the little girl in the river and it was done. The spirit grabbed her and tore off her head. The Sorko at that moment hooked a *desi* which he killed and found that it had eaten some of the flesh from the head of the girl. The mother asked God to curse any of their descendants who ate *desi* thereafter.

A Bela origin story for the taboo is different but still associates the *desi* with human flesh.

One of our early ancestors encountered some fishermen and from them secured a fish which was a *desi.* He went home and put the fish down in his house and asked his wife to cut it up and cook it. His wife was pregnant and was very much

---

[25] For taboo days and other family taboos, see Westermarck, 1926:I, 403; II, 37–40.
[26] Water spirits are often identified with contrary currents.

afraid of the fish. She asked what it was and he said that it was just a fish and to cook it. So she put it in a pot over the fire. The husband ate the fish and then went to visit another woman. When he arrived, this woman smelled the fish on his breath and told him he smelled like a corpse and asked what foul thing he had been eating. He was very ashamed and left the house. A few days later his wife went into labor and the child which she bore looked like a *desi*. Everyone was horrified and he swore a great oath that thereafter if he or any of his descendants ever ate *desi*, they should sicken and die. Now even the smell of the fish renders his descendants sick.

One element of this tale is particularly noteworthy. The sight of the strange fish was frightening. It is doubtless the scaleless, human-like skin of this silurid, rather than its flesh, which accounts for its association with human beings and for the taboo. There is a basic undercurrent in the Negro taboos of this area making *kabi* of animals which eat human flesh.[27] This element was included in the Gabibi folktale about the *desi*. In addition, one Bela tribe has the lion as its *kabi*. "Sometimes these Bela do eat lions," it is said, "but only the right side of the lion. This side comes from the animals the lion has eaten, while the left side comes from the men he has devoured." The crocodile is the *kabi* of the Fulah *dyammu dyal*.

Part of the *kabi* belief is the conviction that there will be supernatural repercussions if the taboo is not observed. The most common result of breaking *kabi* restrictions is blindness. This punishment need not fall only upon the offending party but may be visited upon his kin as well. When a taboo has been unwittingly broken, there are purification rites to absolve one from the attendant curse. Thus, for the Fulani, the excreta of a crocodile will heal a crocodile bite or a wound caused by stepping on a crocodile bone. Such wounds would never heal otherwise.

Gabibi children are believed to be innately repulsed by

[27] This is similar to orthodox Islamic law, as expressed in the *Hidayah*, which prohibits the eating of all quadrupeds that seize their prey with their teeth and all birds which seize it with their talons.

desi. While at an early age, they are given to understand they are not only forbidden to kill and eat the *desi*, but if they see one caught by a fisherman, they should buy it and throw it back into the water. If a catfish is found dead it should be wrapped in cloth and buried. If one observes the taboos, he need never fear to travel on water. This reciprocal aid in the case of the *desi*, whose taboo appears the oldest in the area, is suggestive of totemism. But there is no suggestion of the *kabi* animal being ancestral. A group having a common *dyammu* is neither endogamous nor exogamous. A child takes the *kabi* of his father, but if the mother has a different *kabi* it is respected in the home. The sole suggestion of marriage regulation is a definite desire expressed by the Bela to marry someone of the same *kabi* "so that there will be only one *kabi*."[28] This consideration is not binding but it points to a bilineal emphasis which is distinctive of the Bela.

Religion and Magic

While at the outset we made no distinction between religion and magic, it will be helpful to point out the difference now. Both involve supernatural forces or beings. By "religion" we refer to those beliefs and rituals dealing with supernatural powers which must be supplicated or propitiated. The devotee is on a personal basis with them. He tries to influence them by his favorable acts. Religion may also interrelate the life and afterlife of man. In "magic" there is belief in a mechanical, cause and effect relationship between the magical act and its supernaturally produced, mundane result. Magic is conceptually more like technology.

The most important religious rituals in Timbuctoo are daily prayers, the ceremonies associated with life crises, such as birth and death, and the annual festivals. All of these rituals function to unite the community or segments

[28] A Fulani informant says that among them spouses adopt each other's *kabi* and children inherit the *kabi* of both parents. Sib-linked food taboos are common in the area to the south, as among the Ashanti, Hausa, and Dahomeans.

thereof. Even such special religious acts as almsgiving to avoid community catastrophe or the tying of shereef children to induce Allah to send rain express common interests.

While magic also appears at life crises, it is highly individualized, both in ritual and in purpose. Only the punishment for breaking *kabi* taboos seems to extend to the group. Magical charms and rites protect individuals from disease and harm, cure ills, and produce strength, pregnancy or abortion, depending upon the type of charm. They also assist the wearers in various kinds of business endeavors. Supernatural aid of this latter sort may also result from religious acts such as almsgiving, *Tijani* membership or prayers to the saints. In these cases, as in most of the magic, the purpose is to gain individual advantages.

In connection with this distinction between the uses and functions of religion and magic, the greater importance of magic in day-to-day living seems important. It is entirely consistent with the individualization of economic pursuits. A market economy operating impersonally among strangers does not produce a feeling of unity. One man's loss is not a loss to the total society but is another man's gain. Magic consists of techniques which each can use for his own benefit.

The term "black magic" is often used to describe magic which is used solely to do others harm. In some societies the belief in such magic functions to provide strong sanctions in support of the approved ways of life. The threat of revenge by black magic is a powerful deterrent to abusing the rights of others. Magic of this sort is not common in Timbuctoo. It is most evident in the supernatural powers of craftsmen who use magic to protect their guild prerogatives. Ills and misfortunes are often attributed to supernatural causes, but usually to genii or witches, not to the working of black magic.

Religion and magic operate to explain supernaturally that which is naturally inexplicable, and to influence by supernatural means that which is not subject to technical control. The supernatural thus provides methods of achieving a greater feeling of security. Timbuctoo is full of unfamiliar people, inhospitable areas, and strange customs. These sources of insecurity are explicitly associated with native supernatural beliefs. The genii of unfamiliar towns and strange quarters of Timbuctoo are the most dangerous. Strangers in town are "all" sorcerers. In the contacts of the market some stranger who is a witch may touch you. The native of Timbuctoo does not attribute his misfortunes to his sins against the supernatural order or his transgressions against his fellow man. Divination and protective and helpful magic flourish in this situation.

CHAPTER 7

The Moon Year

A festival is essentially a special occasion and unlike the monotony of everyday life. On holidays one does unusual things and sees a wider range of people. The distinctive customs which characterize festive occasions throw into relief the nature of many social relationships. The annual festivals in Timbuctoo are based on Moslem tradition and affect the whole community. Being religious occasions, the celebrations are closely related to the time schedule of Islam.

Timbuctoo uses the Moslem calendar but applies Songhoi names to most of the lunar months. The Songhoi names[1] clearly do not antedate the introduction of the calendar into the Sudan by the Arabs. Half of the month names are derived from Arabic or are Songhoi words connoting activities fixed in the Moslem calendar. Thus, the third month, *Almudu,* is a distortion of Moroccan *Al Mûlûd.*[2] The next two months are *Almudu Keyna* and *Almudu Keyna Hinkante* or "Little" *Almudu* and "Second Little" *Almudu.* The seventh month *Arredyeb* is derived directly from the Arabic *Rajab.* The important ninth month of fasting, called *Ramadān* in Arabic, is known as *Haome* in Songhoi, which means "Close mouth." The Songhoi call the following month *Ferme*—literally, "Open mouth." It is the occasion of the feast which follows the fasting of *Ramadān.*

[1] The Songhoi months, in order, are: *Dedow, Dedow Keyna, Almudu, Almudu Keyna, Almudu Keyna Hinkante, Koddayer, Arredyeb, Tye Konno, Haome, Ferme, Hina Endyama, Tyibsi.*
[2] Westermarck, 1926:II, 86.

New Year's Celebration

Dedow is the first month of the year. The ceremonies in honor of the new year include a number of ritualistic purifications including lavation and a fire ceremony. The neighboring, pagan Mossi[3] and Bambara[4] have sacred fire ceremonies but the custom as practiced by the Songhoi is like that in North Africa.[5] It is quite possible that the fire ceremony antedates North African influence on the Songhoi, as does the practice of circumcision, but indicative evidence is lacking in this instance.

The appearance of each new moon is the occasion for women to halloo with a wailing cry which notifies all within earshot that the moon has appeared. It is considered advantageous to be the first to pray upon seeing the new crescent. The new year's moon is greeted as any other. After its appearance, acquaintances greet one another, *"Yesi ma tyi ni"* (New Year's to you) and *"Yer koy ma tyerbu ni yesi"* (May God preserve you during the year). Strangely enough, these same salutations are used at the appearance of each new moon, as a sort of reaffirmation of the faith that the good fate already determined for the year will continue.

Moslem days run from sunset to sunset, instead of between sunrises as is our unofficial custom. The real New Year's celebration, following Moslem practice, does not start until the tenth day of the month. During the evening and night of this day, people feast and then bathe, either at one of the ponds around Timbuctoo or in the home. Fresh water is brought into every home from the ponds on this evening for general household use. Following the bathing, a small bonfire is built at the edge of the pond

---

[3] Seligman, 1930:64, mentions a Mossi fire ceremony at end of the rains.

[4] Bambara boys jump three times over a fire when they become "new men" as a result of circumcision (Monteil, 1923: 234–250).

[5] Westermarck, 1926:II, 58–72, considers the Moroccan fire ceremonies of non-Arab origin.

and everyone who bathed there jumps over it three times, saying, *"Yesi guna"* (See the New Year). Arma and Arab women build small fires in their homes and carry out the ritual there. After the fire purification, Songhoi women tie a white cord around their heads, which they continue to wear for three days or until the first time they sneeze.

The significance attributed to these acts varies considerably. There is general belief that, in some way, these ceremonies affect the well-being of the participants during the ensuing year. The water of this night has special but undefined qualities. The Bela believe that the ponds contain water from paradise at this time. The Songhoi and indigenous sedentary Arabs call the water *Dyena* or "mixed waters," in the belief that all the waters of the earth mingle on this evening. This water is also beneficial when taken internally and hence is drunk and used for cooking. The fire ceremony is explained by the Arabs as symbolizing the desire to traverse the narrow path over hell on the way to judgment. Many will fall from this road into the fires of hell. For many Songhoi the fire ceremony has no specific meaning.

The most marked difference in actual practice of *Dedow* ceremonies is between Arab and Songhoi. The Arabs trim their nails and bury the parings in the house. Men and children have their heads shaved; men trim their beards; women put their hair up anew and paint their eyelids with antimony as is still the custom in Morocco.[6] Young Songhoi women may have their faces tattooed on this day. The barber cuts the lines in their skin and fills the cuts with antimony to make the tattoo. The Berabich of the bush are reported to have no fire ceremony at this time and more sophisticated, recently arrived Moroccans likewise omit this ritual.

As the fire and water ceremonies purify the people for the coming year, there are other practices which reassert fundamental social groupings and permit a certain amount of release from the normal restraint of everyday life. Dur-

---

[6] Westermarck, 1926:II, 73–74.

ing the tenth day of *Dedow*, the young children of each quarter of the city go about in groups of as many as forty, engaging gangs from other quarters in street fights, even using clubs in these brawls.[7] No particular patterns of interquarter antagonism are shown. It is each against all others.

Another resort to force is permitted in Timbuctoo on this day under the following circumstances. Everyone has the right to expect *Dedow* gifts from certain of his or her relations and even from non-blood "relatives"—persons who are called by kin terms but who are not actually related. Grandparents, siblings of parents (mother's brothers only, for Arabs), elder siblings, cross-cousins,[8] and all persons called by these kin terms are expected to present gifts. Between cross-cousins, *basey* in Songhoi, a man's children are expected to donate to his sister's children. The Arma are expected to give to the Gabibi who are considered as *basey* of the Arma. If a cross-cousin refuses to produce the expected amount, the thwarted cousin tears the offending relative's clothes and generally belabors him or her. Something of value may be seized and held until the gift is produced. Only old clothes are worn into the streets this day, which suggests that refusal to give the required amount is not uncommon.

The manner of requesting gifts and their amount is fixed by custom. Both Songhoi and Arabs expect a *koporo* or ten centimes from cross-cousins. The traditional Songhoi "tricks or treats" phrases still state the amount expected in cowrie shells, now entirely displaced by French currency. You say, *"nori iyed"* (six cowries) to grandparents, whose gifts in reality may be elaborate if they are very rich. Elder siblings are accosted with *"Ay nor hinka di"* (my two cowries). Uncles and aunts, on the other hand, are greeted, *"Ay ña ka kungu di"* (I eat to be satiated), in the hope of receiving a big meal. Feasting

[7] *Ibid.*, II, 72. Ceremonial fights in this month occur in Morocco.

[8] The children of a brother and sister are cross-cousins. See Chapter 8, on kinship.

and dancing continue for three days and the visiting of relatives goes on until all have been seen.

Birth of Mohammed

The third month, *Almudu*, is marked by the celebration of the birth of Mohammed. Beginning on the evening of the first day, the marabouts and literate Arabs assemble at the mosques and read the *Ibn Mouhibt* aloud from sunset until the evening prayer. Portions of this work continue to be read until the twelfth night, when the feast of Mohammed begins.

The secular preparations for the feast cause quite a stir, particularly noticeable in the market. For several days before the feast, the people from the bush have been coming to town to sell their wares. With their profits, they make purchases to take back to their own communities for the occasion. Numerous articles which are not made in Timbuctoo and which have been lacking in the market, such as large baskets, are now available. The day before the feast the market is alive with activity and the air full of high-voiced conversation and exhilarated cries. An unusually large amount of jewelry is offered for sale. Cobblers are trying to dispose of their stock of plain and embroidered slippers, on which they have been working day and night to profit by the seasonal rush of business. Every young man, who is not already outfitted, is trying to buy a new robe or conclude a deal to secure the money to do so.

The birth of Mohammed is celebrated all night beginning at sundown. Pavilion-like oratories are set up outside the walls of the mosques and less elaborate ones are arranged in other parts of the city. In these oratories, seated on mats, are the marabouts and literate Arabs of the city. The imams of the mosques, teachers, notaries, Madersa students, judges, in fact all of the principal learned men of the community are present. There are some seventy or eighty in all, including the fourteen Arab marabouts and other Arabs who derive no commercial benefit from their knowledge of Moslem religion—who are not professional marabouts, so to speak. At least a third appear to be Caucasian Arabs and many more are culturally Arabs. None is a pure Negro, though many are markedly Negroid. The numerical predominance of Arabs results from the fact that they are the only non-maraboutic group in the population who can speak or read Arabic—the language of the oratory chants. Due to Arab pressure, the French have forced the Songhoi marabouts to include the Arabs in the groups at the oratories for this ceremony. The Arabs are made to feel that they are outsiders but they feel superior, nonetheless, and make caustic comments on the Songhoi Alfa's lack of knowledge of Arabic.

The marabouts are richly dressed in embroidered and patterned silk robes. Many wear luxurious turbans of glossy purple sateen. They install themselves in the oratories after the evening prayer and proceed to chant the *Ibn Mouhibt* in unison from beginning to end, completing it a few hours before sunrise. Some have copies of the book which they read by the light of lanterns. The marabouts in each oratory are divided so that they can read and rest alternately. The holy men partially cover their mouths with their hands or portions of their turban cloths during part of the reading, thereby increasing the eerie quality of their nocturnal chant.

While these religious readings are the *raison d'être* and a focus of interest for the celebration of this night, the secular celebration affects the general population to a greater and very different extent. Arab and Arma women are allowed on this occasion to leave the seclusion of their homes and move about the streets visiting the various oratories or performing the simple ritual of walking three times around the Great Mosque. The women and girls are in groups. Age-mates, whether married or single, promenade together. Arma women, distinguishable by the "scorpion tail" headdresses, always have their Gabibi companions with them. Bela and Gabibi women carry their nodding babies on their backs so as not to miss the fun. Young girls who are too pregnant to appear weep in dismay. Men move with their age-sets[9] also, but tend to be in smaller groups.

Everyone is dressed in his best—new or freshly washed clothes. Turbans and fezzes are common. Ready-made European shirts are apparent under the robes of some of the young men. Even a few tailored white suits are in evidence. The low class Gabibi find such French clothes handsome, while the upper class disdains them. The women wear bright-colored robes and their newly-arranged hair is richly ornamented. There are also gold and silver bracelets, necklaces, and rings for fingers, ears, and noses. The Gabibi have their straw necklaces of "Timbuctoo gold."

The groups move through the moonlit streets, the women's incense burners flickering in the dusk. Girls show off their new robes to the boys they meet. Boys and girls catch hold of one another as they pass. A wealthy man has a musician playing a monochord before his house for the amusement of any who care to listen. Young girls vivaciously dance in the street to this music. When tired, they sit on the sand and listen to the meaningless, rhythmic chant of the marabouts. Here, a wandering male can throw himself on the sand beside a girl to sing and joke and try to slip her away from her companions. Even after the chanting ceases, many young people remain together on the sands. Elsewhere in the city, dancing to the rhythm of drums continues until daybreak. Then the sun is said to dance as, with changing hues, it rises from the desert.

The daylight hours of that day are free from toil. The vendors of daily commodities, such as fresh milk and meat, appear in the market. A few enterprising tradesmen try to sell their wares but the city is dormant after its festive night. With the end of day, the reading of portions of the *Mouhibt* at the mosques is resumed and continued every evening for a week. Many of the Songhoi marabouts say

[9] See Chapter 9, Circumcision and Age-Sets.

they are too tired to resume reading, much to the disgust of the Arabs.

Naming of Mohammed

The eighteenth day of *Almudu* is called the Feast of the Naming of Mohammed. This celebration is of less importance than the preceding one. The *Mouhibt* is read through at night and again during the day. There are tom-toms for the youth at night. During the day, many of the Songhoi again walk three times, counter-clockwise, around the Great Mosque and go to the tomb of a saint outside the walls of the mosque. A blind mendicant installs himself in the tomb, crawling through a small aperture in the front. To all from whom he receives alms, he gives sand from within the tomb. The almsgivers sprinkle the sand on their bodies. Some then go to a nearby "mountain," which is really a hill of wind-blown sand sloping up to the roof of the mosque. The young roll down this hill. Like the *Dedow* purifications, these ritual acts are customary and beneficial but without any known history or specific meaning. As at New Year's, the ceremony is felt to continue the status quo or "to bring the feast back again next year," as they say.

On the eve of the Naming of Mohammed, there is another local ceremony called the "Breaking of the Drum." It takes place in the Arab quarter. A score of Arab slave women sit in a semi-circle before one of the houses, drumming and clapping their hands in unison. Near the center of the group is a woman with a family heirloom—a drum made of half of a large calabash. Crowding around the drummer and filling the street before the house are more than a hundred natives who have come to see the ceremony.

As the tempo of the drumming increases, a group of horsemen ride up. Among them is the son of the emir of Timbuctoo. As they wait at the edge of the crowd, an old Arab slave woman, with her brow and nose marked with charcoal lines, does a grotesque dance. Around her the laughing crowd makes a circle, about ten feet wide, with the drum at one side. The crowd opens and the emir's son rides into the ring. His mount is a spirited beast and, as his rider begins to make him "dance," the horse rears up. The circumference of the watching circle sways just enough to avoid being trampled. Then, stabbing the sand with his front hooves, in mincing steps, the horse advances toward the drummer. The hooves hit the calabash drumhead again and again. The drumhead is either broken or "called broken" and the horsemen ride slowly off, followed by the crowd. The procession proceeds to the house of the emir where he gives the slaves two sacks of grain and a new hide for the drum.

Tradition attributes the origin of the ceremony to an incident which occurred at the time of the Moroccan conquest of Timbuctoo. Those who know the tradition best say it is a detailed reenactment of an episode which took place on the Naming of Mohammed, when the Moroccans first entered the city. From the Arab chronicles we know that the capture of Timbuctoo took place months after *Almudu*.[10] However, incidents between the natives and their overlords were common during the early years after the conquest and one of these, which occurred during the drumming on this feast day, may have given rise to the ceremonial drum breaking.[11]

[10] Es-Sadi, 1900:221–222.

[11] The *Tarikh* also gives a clue as to another possible origin of the ceremony. The Songhoi emperor, Askia the Great, initiated the custom of having a drummer with a ceremonial drum precede his regional viceroys to symbolize their status. One nephew of Askia, jealous of his own brother whom Askia had named a viceroy, threatened to "break his brother's drum" (*ibid.*, 131). This was the beginning of a feud which eventually led to a revolt. It is reasonable to suppose that the Moroccans, years later, could likewise symbolically indicate their deposition of the incumbent authority. The emir is an Arma, a descendant of the conquerors from North Africa.

The drum as a symbol of office is known to be of Egyptian origin. It is found close to Egypt among the Arab Kababish and Negro Baganda. Askia the Great visited Egypt and brought the trait to the Songhoi.

Ramadān

The ninth month is *Haome*, called *Ramadān* by the Arabs. The Arabic name is known to all as symbolic of this period of religious restrictions. The month is characterized by the things one does not do. Eating, drinking, sexual intercourse, smoking, and kola chewing are forbidden from sunrise to sunset. No words of love may be spoken to any woman during the day. A man may have intercourse at night only with his wife, after which they must both bathe before dawn. The unmarried should practice abstinence. The natives will go without food and drink but total sexual abstinence asks too much of some of them. Fast regulations are strict. In the pre-French period a breach of the daylight fast requirements was punishable by death. For such an offense, even the son of a chief was beheaded and his body hung by the feet, like an animal, in the butchers' market. However, if fasting is injurious to the health, it may be dispensed with or even broken off after once being started. Infants and the infirm are thus excluded but the interpretation of this exemption is not liberal. Everyone decides for himself and many who are technically exempt, such as travelers, maintain the fast.

Daily existence is marked by thirst and hunger broken only by indulgence at night. The pre-dawn repast is frugal, as a heavy meal at this time increases thirst during the day. The Arabs tend to arise earlier and, after eating, pray until sunrise. The strict observance of the regulations of this month gains divine forgiveness of sins and helps assure a place in paradise with its violable but perpetual virgins. More than any other practice the fast period binds the whole Moslem community together on the basis of common religion. In this respect there is a marked difference between *Ramadān* and the celebration of the Birth of Mohammed. The latter occasion emphasizes the unity within parts of the community—families, age-groups, sexes, ethnic groups, social classes.

The only special occasion during the month is *Kotome*,

the twenty-seventh day. The Koran is believed to have descended from Allah to Mohammed during *Ramadān* and to have been completed on this day. *Kotome* is celebrated by the public reading of the Koran by both Songhoi and Arabs, and by feasts and dances during the night. This day is celebrated to a greater extent by the Arabs. In the bush the Berabich have their fire ceremony at this time.

The Big Feast

The end of *Haome* and the beginning of *Ferme* is the occasion for feasting, dancing, and gaiety. As in every society, the end of a period of unusual restraint is marked by celebration and emotional release. Repressed desires find expression. The society sponsors excesses over the ways of routine existence and thereby establishes a psychological equilibrium for the ensuing period of workaday life. Even religious sanction supports the occasion, as I was told that it was a sin not to eat well on the first day of *Ferme*. Religion requires that all who are able give alms to the poor so that they too can celebrate this day. Three measures of millet from each member of a prosperous donor's family is the traditional amount. In reality, this is a gesture of opulence usually performed by Arabs. Most of the Songhoi gifts of food follow kin or age-set lines as is customary in the preparation of feasts. On the eve of *Ham Ber*, or the "Big Feast" of the first day, the young Songhoi men send a small amount of money to their mothers-in-law or to the mothers of their sweethearts, if they are unmarried. Clothes or slippers are given to wives and sweethearts. Money also is provided for wives so that they can buy kola to give to their age-mates.

The next morning everyone gets up early, bathes, eats a big meal of couscous or some other special dish, such as the dates eaten on this occasion by Arabs. Then, dressed in their best, the men walk out to the tomb of the Saint Alfa Moya to the east of town. There they form long parallel lines facing the east. The chiefs and marabouts arrive and the imam of the Great Mosque leads the prayer. A few girls go out to watch but do not participate in the prayer. Following the prayer, the new-moon salutation is exchanged with much handshaking. The imam blesses supplicants, as usual, by spitting on his hands and rubbing them on the head of the person being blessed.

The crowd drifts back into the city and begins to visit and feast with relatives and friends. Kola is liberally distributed. In-laws provide their daughters' husbands with tobacco, incense, or boxes of perfumed grease for the body. At noon the age-sets meet at the home of their leaders who provide them with a special sauce which is sopped up and eaten with pieces of bread. The satiated comrades sing and dance into the afternoon. Tiring of this, they promenade through the streets, amusing themselves with companions of the opposite sex or visiting the dances given by wealthy boys. The Songhoi may amuse themselves by watching the Bela dances but not by participating. The Arabs and Arma who own horses are mounted today and their informal races over the dunes attract large crowds. In the evening, the men's age-sets reunite to eat the platters of food which have been provided by actual and prospective mothers-in-law. Visits of thanks to these women are then made. Later the girls join the men and the night is given over to dancing and love. *Mabe*, or the female troubadours, fill their purses with gifts from young swain who desire the praises of their loved ones sung. The festivities continue in diminishing intensity for three nights in all, the daylight hours being devoted to recuperation. In the bush the Berabich celebrate for seven days, but, say the city folk, the desire and necessity for work is greater in Timbuctoo.

The Day of Sacrifice

Tyibsi is the concluding month of the year. It is the month of the pilgrimage to Mecca but for those whom God has not given the strength or means to go, it is no sin not to make the pilgrimage. One way to escape hell is scrupulous observation of the ceremony of *Tabaski* on the tenth day of *Tyibsi*. *Tabaski* morning, all of the men of the city gather at the tomb of Alfa Moy and pray as at the beginning of *Ferme*. Then the imam of the Great Mosque sacrifices a ram, symbolizing the act of Abraham. Slitting the throat of this carefully selected, perfect beast is the signal for everyone to hurry home as fast as possible to make his own sacrifice. It is believed that each sheep which is properly sacrificed will act as a mount on judgment day, on which his slaughterer can ride in safety along the perilous, jagged road over hell. The first man to sacrifice his own ram, after the ceremony conducted by the imam, will be the first to ride into paradise.

Each family should make the sacrifice. If a ram is not obtainable, a male goat or camel or a bull may be substituted. The sacrifice is performed by the head of the family. His robe is thrown back, exposing his right arm, and is drawn around his lower body to protect him from the blood. "In this manner Abraham prepared to sacrifice his son." The sacrificed animal is partially butchered and certain of the viscera roasted and eaten by the family that noon. The flesh is considered less spiritually beneficial. It is from the flesh that gifts of meat are made to the poor who cannot afford the sacrifice. The Arabs do not eat the meat until the second day after *Tabaski*. The fat is considered a worthy portion and the Bela give the rump fat to their mothers-in-law. Poor Bela visit the homes of Arabs and Songhoi, clapping and singing to receive presents of meat. Drums throb throughout the city for three nights.

The Arab concepts concerning the sacrifice are full of status connotation. A ram sacrificed by a wealthy family benefits only three members of that family. If the family is large, several sacrifices should be made, which, of course, results in more meat to be given to the poor. The number of persons who may derive spiritual benefit from the sacrifice of a ram increases with the poverty of the family. As many as nine members of a very poor family may thus receive the same benefit as three members of a rich family. If another male animal is substituted for a ram, the sacrifice brings religious protection only to the head of the family. Any sacrifice made by a Bela or Arab slave is held to be invalid by the Arabs. It is simply slaughter for meat. The sufficient reason for this, to the Arab mind, is that the slave can be sold for the price of a ram and therefore cannot gain the same advantage as a freeman. The import of all these beliefs is the distinction between social classes and between rich and poor. For the community at large, the sacrifice and the gifts of parts of the animal to kinsmen and to the poor serves to accentuate family unity and economic differences.

Looking back over the year, we see that the feasts and ceremonies are common to the whole community—save, of course, the small European group and a lone Christian Syrian family. This common participation welds the inhabitants of the city together. This uniting effect is made more manifest by the existence of the small portion of the community which does not take part. Every Moslem feels his group as an explicit entity contrasted with the nonconformist group. To this extent French occupation has intensified the solidarity of Moslem Timbuctoo.

The yearly ceremonies also accentuate the segmentation of the population. The observance of *Ramadān* alone is almost devoid of practices which highlight differences within the Moslem community. As such it must be considered a most important unifying factor in Timbuctoo. All the other celebrations strengthen the internal unity of the social segments and emphasize their relationships with one another. The yearly festivals demark the Moslem community but stress the importance of differences in age, sex, family connections, ethnic heritage, class position, economic condition, quarter of residence, and extent of religious training. Through the ceremonies of the moon year, prejudices are accentuated anew and social goals reaffirmed.

CHAPTER 8

Kinship and the Family

It is sound practice for an ethnologist to analyze a people's system of kinship terminology early in his field work. The manner in which kin terms classify and differentiate between relatives reflects similarities and differences in patterns of behavior toward the kinsmen so identified.[1] An understanding of the kinship organization thus throws light on a multitude of other culture patterns.

Songhoi Kinship

The Songhoi system of kinship terminology is presented in the accompanying chart. We see that father's brothers and mother's sisters are identified with father and mother respectively. Identification is not complete as the terms also reflect the relative ages of these uncles and aunts compared to the ages of father and mother. Thus an elder brother of father (*baba*) is called "big father" (*baber*) and a younger brother is "little father" (*baba keyna*). A similar system is used to differentiate between mother's sisters. Father's sisters and mother's brothers are distinguished by the terms *hawey* and *hasey*. Their children are grouped under the cross-cousin term *basey*.

It is a common custom among the Songhoi for a man to adopt one or more of his brother's children, soon after they are weaned. As a result, *baber* may really act as the father of his younger brother's child. He calls this nephew or niece by the same term (*idye*) which he uses for his

[1] For an early statement of this hypothesis, see Radcliffe-Brown, 1913. Murdock, 1949, presents the most definitive statement of the relationship of kin terms to social structure.

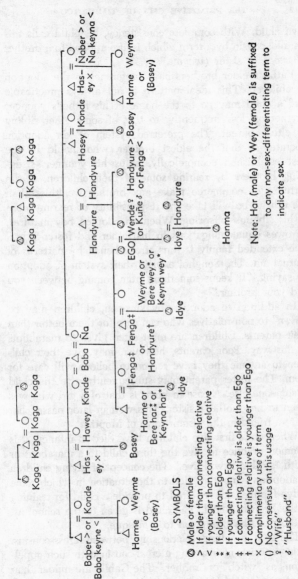

Fig. 8 Songhoi Kinship Terms

SYMBOLS

△ Male or female
⊗ If older than connecting relative
∧ If younger than connecting relative
∨ If older than Ego
*** If younger than Ego
‡‡ If connecting relative is older than Ego
† If connecting relative is younger than Ego
× Complimentary use of term
() No consensus on this usage
♀ "Wife"
♂ "Husband"

Note: Har (male) or Wey (female) is suffixed to any non-sex-differentiating term to indicate sex.

own child. With complete consistency, his child calls this parallel cousin by a term which is also applied to a brother (*harme*) or sister (*weyme*).

Father's elder brothers have preference in the adoption of children. This ideal pattern is not always practicable and a child may go to the home of his father's younger brother or, less frequently, to that of some other sibling of either parent. The preferred system of kin adoption operates so that the eldest brother, who should be the best established economically, helps his younger, struggling brothers by rearing some of their children. If the fortunes of commerce make any brother wealthier than the others, he will take the responsibility of rearing more of his siblings' offspring. When an adopted boy matures, he owes equal obligations to his father and foster-father. The extended family is thus strengthened by patterns of mutual aid. The Songhoi explain their system of adoption by saying, "It keeps something from coming between you and your brother."

In addition to adoption by kinsmen, children may be "given" to non-relatives who can care for them better than their parents. Children are most often given to marabouts in this way. Poor parents, however, may give their children to anyone they have reason to believe will care for them. The foster parent may subsequently give the child to someone else. A case in point is that of a girl who was given to her mother's sister. This woman later passed her on to a friend in the distant town of Mopti.

When one's first two children have died in infancy, it is common practice to give the third child to a marabout or smith "so that it will live." The concept of giving children in adoption is now applied to the situation in which some native families are required to provide a child for training in the French school. The child is given to the school as, in the past, he was given to a mosque.

There is a joking relationship between cross-cousins. Joking consists of insulting a cross-cousin with such appellations as "witch" or "robber." The Gabibi are milder than the Arma in their insults, restricting their teasing to such statements as "You eat too much." At New Year's a man's children are expected to give small presents to his sister's children. If they fail to fulfill this obligation they are beaten and their clothes are torn off by their playful cousins.

It is worth recalling that grandparents, aunts, and uncles, and elder brothers are also supposed to give presents at New Year's. They do this because the recipient has shown his respect for them all year. One way in which respect is shown is to address a kinsman by kin term only and never to use his or her proper name. Thus, if elder brother does not proffer the expected gift at New Year's, younger brother addresses his sibling by name until the gift is forthcoming.

The New Year's gift giving pattern between cousins illustrates a general principle. One of the cross-cousins, the mother's brother's child, has a distinctive status vis-à-vis the father's sister's child. Mother's brother's child, like older relatives, is the donor of the New Year's gift; the other cross-cousin is the recipient. The latter is outside of the paternal lineage of his mother and her brother's child, yet closely allied to the lineage through his mother. The joking expresses the ambivalence of the situation and the gift giving helps to compensate for the status difference between the cousins. This is very apparent in the extension of cross-cousin roles to non-blood relatives. The son or other young male relative of the sponsoring "father" of the circumcision ceremony is called "cross-cousin" by the other initiates during their two weeks together. He must tolerate the jokes and such gibes of his associates as, "You're as big as an elephant"; "You'll go to war and be killed." The reason he is called "cross-cousin" and treated as one, say the Songhoi, is that otherwise he might try to order the other children around because his father was in charge of the ceremony.

Another extension of the cross-cousin term is between all of the Arma and all other Songhoi. The Arma are expected to give New Year's gifts to the Gabibi. Songhoi explain this practice by pointing out that when the Moroccan conquerors came to Timbuctoo, they took Songhoi wives. The descendants of the Moroccans, the Arma, are thus cross-cousins of the Gabibi, who descended from the brothers of the original Songhoi women married by the Moroccans. Unlike real cross-cousins, the high-status Arma give presents to the low-status descendants of the original mothers' brothers. In addition, the Arma who make the donations are adults, while the Gabibi who accost them for gifts are children.

The cross-cousin term is sometimes also used to refer to parallel cousins. In this case the application of the term does not carry with it the joking relationship. The Songhoi themselves do not agree as to whether or not this extension of the term is permissible. This loose employment of the term is probably a distortion of its original use. The Songhoi likewise lack unanimity of opinion as to which kin are preferred marriage partners. The Gabibi state a marriage preference for mother's brothers' daughters. This cross-cousin marriage is entirely consistent with the familiarity of the joking relationship. The Arma, on the other hand, prefer to marry paternal parallel cousins. A match with the daughter of father's brother is the preferred pattern of the Moroccans from whom the Arma are descended. This Moroccan pattern is entirely inconsistent with the Songhoi kin system in which these cousins call one another "brother" and "sister" and may have even grown up in the same household. The Gabibi, who probably express the older Songhoi system, have a positive dislike for marriage between the children of brothers.

It is likely that the old Songhoi marriage preference was for a cross-cousin. If this is so, it is not hard to see why the Songhoi are now a bit confused and extend the cross-cousin term to other cousins. Obviously it is more consistent for the Arma to refer to father's brothers' daughters as marriageable "cross-cousins" than it is to refer to these girls as "sisters."

There are two basic "in-law" terms in Songhoi, *hand-yure* and *fenga*. *Handyure* is applied to those in-laws toward whom behavior is restrained. Parents-in-law and children-in-law are *handyure* to one another. They refrain from talking to one another or even conversing freely in each other's presence. If the situation demands communication between them, the parent-in-law initiates the conversation. Even then it is formal and accompanied by considerable embarrassment and looking away from one another. The older sibling of a spouse and the spouse of a younger sibling observe the same taboos in their interrelations and call one another *handyure*. Other siblings-in-law —younger sibling of a spouse and older sibling's spouse— call one another *fenga* and are quite familiar with one another. Wife's younger sister is considered a desirable subsequent marriage, even though sororal polygamy is not practiced.

Songhoi Families

The Songhoi desire numerous offspring. If there are too many to support, one can always find a foster home for them. Even if a son is given to foster parents he still retains an equal obligation to his real parents. The Gabibi attitude toward a large family of extended kin is illuminating. To have many relatives is considered preferable to the possession of wealth. "All but the very rich want large families," say the Gabibi. There are two reasons for this attitude, in which they differ from the rest of the population. The Gabibi were a serf group whom the Arma never permitted to prosper. The majority of them are still poor. Secondly, the Songhoi family system itself, with its foster homes, stresses the unity of the extended family. Children are always welcome in the homes of the relatives of either of their parents. A child often sleeps at the home of grandparents and eats with foster parents. One who is part of a large kin group can always find something to eat. Wealth is transitory but one's family can be counted on to participate in important life ceremonies. "If I have no family, no one will come to my house when I am married. Everyone will go to the bride's home." Numerous kin, therefore, not only provide security but confer status.

This attitude is further extended in a poor man's philosophizing:

It is better to greet than to give. Everyone knows the Gabibi, Kali Tandia. When he first started greeting everyone, including small children, people laughed at him. Now when he goes about town, people cry out his name in greeting, as though he were rich. Even when Kali walks with the rich Arab, Seku, it is Kali who is greeted in the streets. Seku may give, but he never greets and he may even hit the people who cluster about him.

The extended family is kept unified through regular formal greeting. Before sunrise, at the time for morning prayers, sons go to waken their parents with salutations. Grandparents, uncles, and aunts all receive a morning visit. Younger brother may even waken his big brother's wife with a morning salutation. Old men may spend the entire day greeting their kin and friends in the quarter.

The patrilineal family sometimes assembles as a council to consider serious family problems. With the eldest patriarch presiding, action is taken on such problems as murder of, or by, a member of the family or a robbery committed by a kinsman. Family action is both in the form of correction and reparation. The patriarch of the combined family may make good the damages of an errant relative. If such a one does not heed the reprimands he receives he can be cast out of the family, but not otherwise punished. I was told that even if adolescent brothers and sisters fought, they should be taken before the cadi to be whipped, but this does not appear to be a common practice. Before French rule, murder between kinsmen was always settled by the cadi of the city, while murder between families led to blood revenge no matter what the cadi ordered.

The Gabibi extended family is a cooperative unit, cohesive in poverty. Yet its productive economy is individualized, based on trade and crafts. It lacks the ability to administer strong physical sanctions. Nonconformity can only be punished by withdrawing cooperation. It will be interesting to see if the Gabibi lose their solidarity of kinship and friendship and become like the wealthy Arma and Arabs when they begin to prosper under French protection.

The Songhoi do not consider divorce admirable as do the Arabs. Nevertheless, they usually marry at least twice. A man's second wife is often neglectful and sharp-tongued toward the children of his earlier marriage. Stepchildren complain bitterly about such treatment. Stepmothers are the traditional butt of a derisive verse of the song which is sung by all boys during their circumcision ceremony. On the other hand, the system of adoption operates so that half-brothers and sisters are not always reared together and hence may escape their stepmothers. Foster mothers acquired by adoption are called "mother"[2] and are not at all like stepmothers acquired by a father's remarriage.

Children inherit from their actual parents, not their adoptive ones. Foster mothers, unlike stepmothers, have no reason to try to create a favored position for their own offspring with regard to their patrimony. Foster mothers do not show jealous anger with foster children the way that stepmothers do with stepchildren born to previous unions of their husbands. Adoption therefore mitigates against the conflicts arising out of divorce.

A mother may administer punishment to a child in the presence of his father but not before his "big father."[3]

[2] The "stepmother" term *konde* is sometimes referred to the wife of father's brother or mother's brother. *Konde* is not employed if this person is a foster mother through adoption.

[3] The Songhoi practice of having foster parents and grandparents rear children results in less strenuous disciplinary measures being taken. Real fathers are the persons whose discipline is feared. There is a very low frustration tolerance. Children in their teens frequently have public temper tantrums to escape punishment. Even men in their twenties will break into tears when faced with an unpleasant situation.

As the cultural data on age of development of sphincter control was not germane to this study, they were not collected in the field. However, there is every reason to believe that control is developed late, at least among Bela and Gabibi. These children go unclothed for at least the first six years of their life.

Father's big brothers and sisters are the ones who explain the proper ways of life to a child. From her aunt a girl learns how to dress and to arrange her hair. Uncle imparts the religious and other social values to his nephew. One Gabibi "big father" admonished:

Accept what your mother tells you and provide for her above all others. Do not play with children who have no trade, as they will steal. Work hard at your own trade apprenticeship. Do not attach yourself to the sons of the rich and eat at their houses. Work yourself. After circumcision you must start a trade before you begin frequenting girls or you will become worthless. Get charms to protect you from the evil words of others. Pray. Give half your earnings to your parents and alms to the old and the poor and you are certain of success in life. Do not be like the man who drinks, frequents prostitutes and does not know if his parents are in town or not, or whether they are in good health and properly clothed. Such a man will never succeed, even if he is a marabout.

"Big father" provides for you, arranges your marriage, and teaches you moral values, but he does not usurp a father's position. He always teaches respect for and filial loyalty to your real parents. If a father wants to provide for his children while they are in foster homes, he may not give any present directly. The gift must be given to the foster parent, who passes it on if he sees fit. A child is subservient to all his older relatives until he becomes economically independent.

Young children learn their place during meals. They may not talk in the presence of their father or any uncle, even if he is addressing them unless, of course, they are asked a question. They learn that a wife does not eat in the presence of her husband or his brothers. Arma girls, restricted to their homes, learn how to embroider, make straw ornaments or beaded work. Gabibi girls acquire

---

They were observed pursuing their excretory functions almost at random in the sandy streets, and no repressive measures were ever seen to be taken.

more practical household techniques as they help their mothers grind grain and cook food. Brothers learn not to go about town together lest public comment on their mother's fecundity bring them harm. While Arma boys await their marriages, Gabibi urchins start to earn the money for their first pipes and clothes and eventually for their marriage.

Arab Kinship System

The Arabs have two words for "father"—*buya* and *bâba*. The latter is so widely employed in the Arab world that it can not be considered a borrowing from Songhoi. The fact that the Songhoi have the same term is probably fortuitous.[4] The Arabic word for "mother" (*umm*) is often used by Arabs in Timbuctoo to refer also to mother's sister. The term *khâla*, which explicitly designates this aunt, is also employed. The extension of the "mother" term to apply to her sister is clearly the result of the application of a Songhoi kin term principle to Arabic.

The Songhoi use one term (*ña*) for both mother and mother's sister. Pure Arabic differentiates between these two with separate words. However, by extending the "mother" term to include her sister, the Timbuctoo Arabs achieve the same classificatory arrangement as the Songhoi, except that they now have two ways of designating this aunt. Arab men, more than any others in Timbuctoo, have taken consorts from other ethnic groups. Such unions are powerful avenues of diffusion. It is only Arabs whose families are old in the Sudan who call their mother's sister *umm*.

---

[4] Reduplicated consonant-vowel combinations appear in widely separated areas as parent kin terms (*mama*: "father" in Kariera, for example). The contact between Arab and Songhoi enhances the possibility of borrowing, but the word is certainly of a structure more common to Songhoi than the Arabic. Among the neighboring Bambara, the father term is *fâ* and the mother term *bâ*. One must admit the possibility of Arabic influence on the Songhoi term, even if outright borrowing is unlikely.

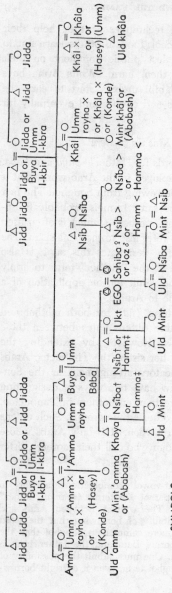

Fig. 9 Arab (Sudanese) Kinship Terms

SYMBOLS

△ Male or female

⊚ Male or female

∧ If older than connecting relative

∨ If younger than connecting relative

† If connecting relative is older than Ego

‡ If connecting relative is younger than Ego

× Complimentary use of term

( ) No consensus on this usage

♀ "Wife"

♂ "Husband"

The siblings of father and mother are, with the above noted exception, indicated by descriptive terms in Arabic. Sex indicative suffixes make the terms explicit (FB—*'amm;* FSi—*'amma;* MB—*khâl;* MSi—*khâla*). The mother's sister term (*khâla*) is honorifically extended to her brother's wife; the mother's brother term (*khâl*) to her sister's husband; and the father's brother term (*'amm*) to his sister's husband.[5] In addition, the stepmother term (*umm rayha*)[6] is honorifically applied to the wives of both maternal and paternal uncles. Significantly, the Songhoi stepmother term (*konde*) is also employed by Arabs for these relatives, as in Songhoi. The Songhoi honorific extension of *hasey* to the husbands of maternal and paternal aunts is likewise adopted by Arabs of old Sudanese families.

Focusing our attention on the terms for mother's brother's wife, we find that there are three. One is a usual Arabic usage (*khâla*); one is a normal Songhoi usage (*konde*); and one is an Arabic term given the wider application of its Songhoi equivalent (*umm rayha*) used like *konde*. In the contact situation between Arab and Songhoi, the Arabs have adopted or adapted kin terminology to bring their system into agreement with that of the Songhoi.

Terms for the children of parents' siblings are derived by combining the Arabic terms for these siblings with "son" (*uld*) and "daughter" (*mint*) terms.[7] Thus, my father's brother's daughter is *mint 'ammi,* and so on. The only change from these Arabic terms is the occasional employment of the Bela term (*ababash*) for cross-cousins. It is quite possible that some Arabs use the Songhoi term for

[5] The Kabâbîsh use the mother's sister term for mother's brother's wife (Seligman, C.G. and B.Z., 1918:123). Their use of the father's sister term for father's brother's wife was not found in Timbuctoo. The other Timbuctoo extensions of the Arab uncle and aunt terms are not recorded for the Kabâbîsh.

[6] The etymology of this word is not clear.

[7] *Uld* and *mint* are, of course, variations of the purer forms *walad* and *bint*. *Ibn* for "son" was not given by Timbuctoo informants. The Kabâbîsh also employ a contraction of the "child" term (*wad*) as an alternative for *ibn* (Seligman, *loc. cit.*).

these cousins but I did not encounter it. An informant who gave the alternate Bela term *ababash* for cross-cousin, used alternate Songhoi terms for uncles and aunts. The diffusion of these terms can be traced to specific inter-ethnic marriages in the informant's family. Thus the term *ababash* enters his kin term system because his mother's brother has a Bela wife and their children give him presents at the New Year, a custom practiced between Songhoi and Bela cross-cousins but not by Arabs recently arrived from North Africa.

It is important to note that *ababash* is not only considered an appropriate term for the half-Bela relatives but is applicable to other cross-cousins as well. The term itself is considered to be an Arabic word. The diffusion of some kin terms is not quite so simple as, for example, the Arabs' adoption of the Songhoi term *hasey* for mother's or father's sister's husband. This man is always an Arab. The borrowing of *hasey* therefore involves: (a) the recognition of the fact that relatives (the Songhoi wife or mother of an Arab, for example) employ the term for their father's sister's husband and (b) the application of the term to the specific relationship with an Arab.

The distinction between different sorts of cousins is important to the Arab. Some are preferred marriage partners; others are not married. The true Arabian pattern is a preference for father's brother's daughter.[8] This has the advantage of keeping the patriarchal family a closely knit unit in spite of drawbacks which they recognize; i.e., greater likelihood of weak progeny and of quarrels between the husband and the girl's parents. Arab town and tribal chiefs in the Sudan are most likely to marry this cousin in order to strengthen their claim to chieftainship. A third of the marriages between Arabs in Timbuctoo are between cousins. Half of these are with father's brother's daughters. Slightly fewer marriages are with mother's brother's daughters. The two other kinds of first cousins

[8] Westermarck, 1914:53–56.

are taken to wife only rarely.[9] Many Arabs consider that their relationship to their mother's family is much more friendly than that with father's kin. Generosity marks the former, while jealousies born of shared inheritance characterize the paternal family.

It is possible that the frequent marriage with mother's brother's daughter is the result of Songhoi influence. There has easily been enough intermarriage to introduce this emphasis. There is a small but constant influx of Arab men into Timbuctoo, drawn by the commercial opportunities. The resulting preponderance of Arab males forces many to marry non-Arab women. Two-fifths of all Arab marriages are with Arab Negro slaves, Songhoi, and Tuareg. Most marriages of this sort are with lower class women. Gabibi mates are thus ten times more common than Arma. The children of all such marriages are considered to be Arabs.

All remote kinsmen through paternal lines are called "father's brother's children" (*ulâd 'amm* or, differentiating as to sex, *ulâd 'amm* and *minat 'amm*). The shereef refer

[9] The sample studied consisted of 180 marriages of Arab males covering three generations. Not all of these families are in Timbuctoo. All involve people of the city or people whose children came there. Several marriages of one man are treated as separate marriages. Individual men showed no tendency to take their various wives from the same tribe, family, town, or ethnic groups, with the following exceptions: owners of many slaves frequently had several slave wives; a few cases of successive marriage to two sisters occurred; the smiths and Berabich tend more than any other groups to be endogamous. The smiths of various Arab tribes intermarry and are supposed to be a caste. One Kunta smith took a Gabibi wife, however.

The 180 marriages were divided as follows:

With Arab women	107	With non-Arab women	73
Father's brother's daughter	17	Gabibi	30
Mother's brother's daughter	11	Arab slave	26
Mother's sister's daughter	2	Bela	8
Father's sister's daughter	2	Daga	4
Total first cousins	32	Arma	3
Other Arabs	75	Alfa	1
		Bambara	1

to one another by these terms even when no relationship can be traced. Being descendants of Mohammed in the male line, shereef are sure of the relationship. Likewise, patrilineal tribal groups are known as the "children" of their original progenitor, i.e., the *ulâd Dris* (children of Dris). Distant relatives in mother's patrilineal family are called "children of mother's brother" (*ulâd khâl*). These terms are sometimes used to refer to any relative of father or mother, irrespective of patrilineality.

The distinction between lineages and the descriptive tendency in the terminology are broken in the grandparent generation. Mother's and father's parents and their siblings are all designated by the same term, with a sex differentiating suffix (*jidd*—male; *jidda*—female). There is a special term in Timbuctoo which is sometimes used to distinguish grandparents from their siblings. Translated literally, these grandparent terms are exactly like those in English—"grand father" and "grand mother" (*buya l-kbir* and *umm l-kbra*). The use of a single term for relatives in the several lineages appears inconsistent with the strongly patrilineal character of the Arab extended family. It is, however, consistent with the extraordinary reverence and respect which is paid to aged persons. Great age actually produces a condition of holiness. Old people are more greatly endowed with *baraka*. This principle outweighs lineage in the kin term system.

In-law relationships are often precarious. We recognize the distinctive character of this relation in our jokes about mothers-in-law. But whereas we are apt to think of in-laws in terms of friction with them, the Arabs experience a feeling of shame in their presence.

Marriage creates a doubly ambivalent situation which finds its expression in in-law avoidance customs. In Arab patriarchal society, the control and allegiance of the wife is shifted from the wife's parents to the husband. It is difficult to change these old bonds which conflict with the newly created alignment of control and loyalty.

The other ambivalence arises from the introduction of a new sexual union in the domestic circle. A daughter or sister is not regarded in sexual terms, due to potent incest taboos. Upon her marriage, there is brought into the family circle a man whose connection with her is basically sexual. As a result, the Arab husband and relatives of the wife experience a sense of shame in each other's presence. In-law avoidance patterns function to separate people whose close association would breed friction in the extended family.[10]

The Arabs have two basic in-law terms, each sex differentiated. Their use is strongly influenced by the Songhoi equivalents.

Figure 10

BASIC IN-LAW TERMS (ARAB)

Relationship covered by Arab term	Included relations in English terms
avoided male in-law: *nsīb*	father-in-law, son-in-law; younger sister's husband, older brother of spouse
avoided female in-law: *nsība*	mother-in-law, daughter-in-law; younger brother's wife, older sister of spouse
familiar male in-law: *hamm*	older sister's husband; younger brother of a spouse
familiar female in-law: *hamma*	older brother's wife; younger sister of a spouse

The shame of being familiar with avoided in-laws is "like that one would feel if caught stealing." One is ashamed to eat with these relatives or speak to an avoided in-law of the opposite sex. If a man has to address his father-in-law, he does not shake the other's hand, as is customary between friends, but covers his own head with a piece of cloth or lowers it and keeps his eyes on the ground. They may speak only about necessary practical matters but no casual conversation is permitted. If a per-

10 Westermarck, 1914:315–317, attributes the in-law avoidance pattern to "sexual shame felt inside the domestic circle" and shows similar behavior between sons and their parents at time of son's marriage. Murdock, 1949:279–280, sees the function of such avoidance to be the preclusion of intercourse.

son was a relative or comrade before becoming an avoided in-law, the restrictions are somewhat less stringent. Any discussion of sexual matters, however, is strictly taboo.

We have noted that certain brothers and sisters-in-law may be casual with one another. This is consistent with the not infrequent practice of marrying a deceased or divorced wife's younger sister. A deceased husband's brother may also marry his sister-in-law, in order to keep the family unit in the same lineage.

Arab Family

The ramifications of the extended family of literate Arabs are recorded in a family genealogical history (*ta-rikh*). The record itself and the responsibility for maintaining it pass down the male line following primogeniture. The paternal ancestor of my shereef friend, Mulai, came to Timbuctoo from the oasis of Touat five generations ago. The family *tarikh* is in the hands of an uncle but as Mulai is the son of his uncle's deceased eldest brother, he will eventually inherit the record. He already knows the paternal sequence back twenty-three generations. There is another *tarikh* which relates this family to their ancestors in Arabia but Mulai knows only of its existence. Quite naturally, the extended families of mothers and wives are little known beyond those individuals with whom one has actual contact or whom one avoids, as the case may be.

The written genealogy is an academic thing. It is family behavior which counts. Every morning after breakfast a man goes about town and exchanges greetings with his parents, uncles and aunts, brothers and sisters. On Friday morning he will include even more distant relatives. That afternoon he shows similar regard for his dead paternal kin by praying at their graves.

On the other hand, an Arab will tell you that he would rather be rich than be part of a large extended family. "When a man has money, he gets many relatives which he never knew he had before." But every Arab man wants many children of his own. They are a manifold blessing, both economic and spiritual. They assure one's old age.

Some may become powerful marabouts. In any case, there will be many to pray for their father after he dies. During his lifetime they are a physical defense against insult and aggression. As the desire for progeny is common to all Arabs, the very existence of a larger family is a credit to the father. A poor man does not look with apprehension at the prospect of more mouths to feed. He has faith that "Allah will provide."

The free Arab population in Timbuctoo is small—less than five hundred persons. As a result, every Arab knows the family history of most other Arabs. Songhoi and Bela families are beyond their ken unless they are interrelated. In this case one cannot escape acquaintance with in-laws and joking cousins. But even as closely knit as the Arab extended families would seem to be, the Songhoi accuse them of quickly forgetting their responsibility to kin who live in other towns. Thus, on one occasion, the public crier of Timbuctoo had to urge the Arabs to send food to their kin in the oasis of Araouan, which was known to be facing starvation.

The daily routine of the primary family provides cohesive forces. Father and mother pray together in the morning. Then they and the children share a common bowl at morning and noon meals and take their afternoon tea together. In the evening the wife may eat different food from the others.[11] Husband and wife converse freely, but adolescent children must show filial respect by not speaking at meals unless addressed by their parents.

The Arab's house is his sanctum. The only males who may enter in his absence are his sons and grandsons, his younger brothers, and his wife's close male relatives.[12] Even when he is at home, all other men must wait at the

[11] Sample Arab meals: Breakfast—purchased bread, eaten with a sauce of sweetened, melted butter, followed by tea. Dinner—rice or couscous with meat and vegetable (in season) sauce, homemade bread. Tea. Supper—sauce from noon meal reheated with fresh rice or couscous, millet and milk gruel for the wife.

[12] Close male relatives of Arab wife who may see her: brothers, father, and his brothers.

door until his wife has had an opportunity to retire from view. Any woman, however, has free access to the house. Surveillance extends also to the children. Strangely enough, young children are more closely restricted to home than are adolescents.

Young girls are taken by adult relatives to dances, but a small boy is fortunate if he is even allowed to attend a neighbor's party. Adolescent girls are permitted out alone to attend weddings and name feasts, where they will be with other women. Boys are not given complete freedom of movement until they are fifteen. Younger boys are kept under strict supervision. Paternal relatives, who see one of their young kinsmen playing in the market, send him home with a sound thrashing. But if the family is poor, the boys are free to come and go as soon as they can earn money. The wealthier families turn their pre-adolescent lads over to marabouts for day-long instruction. They are scornful of the Songhoi practice of letting children run in the streets and market "where they learn to steal things they want."

This general restriction to the home of all of the family except the father means that he must do the marketing if he is not fortunate enough to have a household slave. Even then the man purchases the meat and Arabs eat much meat, being firmly convinced that "meat makes flesh." Force of necessity may send widows or divorcees to market but even this is undesirable.

This picture of a happy, cooperative, conjugal family is distorted by the prevalence of divorce. Spouses may yearn for a change of mates, but the introduction of step-parents and half-brothers and sisters into the family creates continual friction for the children. Arab wives are confined to their homes and dominated by their husbands, but Arab mothers dominate the lives of the children in the home. Stepmothers are invariably considered bad. "Even if they are kind, their stepchildren will speak evil of them." The usual complaints are about the quantity and quality of the food and of inequitable treatment between step-children and the stepmother's own children.

There is generally recognized ill feeling between half-siblings in the same household. The partiality of mothers for their own children is the usual source of this friction. Some children falsely accuse their stepmothers of misdeeds so that the husbands will turn against them. Children with bad stepmothers become bad themselves. The resultant antagonism of the father toward the child sometimes results in the latter being cast out of the home while yet a youth. One stepmother, who had married her sister's husband, even contested the paternal inheritance of her stepchildren. Stepmother and her children are a constant source of misery in an Arab home, and almost every home has them.

Bela Kinship

The kin terms of the Tuareg slaves are, of course, in a distinct language. They reflect a somewhat different kinship pattern. The fact that the maternal family is much more important than among the Arabs is not evidenced in the structure of the kin terminology. It is only observable in the behavior patterns between the clearly differentiated relatives.

Tuareg terms for siblings of parents, for grandparents and their siblings are agglutinative words consisting of morphemes meaning "father," "mother," "brother," and "sister."[13] Thus, *abba* is "father" and *anna* "mother." *Tisnabba* is "father of father" and *tisnanna* means "father of mother." *Wŭletmasnabba* is "sister of father," *wŭletmasntisnabba* indicates "sister of father of father," and so on. The "mother's brother" term *angatmar* is extended to mother's mother's sister's son and mother's mother's brother's son. While these relationships can be expressed in other terms, *angatmar* is usually employed.

There are three basic types of "cousin" terms: *ababash* (cross-cousin; feminine form is *tababasht*), *tangaten* (matrilineal parallel-cousin), and *arammeden* (patrilineal

[13] Nicolaisen (1963:449–453) found that terms for primary relatives were extended to others when used in reference, rather than address.

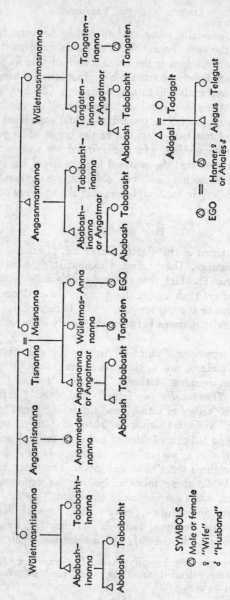

Fig. 11 Tuareg (Bela) Maternal and Affinal Relatives

SYMBOLS

⊘ Male or female

♀ "Wife"

♂ "Husband"

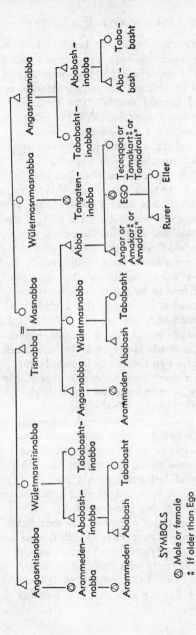

Fig. 12 Tuareg (Bela) Paternal Relatives

SYMBOLS

⊗ Male or female

△ If older than Ego

○ If younger than Ego

parallel cousins; literally "son of brothers"). These terms all refer to cousins of one's own generation. Mother's mother's sister's son, who is usually designated as *angatmar*, may also be indicated as *tangateninanna*, or "mother's matrilineal parallel cousin." The same term always designates this man's sister, but while her child is *tangaten*, his will be *ababash*, or cross-cousin.

There is a joking relationship between cross-cousins. You can steal from them with impunity. They may be struck without engendering malice. You may curse them and it will not bring them misfortune. "May a thunderbolt fall on your head!" is a serious curse against anyone except cross-cousins, for whom it is a big joke. At the funeral of a cross-cousin "you must hit his corpse or people will say you have a bad heart." Men are expected to make free with their female cross-cousins. With such a familiarity pattern it is not surprising to find that marriage to such cousins is supposed to be the preferred match. This preference is emphasized by the fact that brothers and sisters-in-law, even when they are not cross-cousins, are treated exactly like joking cousins. A man can be exceedingly familiar with his sisters-in-law, even if they are married. The Bela do not marry two sisters simultaneously but they may divorce one to marry the other or a widower may marry his wife's sister. A man sometimes marries the wife of a deceased brother but this is not common.

In contrast to the familiarity with a spouse's brothers and sisters, parents-in-law must be shunned. A man avoids not only the presence of his mother-in-law but even the use of her personal name. His restrictions with father-in-law are somewhat less stringent but each is very formal in the other's presence. A woman must avoid the presence and name of both of her parents-in-law.

The children of father's brothers are considered "prime enemies." They are always ready to ridicule and are never ready to help, except sometimes to come to your defense in a fight, and then only with very bad grace. Occasionally paternal kin may even fight against you. It is mother's kin who will stop a fight or give aid. The Bela say that paternal kin know that you will inherit wealth which they might otherwise receive, and so "they would rather see you dead." Quite a contrast are mother's sister's children. "They are like brothers and sisters." If you are in need they will provide, as to their own brothers and sisters. The best one could expect from any other cousin would be a loan.

The Bela sometimes give children to relatives to rear, either permanently or on a part-time basis. This is done only when there are many children and when a relative requests a child. Under such circumstances a refusal would be considered miserly, as the custom provides additional workers for relatives who have few children. For the parents of many children, the economic burden of child rearing is eased. But not just any relative is given a child; only maternal kin of either sex can become foster parents.

Marriages are not limited to or excluded from any lineage groups. Analysis of an extended genealogy, including eighty-two marriages, indicates that only a fifth of the marriages are with cousins of any sort.[14] In spite of the stated preference for cross-cousin marriage, parallel cousin marriages are even slightly more frequent. First marriages, which are arranged by parents, are more likely to be with cousins than are marriages with self-chosen

[14] In the sample of 82 Bela marriages, only 16 were between cousins. It is possible, of course, that the informant did not know all of the interrelationships in the extended genealogy of his own family. The cousin marriages were divided as follows:

Mother's sister's daughter	4	Mother's brother's daughter 3
Father's brother's daughter (incl. 1 brother-sister exchange)	4	Classificatory cross-cousin (distant) 3
Classificatory mother's sister's daughter	1	Cousin (exact relationship unknown) 1

Two-thirds of the cousin marriages are first marriages. One quarter are of stepchildren marrying cousins to whom they became related upon the remarriage of their parents. There are two cases of marriage to "sister's daughter" but in each no actual blood relationship exists.

mates. The marriages of stepchildren of either parent are most apt to be with kin, which strengthens the family ties.

Bela Family

To a Bela his family is an economic asset. A single man soon spends all he earns on food and clothing. He needs a wife to economize. He also wants children to help him in his work and care for him in old age. "A man who has no children has wasted his life." He is not really a man until his seed has borne fruit. Ishkrash, a Bela, told me that four or five children was an ideal number. The more sons among them the better, as only men will provide for their father. Ishkrash has had four children, all daughters. Two of them have been given to their maternal grandmother, while Ishkrash hopefully waits for sons. His wife, quite naturally, wants some daughters to help her in the hut.

It is practically impossible for a Bela to support more than four or five children. If there are more, some have to be placed in relatives' homes. A large family thus tends to break up, children being sent, or attaching themselves, to other families where they can get a decent living. The rate of natural increase is such that most families do not reach these non-economical proportions. This is the reason that foster homes are so readily found. Couples who have few children keep an eye on the offspring of their more fecund relatives. If there are many children in a family, a request to adopt one would be met with favor. But even the request of a wife's brother would be refused if there were need for the child in his own home. The average number of children a Bela woman bears to grow to maturity is less than four.[15] One unusual man, by dint of

[15] The average number of grown childern in 37 Bela "completed" families was 3.5, with the maximum 7 and the minimum one. These completed families sometimes include children of successive marriages. On the other hand, the additional children born to divorced wives are unknown. As long as there are no contemporaneous double marriages the number of half-siblings reared together is the best approximation of the number of living births per couple.

three marriages, has eleven children. Most of them are being reared by their mothers' brothers.

The Bela feel much as the Arabs do toward extended kin. Wealth is preferable to many relatives, who consume one's sustenance. One can always win friends and relatives with gifts, as a Tuareg folktale shows. The tale is worth repeating, even though its original moral was probably quite different.

When the Tuareg were the most powerful people in this region, there was one young man who could get no recognition from his fellows. He went to a smith and promised him a goodly gift if he would make a beautiful sword and a strong lance so that the youth might kill many men and gain the respect he so desired. When he had left, the smith went into the bush and cut down a tree. From its trunk he carved a great wooden platter of the type used to bear the food in a feast. When the Tuareg returned and asked for his sword and lance, the smith gave him the platter. The Tuareg was very angry and said, "What is this? I asked for a good sword and lance." The smith explained that to gain the respect the Tuareg desired, it would be much better to take the platter and fill it with food for his friends[16] and relatives. If he did this everyone would admire and respect him. The Tuareg thought about the idea and finally carried it out. In later years he became chief of the tribe. Each year thereafter he sent the smith a cow as the gift he had promised if he gained renown.

Age is an important factor between siblings. Age differences are expressed in the composite terms for "older brother" (*amakar*) and "younger brother" (*amadrai*) and the same distinction is made for sisters (*tamakart* and *tamadrait*). Before a young man is married, his older brother has much the same control over him as his father exerts. Older brother can demand his services and direct his work. In the absence of father, this brother's word is law. He or father will arrange the younger man's marriage, which marks the beginning of independence.

Before that time all that a son earns should be turned

16 The omission of this word would change the moral to an emphasis on kin rather than on wealth.

over to his father. All the produce of any field allotted by a father to his son is given to the parent. In return, the father clothes and feeds the children. The family meals are highly informal. Only if there is little to share does the family eat together. Otherwise a wife eats when she is hungry; a man when he comes home, frequently with friends; and the children when they arrive home, often with their comrades.

Bela children are under very little restraint except when their services are required by their parents. They are free to circulate with their friends in the quarter or to haunt the market for small gifts or stolen tidbits or an odd job. Drumless dances, to the rhythmic clapping of hands, are organized by age-groups. A girl's group may give a dance to honor a youth of eighteen or twenty who has received his first turban. This marks his arrival at maturity and he also receives gifts from his age-comrades. He distributes these presents to the poor and aged of the quarter. This first gesture of social responsibility stands as a portent of his approaching marriage. Then he will be free of all economic control; will send his parents gifts or help them if they are in want. But the carefree days are gone. Freedom brings responsibility for his own family.

Diverse Systems in Contact

Two types of effect seem to have resulted from the diffusion of traits among the three major culture groups. Heterogeneity has been increased and the integration of the family units has been weakened. The growth of heterogeneity is striking in the prevalence of numerous kin terms employed for the same relationship in the same group. This tendency is most marked among the Arabs. Their patrilineality and frequent intermarriage with women from other groups are clearly the responsible factors. However, the longer these intercultural marriages continue in a closed system, the more homogeneous the total group becomes. Comparison of Arab and Arma makes this clear. The Arma descend from Arabs who have mingled with the Songhoi for over three centuries. Today Arma and

Gabibi culture are practically identical. Yet even after this long, Arma and Gabibi express different kin preference for marriage. But both are confused as to whether father's brother's daughter is the equivalent of *weyme* (sister) or *basey* (cross-cousin).

The Arab extended family has suffered from lack of contact among kinsmen. Kin in one's own community are important, but the mobile Arab can only pay deference to his ideals of a large patriarchal family by recording or memorizing his genealogy. Moslem influence on the Bela matrifamily has brought conflicts. Inheritance in the male line divides the family rather than uniting it. Bitterness between lineages may become so strong that a man may not even speak to his joking cousin.

The diffusion of culture traits and their integration into new combinations are processes which go on in societies quite apart from any urban setting. From one point of view, the city is simply a milieu in which culture contacts are multiplied and intensified.

CHAPTER 9

Circumcision and Age-Sets

Circumcision Ceremony

Circumcision is not mentioned in the Koran but is required by Islamic law based upon the customs of the Prophet. The age at which boys are circumcised is not fixed. Songhoi boys are usually circumcised before puberty, sometimes before their tenth year. Older boys who are still uncircumcised are the object of ridicule. The Arabs tend to be circumcised earlier, even as young as three. The Songhoi custom of excision of girls was discontinued in Timbuctoo centuries ago, when many died as a result of the operation, but it is reportedly still practiced at Kabara, a few miles away.[1]

The Songhoi circumcision ceremony is held whenever there are enough uncircumcised boys of the proper age to make a large ceremony possible. It is known as a "boy's first marriage," both ceremonies involving feasts, gift-giving, and the ritual use of henna on the boys' hands.[2] The interval between initiations is usually three to five years

[1] According to Dupuis (Yakouba), 1917, under *bangu* in dictionary. In this connection Es-Sadi records that Sonni Ali, around 1468, ordered thirty virgin daughters of marabouts of Timbuctoo to be brought to him as concubines. They were forced to begin walking to Kabara but stopped, exhausted, en route. Sonni Ali had them executed on the spot which is still called "The threshold of the virgins' fate" (1900:107). This probably refers to the spot where the girls' initiation used to take place, the story about Sonni Ali being apocryphal. If this interpretation is correct, the ceremony must have been discontinued by the seventeenth century, when Es-Sadi wrote.

[2] Dr. Raphael Patai has called my attention to the fact that, in Arabic, *khitan* means both "circumcision" and "wedding"

and the number of initiates in any one circumcision group is approximately one hundred and fifty. Most of the initiates are Songhoi, although a few Arabs from shereef and Kunta families are included. These Arab families have been in Timbuctoo for generations but not as long as the Arma who have entirely lost their Arab identity. The boys from shereef and Kunta families always have special roles in the ceremony. Other Arab extended families, more recently settled in Timbuctoo, have their boys circumcised separately along with the children of their slaves. Such groups are smaller and the ceremony, like that in Morocco, does not follow Songhoi custom.[3] The Bela are always circumcised separately from the other groups and by distinctive Tuareg ceremony. Even for the acquisition of the "mark of brotherhood in Islam," the marks of ethnic difference are emphasized.

The Songhoi circumcision ceremony is initiated by some wealthy man who is the patron and bears the brunt of the expenses. Before French occupation, patrons were always Arma, Alfa, shereef, or Kunta. In recent years, at least one Gabibi has been able to become rich enough to be patron of the ceremony. The patron is known as the "father" of the circumcision. He usually has a son or close relative to be circumcised. He announces through the public crier, through his age-group, and through his friends his intention to foster the ceremony on a certain day. Interested families bring their children to his house where their names are inscribed on a list of neophytes. The larger the group, the more renown the patron receives. The "father" then selects a large house or has doors cut between adjoining houses if the group is to be large. Occasionally, for very large ceremonies, there are joint sponsors who provide several houses. The house

---

and that originally the two rituals were combined in the Middle East.

[3] For comparison of the Songhoi ceremony with that in Morocco and that of the Bambara, see Miner, 1942:625–631. The complete circumcision song in Songhoi, and translation, is included in the article.

of the circumcision is called *bangu* or "pond" and apparently the rite used to be conducted at the edge of one or another of the ponds which surround the town.

The house is carefully cleaned and repaired. The marabouts of the city come and chant the Koran into sand, which is thrown onto the ground to expel the genii from the house. Gabibi magicians make bone charms which are buried in the four corners of the room. All of this is to make sure that none of the boys will die as a result of the operation.

The circumcision is held on a Monday after a *kambu* has been consulted to see if the day is propitious. The children assemble in the early afternoon at the house of the "father." They are accompanied by their parents, uncles, and aunts. While the adults wear their finest clothes and richest ornaments, the boys are clothed only in very old garments which are soon to be discarded. The "father" provides a feast for the boys "so that they will not be afraid." Then all of the marabouts of the city give the boys their blessing and provide them with Koranic charms ordered by the parents in advance. At least six *tira* are tied around the neck and arms of each boy and the sons of the rich are provided with many more. These charms are specific for the circumcision and are afterward discarded.

The next part of the ritual is the hennaing of the palms of the hands.[4] This is done by four Gabibi women. The first four boys to have their hands hennaed have special titles: *falanga, falanga wende* (wife of the *falanga*), *falanga handyure* (older brother-in-law of the *falanga*), and *falanga fenga* (younger brother-in-law of the *falanga*). The four *falanga* are chosen from the sons of the family of the patron and from the shereef, Kunta, and marabouts' boys. The oldest boy among the initiates is apparently sometimes selected as *falanga*. After the four boys have henna put on their hands, the remaining participants

---

[4] This part of the ritual may be executed before or after arriving at the *bangu*.

are brought up four at a time. Meanwhile, the maternal aunts give money gifts to the assembled Gabibi and to minstrels who sing the praises of the boys. Then there is dancing to drum rhythms until late in the afternoon, when the boys are carried on the shoulders of the men to the house of the circumcision. The women, including crying mothers, and the fathers, who cannot accompany their sons, bid the boys "goodbye" and give them their blessing.

The boys enter the *bangu* and await the coming of the barbers who are to do the actual circumcision. In the room are four inverted mortars on which the boys are to sit during the operation. An old man is sent to inform the barbers that all is ready. They come to the house in single file led by their chief. While they pass through the streets, the boys and girls of the city are kept indoors, as a chance meeting with the barbers at this time is believed to be fatal. The barbers approach the house so as to arrive from the east. At the open door the chief incants a few words, spits on his hands and taps on the door. Each succeeding barber does the same before entering. They speak not a word until the operations are completed.

The aspect of the barbers is terrifying. Their faces are painted white with black on the forehead and cheeks and around the eyes. They wear large yellow turbans and tattered robes and are covered with charms. Each carries a pouch for his equipment. With sullen mien they enter the dusky room. The emotional tension of the children is such that some cry and others see these devils incarnate turn into charm-covered dogs. The barbers install themselves before their mortars and gesture for the boys to be brought to them. The barbers take out their knives or scissors, spit an incantation onto them and cut the boys' foreskins. The four *falanga* are taken first, then the other relatives of the patron, and finally the Gabibi and slaves. The last one to be circumcised, usually a slave or poor serf, is called the *koro*. Ground acacia seed is put on the wounds of the boys, who are also given cake to eat, as eating is believed to be healing. All of the boys are circumcised by sunset and when the operations are completed, the assembled male relatives chant the *fātiḥah*. The foreskins are counted by the barbers as a tally on how many circumcisions they are to be paid for. Thereafter, the foreskins are buried or used to make charms.

For two weeks[5] after the operation the boys remain in the house of the circumcision under the surveillance of the barbers, who resume their normal appearance. The neophytes wear their old clothes and amuse themselves to their hearts' content. The families of the boys are expected to make food donations to the patron, as do the fellow members of his age-group. The "father" sends prepared food for all of the boys. They receive a wheat flour gruel the first day and thereafter have wheat cake and mutton. The barbers force the children to eat, if they are not inclined to do so. After these bounteous meals, the boys wipe their hands on the *koro*. The boys cannot drink during the day but are allowed water with tamarind or with honey at night.

On the third day cane-like sticks called *dyow-bundu* are brought to the boys. The barbers are "paid" a small sum for each of these, though the patron really provided them. Beginning this day and repeated twice every day of the forced isolation, the boys form a large circle with the barbers and the very young lads in the center. Seated thus, beating the ground with their sticks and led by the barbers, who set the rhythm with gourd rattles, they learn, little by little, the circumcision song. Among the more intelligible of the thirty-one stanzas, some of which are but ritual gibberish, are these:

[5] The Songhoi circumcision ceremony shows some similarities to Hausa cult initiations. The latter are for single neophytes and do not involve circumcision but the period of seclusion is fourteen days. The sponsor is known as "father." Ritual songs and rhythms are learned in both cases. Hausa circumcision is carried out by a barber and the details are the same for both pagan and Moslem (Greenberg, 1946:23, 50–51).

1.

In the name of Allah, Ali
Yaya,[6] peace be with you
Children of the circumcision,
peace be with you
May we enter in contentment
May we leave in contentment
May Allah accept us.

2.

Ali Yaya, Father, our Father
Oh! Father, our Father
Father of the *falanga*,
our Father
Bless our Father
Bless our Father
May Allah accept us.

3.

Ali Yaya, Barber accept us
Oh! Barber accept us
Red gold, *bosso*,[7] accept us
The day that we arrive at this
mother's house
Or we arrive at this beloved
house
May Allah accept us.

4.

Ali Yaya, the platters are be-
side us
Oh! the platters are beside
us
Falanga's platters are beside
us
You eat your full platters
You drink your full platters[8]
Contentment with unempty
platters.

5.

Ali Yaya, Stepmother spoils
my fun
Oh! Stepmother spoils my fun
Bad Stepmother spoils my fun
Bad Stepmother, your father
has no turban.[9]

6.

May the marabouts assemble
May the Kunta assemble
May the shereef assemble
You all should assemble to
bless us.

Beginning also the third day, the boys go out just after
noon and sit in the hot sand, piling it on their healing

[6] Given as the name of the originator of the song, Ali Yaya,
constitutes an introductory refrain. It may be derived from
"hallelujah."

[7] The *bosso* is a tree, the sap of which is used as a remedy.
This term and the "gold" are complimentary synonyms for
"barber."

[8] Drink the sauce which is served with the rice.

[9] Meaning "your father is not married," as married men wear
turbans. The informant gives this meaning but "your father is
not circumcised" is also a possible meaning.

genitals which are bandaged with a piece of cloth called a "turban." After the actual circumcision the boys may be visited by married men, but youths, who may have been having illicit intercourse, are felt to be a danger to the boys and can only visit them after four or five days have elapsed. The night of the seventh day after the operation is the time for the *hari futu* (dirty water). Toward midnight the boys are all washed in hot water and their bandages are removed. Wood or kola charcoal is put on the wound along with a clean "turban." The four *falanga* are taken first for the bathing and when all are clean, there is a feast of boiled rice and honey.

The *hari gumo* (big water) takes place a week later. The boys are washed again and mats are spread on the floor to keep them clean. In the lamplit room the "father" comes and reads his list of initiates, distributing two, new, white robes, a fez-like *chechia,* and a pair of sandals to each boy and to the barbers. The latter also receive all of the boys' old clothes. The parents of each boy pay the barbers a franc and enough millet to provide each with a sack of grain. The next morning, after eating, the youths file to the cemetery behind the barbers and a Bela who carries all of the *dyow bundu*. There the sticks are deposited under a tree and the boys circle around it seven times, singing. It is believed that if thereafter anyone touches the sticks, he will go crazy.

After disposing of the *dyow bundu* the boys go to the house of the patron where they form a circle about him and sing three times the section of the circumcision song giving thanks to the "father." He distributes money and more grain to the barbers. His relatives give more presents and also gifts to the *falanga*. Then all of the boys, accompanied by the barbers, visit the homes of all the initiates and receive further donations. Thereafter there are three-day feasts at the homes of the initiates and then the festivities are over.

The Bela, who are never included as initiates in the Songhoi ceremony, are circumcised about the age of eight. Whenever there are a number of boys of the proper age, one of their fathers visits a Bela of the quarter who knows how to circumcise and makes arrangements for the boys to be brought to him. This Bela has no particular profession or status and is just a farmer like the rest. On a designated day the children go to the house of this man and pay him a small amount and are circumcised. After the foreskin is cut off, glowing hot wood embers are ground up and applied to the wound. Then all of the children go home. A marabout gives each child a charm to protect him from danger and sorcery. Unlike the Songhoi the Bela wear these charms forever after. Every day the children leave their homes and meet together to sit in the hot sand. They eat at their own homes, however, and are fed butter and meat, which is believed to hasten the healing. When the wound begins to heal, butter is also put directly on it. On the seventh day the father takes his child to a marabout who reads Koranic verses and then, with his hand on the child's head, spits onto the circumcision wound. During the next seven days the boys wash together at the ponds where they play and amuse themselves.

Age-Sets

Most adult natives of Timbuctoo belong to a fraternal organization of some sort. The Songhoi term for such groups is *koterey*. The *koterey* are "age-sets" or mutual aid associations of people of the same sex and about the same age. The *koterey* helps its members when they need economic assistance. The cooperation of the *kondey* (age-mates in a *koterey*) is mandatory for the feasts required at marriage and childbirth. The group participates in the funeral of a *kondey*, helps a member construct a house, gives financial aid to a destitute associate or disciplines an unruly one. The *kondey* are also active in organizing dances and feasts for holidays.

True age-sets, like the *fla-n-ton'* of the neighboring Bambara,[10] cut across the entire society so as to include all persons of one sex within a particular age bracket.

[10] Monteil, 1923.

In such a system both sexes may have age-sets which parallel each other and are closely linked in cooperative enterprises. The heterogeneity of Timbuctoo is reflected in its *koterey* system. There are not only separate *koterey* for the sexes and age-groups but for the various quarters of the city, the major ethnic groups and some status classes as well. The Songhoi, Arabs, and Bela have separate and distinct systems. There is a loose confederation of all Songhoi *koterey* which permits them to function on a community-wide basis when necessary, but this organization does not include the Arabs or Bela.

The following diagram illustrates how the community is divided into *koterey*. The primary differentiation is along ethnic lines. Subdivision on the basis of sex is common to all. The Arab organizations are unique in that they are not age-graded but are divided into separate units for freemen and slaves. The Songhoi and Bela have age-sets. The range of ages indicated for each is not fixed but approximates a ten-year span. Below the youngest *koterey* are play groups of uncircumcised boys and pre-adolescent girls. The Songhoi age-sets are further divided into separate *koterey* for each quarter of the city. Every block in the diagram, therefore, represents a separate *koterey*. The figures indicated in one series of *koterey* represent the approximate number of members in that system.

A Songhoi male *koterey* includes all of the men or boys of one quarter who were circumcised during two or three successive ceremonies.[11] The hierarchy of *koterey* includes about six age-sets. As one lad in the youngest *koterey* described the ascending series above his own group, "There are the *koterey* of my older brother, father's younger brother, my father, and my grandfather." The oldest generation ("grandfathers") is sometimes divided into two *koterey*, like the other generations, but the older *koterey* amalgamate as their members die off.

---

[11] The age span of initiates of a circumcision ceremony is about four years. The age span represented in a single *koterey* is about ten years. Among the Bambara, three circumcision "classes" usually make up an age-set.

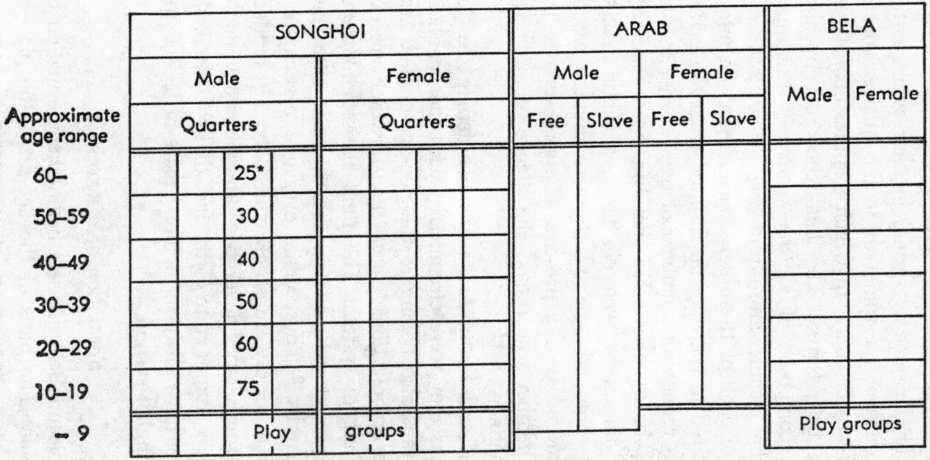

Fig. 13 *Koterey* of Timbuctoo. Figures (*) indicate approximate number of *koterey* members in one city quarter.

Each *koterey* maintains close relations with those groups in other quarters of the city which were circumcised at the same time. They also have special ties to the female *koterey* of the same age-group in their own quarter. The older groups of the same sex in the quarter constitute a series of higher courts to which disputes on *koterey* matters can be referred. The final court of appeal is the *dyemãa*, composed of all the *kondey* of the quarter in which the dispute arose plus the officers of the oldest *koterey* of each of the other quarters. One dispute which was referred to the *dyemãa* resulted from the inability of the three remaining members of one *koterey* to agree on a chief. The *dyemãa* ruled that the three *kondey* would have to join another *koterey*. They were also fined a cow and one thousand kola which were divided among the three hundred *kondey* present. The same fine is imposed on any member who breaks the silence required at these large meetings.

Shereef and Kunta Arabs are included in the Songhoi *koterey*, as they were circumcised with the Songhoi boys. These Arabs also belong to the non-age-graded Arab co-operative organizations (*larab terey*), which are external to the Songhoi system. The Bela age-sets for men and women interact with one another but not with the Songhoi or Arabs.[12] Thus, while everyone participates in a cooperative society, most of which are age-graded, the various groups have never been drawn into a single system. This is true in spite of the fact that the Arma, shereef and Kunta have all been included more or less completely in the Songhoi system.

Formation of a KOTEREY

Songhoi and Bela age-sets begin their formation before circumcision. The basis of the age-set is the play group. Songhoi *horey kondey* or "play comrades" have an or-

---

[12] I knew of one Bela who participated financially in a Songhoi *koterey* as a result of his maternal great-grandfather having been a Gabibi. His principal activity was in his Bela age-set, however.

ganization with three popularly selected officers.[13] Both boys and girls have such groups. They have no dues assessments, unlike the real *koterey,* and are solely for purposes of amusement, particularly for the dances which the girls and boys hold jointly. It is in these play groups that individual leadership becomes expressed and recognized. Chances for leadership are usually enhanced by family wealth, as richer children can act as hosts to their comrades. The Bela play groups choose an older person as patron and chief of the organization. A "little chief" is picked by common consent from the group itself. The play group, as a unit, becomes part of the age-set system when the boys are circumcised.

The Songhoi play group organization is given up after circumcision. The initiates join the preexisting *koterey* above them, or if the discrepancy in age between them is great, the chiefs of the oldest men's *koterey* in the quarter take steps to organize a new age-set. The excision ceremony having been abandoned, girls join existing age-sets or form new ones when the boys of a parallel play group are initiated. A new female *koterey* is formed on the initiative of the oldest women's group.

As there was no new *koterey* formed during my stay in Timbuctoo, we must rely on an informant's account of the ceremony.

The elders announce that the time has come to form a *koterey* and the news is given out. The meeting starts after sunset and continues late into the night. The boys form a big circle with the old men in the center. There is a slave called the *basuda,* who repeats aloud what the old men tell him, because a chief should not raise his voice before his inferiors. The *basuda* says that the boys must put aside all discord and select four chiefs among themselves.[14] They are then chosen by common con-

---

[13] This is the equivalent of the Bambara *n-Tomo* which is also abandoned after circumcision. The officers of the Songhoi society are the *emir* (chief), *alkaidi* (commissary) and *alkaidi keyna* (sergeant at arms). The girls' play group includes a singer (*don koy*) in the place of the sergeant at arms.

[14] The four officers are *aseku* or *alkaidi* (chief), *aseku keyna* or *emir* (deputy chief), *alkadi* (judge), and *ko yo boño* (ex-

sent. The group is likely to select the oldest boys and the leaders
who have already proven themselves as *horey kondey*. The
elders ask that each of the new officers give a sheep and two
hundred kola. This amount is the customary request. Only a
smaller number of kola is usually given. A few rich boys, out
of vanity, may give the whole amount. The new chiefs then
call each of their comrades by name. Each comes into the center of the circle and is told to give a sheep and fifty kola. The
boys are already supplied with kola and each gives ten to
the *basuda*, this constituting the payment. The kola is shown
to the chief and then given to the old men for their *koterey*.

The elders then call for all of the youths who have standing
quarrels with one another to make themselves known. The
basuda brings them forth and they stand motionless in the center of the circle. The chief elder demands from each a donation
of a sheep and two hundred and fifty kola. Payments of ten or
twenty kola are made except for the proud and vain who pay
the full amount. The elder tells the *kondey* that they have
formed a great society and must forget their differences. It is
not a society for amusement. It is serious and all members
must get along together. They must forget differences—the
shereef, the Arma and the Gabibi are all equal in the *koterey*.
If the Arma should say that they would not eat wtih the
Gabibi, there never would be any harmony among the *kondey*.
The elder continues by warning the newly selected chiefs not
to consider the members as their slaves. Then in the name of

---

ecutive). After the selection of the *aseku*, he nominates the
other officers who must be approved by the *kondey*. In addition, the *aseku* appoints a Gabibi or slave as *basuda* (crier and
runner). This individual is not considered an officer. During
meetings he is always called *al musta habu*. He is the counterpart of the "linguist" of an Ashanti chief or the *tonukwe* of
the Dahomean chief. Note the three instances of alternative
Songhoi and Arabic titles. The Arabic titles probably result
from the inclusion of shereef and Kunta in the *koterey*.

The women's *koterey* officers are: *wedye ber* (big chief),
wedye keyna (little chief), *ko yo boño* or *saousi*. The chief of
all the *koterey* of the city, of both sexes, is the "grand *aseku*"
selected from the four *aseku* of the oldest *koterey*. The *koterey*
are autonomous except in their prerogative of appeal when
kondey refuse to accept the decision of their chief. Yakouba indicates that *aseku* exert ratifying control over decisions of their
corresponding *wedye ber*.

Allah, he asks the young men involved in discord to shake hands.

Addressing the whole society, the elder asks if they are content with their new organization. Anyone who is ill content can rise and express his grievance. If it is ill-founded, he is told that he can leave and is read out of the society with the *kamba banda alfatha*. This consists of chanting the Arabic *fātiḥah* but instead of turning the palms upward, they are turned down. Said thus, the *fātiḥah* constitutes a curse on the individual and he will surely never succeed among his comrades who will regard him as a stranger.

Members are now responsible for giving material aid to one another whenever unusual expenditures are necessary —particularly at marriage and other family ceremonies. The amount of financial aid required is assessed the members when the occasion arises. Those who cannot pay are expected to contribute produce or labor. The chiefs of the group must contribute double the individual assessment placed on the members. If the age-set project is the building of a house for a member, the corresponding *koterey* in all quarters are asked to assist. The corresponding women's society of the quarter contributes tobacco and kola and prepares the donated food for the workers.

Hina Hina

In addition to such cooperative effort, the younger age-sets also organize dance parties, called *hina hina,* in connection with the seasonal holidays. The *hina hina* is held by corresponding women's and men's *koterey* of one quarter. The *kondey* of the same age in all of the other quarters are usually invited. Sometimes interquarter friction results in the exclusion of one *koterey* or another from the invitation list. Sankore turned a cold shoulder on their age mates from Badyinde "because the people of Badyinde were rich and tried to lord it over those who really come from the most noble families."

The young women who are to be the hostesses contribute money to their leader. The men send money, tea, and sugar in advance, and meat and butter on the appointed day. The women prepare the food and that evening send bread and platters of stew and couscous to the chief of the men's age-set. The men foregather at their leader's house for the feast. The women always hold their feast separately and often in smaller groups at several houses.

Later in the evening the men and women, dressed in their finest robes and jewelry, assemble in the large courtyard of one of their chiefs. Married women who have borne no children are not permitted to attend this mixed function. A cleared dance space is left in the center of the court. Around it sit the young women and the men cluster about the outside of the circle.

At one side of the cleared space are the Arab slave and Gabibi drummers. There are calabash drums, wooden Bambara drums, and the *koterey* drum with its skin head drawn over half of an empty oil barrel. Near the drummers is another essential piece of *koterey* equipment—a gasoline lantern. Its glaring light illumines the courtyard and covers the surrounding mud walls with grotesque shadows. The rhythms of the drums are taken up by the girls who clap their hands in unison. Meanwhile, the professional praise-singers circulate among the men. A young swain pays a *mabe* and tells her the name of his sweetheart. The *mabe* shrills out the name of the girl and her *dyammu* and sings extemporaneous praise of the maid, her family, her ancestors, and her admirer. The young man's name is chanted by the clapping women. The girl, if not too bashful, comes forward and dances to the pulsing rhythm of the drums, the clapping hands, and the chant. The girl rejoins her comrades, another heroine is chosen and a new eulogy begins. As the evening wears on, the groups repair to their houses for more feasting, after which they reassemble to sing and dance through the small hours of the night.

Somewhat similar dances are held by the paired *koterey* of any quarter on the invitation of a chief. There are no feasts for such a party, but tobacco, kola, and beverages may be provided by the host. The *mabe* are absent and the girls dance two at a time when called out by the host. The officers of the men's *koterey* dominate the male dancing with their graceful sword dances, in which sticks replace the weapons. Such amusement is a continuation of that of the play groups and is discontinued as the *kondey* grow older.

Arab Cooperative Societies

The religious orders are cooperative societies of Arab origin which affect only a small part of the population. Their religious aspect is quite unlike the *koterey*. But the Arabs have other mutual-aid associations which are closer counterparts of the Songhoi societies. *Larab terey* is the principal of these. This society includes all the free, circumcised Arabs of the community. Male slaves of the Arabs have a comparable organization. The Arabs may have borrowed the idea of this society from the Songhoi *koterey* in which few of them participate. While the age-graded character of the *koterey* is absent, cooperation among members for weddings and naming feasts is the prime function of the Arab society.

Contributions are made to every groom and father. For a wedding feast the members give the groom a cow and four sheep—but only if the bride is a virgin. Hundreds of kola are donated; the barber who shaves the groom's head is paid; the gift to the bride's companions provided; and any money remaining from the collection is given to the groom. Members participate personally in the wedding festivities and the naming ceremonies of the first children. The donation of two sheep and money is expected for this latter celebration. For the successive children, solely a money contribution is sent to the father.

There are two officers of the Arab *terey. Al qa'idi*, president and treasurer, is normally elected for life. The present incumbent is the son of his predecessor. The other officer is *al wazir*, who is the speaker, giving orders for the *qa'idi*. He also collects the money assessments. Either officer can be removed by a majority vote. The *wazir* was recently so ejected from office for misappropriation of funds. In case of a tie in such a vote, the decision is reached by a drawing made by a non-Arab.

Arab women have a somewhat similar organization which operates less as a unit due to the greater restriction placed on Arab wives. The chief of this group has as *basuda* a personal slave, who distributes the kola announcing the marriage of one of the members and delivers the gifts of food for ceremonial occasions. For this service she receives small money gifts from the members on the holidays. Married women can attend marriage and naming parties with other women, but the women's group never joins the men's for dances in the Songhoi manner.

Some Arab women hold a unique sort of dance which is attended by men. It is held solely by divorced and widowed women for the purpose of making themselves known to the men. Such a party is held on the evening following the divorce of one of the women. The unattached and previously married women dance and sing. The assembled men join in the singing as they watch the women and discuss their merits. Sought-after girls are given presents of jewelry or charms from the persons of their admirers. The dance gives the relatively confined, but much marrying, Arab women an opportunity to get new husbands.

Age-Set or Insurance Company

At one time it seemed probable that Songhoi society had once been completely age-graded, like the neighboring Bambara, and that the system had been fractionated, secularized, and individualized in Timbuctoo. Subsequently published work on the Songhoi suggests, however, that there may be more organization of age-groups in Timbuctoo than in the rural hinterland. The situation in the villages is still far from clear. Young boys and girls form separate little associations which are sometimes age-graded but circumcision classes do not appear to form lasting groups. The type of organization of Songhoi age-groups found in Timbuctoo is thought to be limited to that region.[15] On the other hand, similarities between *koterey* and non-age-graded cooperative associations in other parts of West Africa[16] give evidence of a wide-spread tradition of such associations. The *koterey* system in Timbuctoo may be a specialized development upon that generalized base. Rather than trying to construct a hypothetical history of that development, it will be more useful to indicate how the *koterey* of Timbuctoo differ in nature from a fully age-graded social system.

The Bambara *fla-n-ton'* constitute a social expression of interlocking schemes of life in which biological and social maturity develop simultaneously. Those who are ritually reborn into adult life together maintain their bonds of mutual interdependence thereafter. They also continue to respect the seniority of those who previously became full members of the society. Everyone's position in the

[15] Rouch, 1954:39.

[16] The Songhoi *koterey* resembles the *gbĕ* of Dahomey (Herskovits, 1938:1, 250–256). The *gbĕ* is a mutual aid society which provides financial assistance to members at life crisis ceremonies, such as funerals. Like the *koterey*, the *gbĕ* has four officials, holds dances, and regulates disputes between members. The membership consists of "a group of young men —sometimes women are included—who have grown up together." Elsewhere (*ibid.*, I, 299) Herskovits states that men who have been circumcised together in a group ceremony and subsequently isolated until cured regard one another as "brothers by the same knife." Should one be a stranger to the others, he must be made a member of the "society" to which they belong. It seems probable that this society is a *gbĕ*, or possibly a *sŏ* or *dŏkpwĕ*.

The *dŏkpwĕ* includes men of various ages, although the young are the most active as these cooperative societies provide manual assistance to their members, as do the Bela age-sets. The speech at the installation of the chief of the *dŏkpwĕ* bears similarities to that delivered upon the formation of a new *koterey* (*ibid.*, I, 63–77).

Bascom reports cooperative societies, *ęgbę*, for the Yoruba (1944:65–66). It is noteworthy that upon the expansion of the monetary economy of the area, members of these societies ceased giving their labor when called upon. They paid for a laborer to do their work or contributed money directly.

system is determined at birth. Being a member of an age-set is part of the process of life, as natural as adolescence, childbirth, and death.

In contrast to such a system, the age-sets of Timbuctoo are not organized into a single system. While each of the separate systems functions to integrate an ethnically distinct group, the separation of the systems functions to enhance the ethnic cleavages in the community. The division of Songhoi *koterey* by city quarters makes for more manageable age-sets, but can not provide a mechanism for control of the ethnically heterogeneous quarters.

A significant concomitant of the diversity of systems and their lack of over-all organization is the fact that membership in a cooperative unit is not mandatory. Nor is membership exclusively a function of age. Some Songhoi are said to have given up their age-set membership. Those who have left the *koterey* felt that they had to pay a lot and received little in return. Other young Songhoi, of different opinion, see the advantage of cooperative associations. They join the *koterey* of other quarters in order to secure the assistance of more *kondey* for future weddings and naming ceremonies. Some Bela join additional age-sets, either older or younger than their own, if they have many fields to cultivate. The reason for this is that Bela age-mates work one day a year in each other's fields. The participation of a Songhoi in additional *koterey* is purely financial. In such respects, the *koterey* is like a mutual insurance company. As a basis of social organization, the principle of voluntary association is antithetical to that of age-grouping. The interoperation of the two in Timbuctoo suggests why the former is better adapted to the mobile, heterogeneous, commercial milieu of the city.

CHAPTER 10

Mating

Men in Timbuctoo feel that lighter skinned women are more attractive. Aesthetic values, as always, are status linked. Light skin color is associated with the high status groups—Tuareg nobles, Arma, and Arabs. Conversely, the slaves are the darkest skinned and the serfs—Daga and Gabibi—are intermediate. While there may be very Negroid persons of status, slaves almost never show Caucasoid traits.

Feminine pulchritude, which all but Bela can hope to possess in a woman, also includes long hair, thin nose and lips, well-developed but not matronly or pendulous breasts. Some like a well-developed posterior. Most of these traits are Caucasoid but the gluteal emphasis is Negroid and interesting to the Gabibi. The preferred breast shape is largely an expression of age difference. The conical breasts of the Negro, however, do tend to become pendulous early, while the hemispherical breasts of the mixed blooded Daga women retain their pleasing form late in life. The beauty standard of obesity is found among the Arabs and particularly among the Tuareg nobles, but the low fat content of the diet and the dessicating desert air make obesity rare in Timbuctoo.

Of course, in a wife one may look for other traits, such as wealth or ability to grind grain. But this concerns marriage which is a different thing from ordinary sexual attraction. Personal cleanliness, well-groomed hair, jewelry, and pretty clothes are part of any woman's charm. A body well-anointed with shea butter may repel a European but it attracts the African.

Extramarital Sex Relations

It is considered abnormal if a youth does not have affairs during adolescence. Sex play begins well before that time but it is said that immature girls can rarely be sufficiently aroused to submit to intercourse. The extramarital deflowering of any girl against her will is a serious offense. The culprit is brought before the cadi and is forced to marry the girl if she and her parents so desire. Otherwise he pays a heavy fine to the parents. If the girl is immature, such a wedding is postponed until she reaches adolescence. Virginity, however, has value largely in the eyes of Moslem law, marriage custom, and among the élite classes. Few Gabibi, Bela, or Arab slaves are virgins at marriage.

Sex is a favorite conversation topic among unmarried boys. The same is true for Arab married men but married Songhoi are more discreet even though they are more adulterous. The Arabs restrict their amours more to numerous, secret, contemporaneous, and short-lived marriages. Gabibi youths spend much of their time together bragging about the number of girls with whom they have had intercourse, discussing the names and qualities of their sweethearts and the presents they have given them. "Having a sweetheart is just like being married, except you are not. You lie with the girl and give her clothes and presents all the time." A girl is not supposed to carry on more than one affair at a time. Such liaisons may eventually lead to marriage, compatibility rather than pregnancy being the determining factor.

Competing youths may spend their money on *mabe* to sing the girl's praises and extol the swains' virtues until she selects one of them. Once paired off, sweethearts commonly enjoy one another nightly or at least once a week. Coitus two or three times a night was one unmarried Songhoi braggart's boast. One Arab, however, has the local reputation of having intercourse ten times a night. He is supposed to have lost a number of wives because of his sexual demands.

Some girls recognize the economic possibilities of the presents received from admirers or are overcome with the sensuality of their new-found bodily function and welcome numerous lovers. Such a girl is still acceptable in marriage to Gabibi as long as she does not accept money for her favors. There is even an advantage to such departure from the "single lover" standard. It is commonly held that if a girl is frequented by a number of different young men she will not become pregnant.

It is said that even in the old days, when the law required the stoning of fornicators, parents of the expectant mother of an illegitimate child would keep her out of sight until time to be delivered. Then she would surreptitiously leave town and bear her baby in the bush where the child would be killed or abandoned. The strong taboo on bastardy was associated only with the high status groups which placed great value on virginity and secluded their women. The Bela, whose premarital sex relations are very free, ridicule the mother of a bastard but, far from killing the child, make it clear that the father has no claim to it. In spite of this fact, they consider the recognition of the procreator as essential. His name is wrung from the girl during her labor in bearing the bastard child, if not before.

All Songhoi bastards were not abandoned in the bush. "*Wallahi, ni tyi dyafan!*" (By Allah, you're a bastard!) is a well recognized insult which is sometimes an accurate statement. While natives are apt to attribute the present frequency of bastardy to changed conditions since the arrival of the French, the pre-French descriptions of Timbuctoo comment on the promiscuity of the population. The Caucasian racial traits in most Gabibi indicate illicit mixture, as was pointed out earlier. The devices employed by lovers to circumvent parental control were as applicable in the old days as they are now.

A young man who visits a Gabibi girl is expected to sit on a separate mat from hers and discuss personalities and the events of the city. In actuality, the subject quickly gets around to sex and the couple soon finds other

ways of treating the subject than talking about it, unless
a watchful father is present. But fathers sometimes retire
early or leave for age-set meetings and daughters leave
on the pretext of similar gatherings.

If an unmarried girl becomes pregnant, the father of
the child may marry her. The customs related to such an
arrangement certainly indicate that the sanction of death
was rarely applied to illicit lovers. The marriage of fruit-
ful partners in love is not a device to hide the fact of unmarried pregnancy. The couple is not supposed to be
married until *after* the birth of the child. The basic idea
is to assure the man that it is really his child. In a system
which anticipates a girl's having a series of single affairs
of varying duration, such a practice is entirely consistent.
One can count back from the birth of the child and ascertain who the father is.

If it is discovered that a man has married a pregnant
woman, the marriage is automatically dissolved. If the
man swears on the Koran before a marabout or cadi that
the child is *not* his, he may remarry the woman forty days
after the child is born. If a father waits until after his child
is born and then marries the mother, the child is recognized
as his offspring but can not inherit. But the father may
give the child all he desires during his lifetime. Unless a
man marries a girl without knowing he has made her
pregnant, there is no cause for him to swear falsely as to
the paternity of the child and make a bastard of it.

If need be, a man will take a false oath on the Koran.
It is not unusual to swear to untruths. Such testimony has
validity even in the face of other evidence, for priority of
oath is recognized. If three witnesses swear that the man
was frequenting the girl when she became pregnant, he
will not deny it. But it is said that if he has already sworn
the contrary to be true, no amount of later testimony of
witnesses makes any difference.

If the parents of an illegitimate child do not marry,
the father of the child is expected to indemnify the father
of the girl. This compensates him for the reduced bride
price he will receive upon the marriage of his errant

daughter. But if the couple does marry, the father-in-law receives only a small bride price.

Abortion is attempted by unmarried girls but with a certain amount of hesitancy because of the recognized danger of physical complications. The eating of large quantities of honey is supposed to induce miscarriage. The leaves of the baobab tree are crushed and put into a cake, which, when eaten, is said to be an abortifacient.[1] Gabibi cord charms are frequently worn around the abdomen to produce abortion or avoid conception. Maraboutic charms and water containing the Holy Writ are also used by girls for the same purposes.

Songhoi and Bela unmarried youths can find sexual satisfaction with Gabibi and Bela girls whom they may later marry. Unmarried Arab men, transients in the city, and all the single men too old or unattractive to find willing sweethearts, frequent prostitutes. There are about fifty such *idye futu* (evil children) in the city—about five per cent of all women of childbearing age.[2] They are confined to no area, each living in her own house and soliciting in the market place when business is dull. They come from all classes and ethnic groups but are preponderantly Bela, Daga, Arab, and Arab slaves. As a result, prostitutes are more prevalent in the grass hut suburb of Arab slaves to the north of the city and the Bela area on the eastern edge of the town. A few beautiful and wealthy courtesans have houses in the city. Prostitutes themselves express no class preferences. Any man with the price is welcome.

Women usually take up prostitution through force of necessity or a desire for greater income, along with lack of paternal or marital control. Arab girls driven from their

[1] These abortifacients were described by men. It is likely that the essential ingredients were not known or that it is simply customary to refer to the concoction by its flavoring ingredients —honey or baobab leaves. The term "lime juice" is so employed in Dahomey (Herskovits, 1938:1, 269, fn. 1).

[2] The French doctor has a list of thirty known prostitutes who are required to visit his clinic twice a week. He states that there are doubtless many others. The natives estimate a total of forty or fifty.

paternal homes for repeated illegitimate pregnancies, Arab women abandoned for adultery, or poor, unmarried women who have no male relatives may all turn to prostitution. The Bela are the most brazen in selling their sexual favors. Many married Bela women prostitute themselves while their husbands are away. Some find this occupation so far preferable to that of being a wife, that they leave their husbands, returning double their dowry, in order to be free. No husband would remain with a wife he knew to prostitute herself. It is felt that once a woman starts renting the use of her body, there is no way to break her of it. Even in the old days, when the kinsmen of a prostitute beat her in public, it was to no avail.

Marriage and Status

Men may theoretically acquire wives from any status group, a slave mate of a master being distinguished as a concubine. In actuality, it is only men of high status groups who have this freedom of choice. Men of low status are limited by the fact that the high status women do not marry inferiors. Even between high status groups, such as Arma and Arab, women are largely limited in marriage to men of their own ethnic group. Arma and Alfa intermarry freely but only one Alfa and three Arma women have married Arab men. In two of the three Arab-Arma marriages, the Arabs are locally prominent. In the third case, the Arma family is very poor. The Arab-Alfa marriage was turbulent and of short duration. Only one Arab woman is married to an Arma, the brother of the emir of Timbuctoo.

In spite of the relatively low status of the Gabibi, three Arab women are now married to Gabibi men, a situation which would have been broken up by force in pre-French days, if it had ever arisen. Without the barrier of physical force, the following matches occurred: the Arab daughter of a slave concubine married the son of the Gabibi chief of the town quarter of Sankore; a daughter of Arab Kunta and shereef parents married the brother of the wealthiest Gabibi in the city over the strenuous objections of her

relatives, who refused to participate in the marriage ceremony; a third Arab daughter, this one with a Gabibi
mother, married a Gabibi.

The legitimate children of Arab men are accepted as
full-fledged Arabs, no matter what their maternity. Under
a strongly enforced patriarchal system, the cultural marginality of children of non-Arab mothers is not very apparent. However, we find that of the four Arab women who
have married non-Arabs, three are the daughters of non-
Arab mothers. The out-marriage of the only girl who had
an Arab mother was the only one which stirred up a great
furore. This is only in part accounted for by the fact that
it was a match with a Gabibi, as the other marriages of
Arab girls with Gabibi men were not vigorously opposed.
In the only one of these marriages not involving a Songhoi man with unusual political or economic connections,
the marriage is with a person of the same background as
the girl's mother. The cultural influence of the mother
upon the daughter is obvious.

Since the French no longer permit the use of force to
maintain the old status lines, wealth and political position
have taken on new meaning. A wealthy Gabibi is no longer
pillaged by the Arma. A poor Arma cannot now recoup
his wealth by looting the goods of his "inferiors." In this
situation, marriages are beginning to reflect a departure
from the old standards. It is the culturally marginal people who first reflect the change.

The old status equivalence of Arab and Arma and the
superiority of both to the Gabibi is seen in the fact that
the man of each group must be outstanding to contract a
mixed marriage with an Arab or Arma woman, but Gabibi
women are taken readily by all three. However, the Gabibi
were serfs or clients, not slaves, so their women do not
become marriage partners of the Bela or Arab slaves.
These two groups, at the bottom of the status ladder, do
intermarry to a slight degree, their status equivalence being indicated by the fact that the wife may be from either
group.

First marriages are arranged by parents or other older

relatives. In these marriages the status of the partners is important. A man's first marriage should be with a woman of equivalent status and from the same ethnic group. Thereafter, he may marry as he chooses.

A man's age at marriage is usually around twenty. If the father is wealthy, the groom may be only fifteen years old. If the family is poor the man may be thirty before he acquires enough money to marry. The Bela can marry and work paternal lands, but the Gabibi are usually so poor that they can expect little assistance from their fathers and so must become self-supporting before marriage.

Songhoi girls are first married shortly after puberty. Bela girls may be married even before puberty although they do not cohabit with their husbands until sexually mature. In all the groups, therefore, the bride is usually younger than the groom. In fact, if the bride were obviously the elder, the groom would be teased about "marrying his mother."

Arab Marriage

The marriage ceremonies of the various people of Timbuctoo are distinctive. However, the dominant pattern is the Islamic one, fully exemplified by the Arabs. Variations from that pattern will be indicated following the presentation of the local Arab marriage practices. The Arab father is responsible for his child's initial match. Other patriarchs —paternal grandfathers and uncles—also take a hand. Families of any means plan the match and arrange the engagement so long before the proposed marriage partners are mature that there is no question of consulting them. If the engagement has not been so arranged, the young man may indicate to his father his desire to marry a particular girl. He would not think of doing so directly. He might indicate the object of his affection to his paternal grandmother, who would tell her son. If that grandparent were not living, the maternal grandmother would do. As this old lady is the avoided mother-in-law of the boy's father, she must pass the information on through her daughter. So strong is the antipathy toward discussing the matter directly with parents that if there are no grandparents, some unrelated person with a "golden tongue" is used as an intermediary. The father's answer, derived from consultation with his father or elder brother, comes back through the same channel. Other prospective mates may be suggested to the youth for his opinion or the dogmatic decision of his elders may be handed down.

Once the decision to arrange the match has been made, the youth's paternal uncle sends one or more intermediaries to the father of the girl. The *pourparleurs* are usually marabouts or other persons of status. When the father of an eligible girl is greeted by a delegation at his door with the words, "We have come to bring a great gift in the service of Allah," he knows a proposal of marriage is in the making. If the match does not appeal to the father he will tell the intermediaries that his daughter is already promised to another. The white lie is just plausible enough to cover the awkward and insulting refusal of the proffered marriage. Sometimes, the girl may actually have been promised to another.

If the father has no objections to the match he will refer the petitioning visitors to his father, if he is still living, or to his elder brother. If none of these relatives is alive, he will say that he must consult his older sister or the mother of the girl. The mother is always notified of the proposal even if she has been divorced by the father. Her opinion of the match is not important unless she comes from a more powerful family than the father. In that case, she may even block a marriage. The final decision is made known to the intermediaries who transmit it to the young man's uncle. The fiction of a "previous engagement" is used for a refusal at this point also.

If the suit has been accepted, the uncle sends his representatives back to the girl's father with a gift of kola. The number of kola nuts is traditionally some multiple of a hundred, plus an additional kola for the patriarch responsible for the hand of the girl. It is said that if the extra nut is not given, the whole lot will be returned and the marriage is off. However, some Arabs simply transmit money to their intended in-laws, who buy the requisite kola themselves. Kola nuts are used to chew but their ceremonial function is evidenced by their frequent association with rituals, as in the creation of a fetish and the formation of an age-set. The transmission of kola signifies a binding association of some sort.[3]

When the kola are received, the date of the marriage is decided. Unless the girl has not yet reached puberty, the marriage follows shortly after the engagement. The kola transaction constitutes the engagement. If, for any reason, the engagement is broken, the kola are returned to the young man's family. Such a gesture is unusual as it results in an undying enmity between the families.

The kola nuts serve as wedding invitations. Aside from the patriarchal nut and the ten per cent which is given to the intermediaries, the rest are divided in half—one portion for the bride's paternal family and the other for the mother's kin. Arab slaves go about town inviting the male relatives of the girl's father to the "division of the kola of my daughter's marriage." The female relatives of the mother are likewise invited to the division of the kola. On the appointed day, before sunrise, the men assemble and receive their share of the kola nuts, the number being proportional to the proximity of relationship. The date of the marriage is announced at the same time. As small a portion as a half-nut may be sent to a distant relative along with the information as to the wedding date. When the male relatives have received their kola they depart. After sunrise the women of the mother's family come for the partitioning of the other half of the nuts and to learn the marriage date. The close relatives of the boy also send kola to all their relatives informing them of the marriage.

The day before the marriage the intermediary brings the bride the customary gifts from the groom. They con-

[3] Gifts of kola nuts are also part of the Bozo engagement rites. The Bozo antedate the Songhoi in residence in the western part of the Niger Buckle (Ortoli, 1939).

sist of three robes and five pairs of slippers.[4] One of the robes is of the poorest cloth. It is in this garment that the bride will be forcibly carried to the groom's house to consummate the marriage. The robe may get torn in the bride's struggle for her virginity and anyway it is given to the attendant wife of a smith after this initial use by the bride. The other two robes are black and white respectively and are of the finest cloth that the groom can afford. One pair of slippers is finely embroidered in silk.

The slaves and serfs of the families remind the relatives of the marriage and the day arrives. The bride's kin come to her house and there is drumming and dancing for their amusement. The bride, however, may not participate but remains isolated in a back room of the house. Before sundown the male relatives of both families, with the exception of the fathers of the marriage partners, assemble at the girl's house. It is said that the fathers make the marriage but actually each has a representative who replaces him. These men even refer to the bride and groom as "my daughter" and "my son." Before the assembled families, the paternal representatives decide the amount of the dowry to be paid by the husband and conclude the contract—for Moslem marriage is a contract and not a sacrament.

The bride's "father" begins the dowry discussion by stating the amount desired and the ritual haggling begins: "Your daughter could bring that much in marriage but you should leave off some of the demand in the name of Allah." The amount is halved "for Allah." Further reduction for Allah is requested and the amount is again halved. The "father" of the groom asks another reduction "in the name of all the assembled relatives" and the remaining

[4] These numbers are considered traditional by one informant. Actually, for all the population elements of Timbuctoo, there is little uniformity of opinion as to exactly what gifts are required for any ceremony. The situations requiring gifts and the general nature of the gifts are recognized but details as to sort and amount are quite variable, in spite of the fact that they are considered to be fixed.

dowry is reduced a third. Another request is made in the name of the groom's "father" himself. The ensuing deduction varies from one to five dollars, depending upon the amount remaining. If the amount is still considered extremely high, the groom's representative says that Mohammed's daughter did not bring that much, which draws the retort, "I know Mohammed's daughter did not bring it but I will not marry off my daughter for less." The question, at this crucial turn, is given over to the assembled relatives who, in the name of their Moslem faith, discuss the matter and decide on the sum which Mohammed received for his daughter. "It is known that Mohammed received the equivalent of five hundred francs,[5] a blanket, and a slave in the marriage of his daughter." Slave transactions now being forbidden, this part of the dowry is often not considered but rich families will include up to two hundred francs as "the price of a slave."

The final dowry, including the price of a blanket, will range from twenty-five dollars for poor families to fifty dollars for the rich. These amounts may appear small but they actually represent a man's average income for a year. As soon as the amount is decided, proceedings stop until part of it is paid. The representative of the groom usually has the blanket and a down payment on the dowry at hand. The blanket always goes to the bride and is used on the marriage bed. If the groom cannot provide a blanket immediately, it is given to the bride as soon as possible after the marriage. Local Moroccan families give a handsome rug in lieu of a blanket but rugs are foreign to matusing Timbuctoo. The money payment is divided among the girl's relatives or, if only a small amount, it may be given to the slaves and serfs celebrating the marriage. The money dowry is frequently not paid in full, a payment of as little as twenty-five cents being made in some cases. The remainder is never paid unless the man divorces his wife, in which case he must pay it. The Arabs express no preference for or against full payment at the time of

[5] About $12.50 in 1940.

marriage. Non-payment obviously constitutes a sort of insurance against divorce.

After the dowry payment the paternal representatives formally join hands and seal the marriage contract, with appropriate statements of acceptance of the dowry and transference of the bride from her father to her new husband. A marabout and the assembled guests pray for the good fortune, numerous offspring, and good family relations of the couple. Following this ceremony the wife of an Arab smith joins the bride and is her constant companion during the next three days. The wives of smiths are skilled leather-workers and the bride's attendant uses her skill to make a number of leather cushions for the nuptial bed. In addition, the smith's wife feeds the bride with her own hands, massages her when she tires, and accompanies her everywhere—even to the marriage bed, as we shall soon see. The bride's head is covered with a white cloth during her seclusion and in her hand she holds a knife or piece of steel. She may speak only with intimates.

When the bride gets her companion, the smith joins the groom who is similarly restricted to his house. His head is covered and a sword or dagger is always by his side. The smith carries the weapon when they leave the house. He gives the groom his food and drink and accompanies him even when he urinates, which is quite a concession for a modest, squatting Arab.

It is quite clear that the new couple are in a dangerous supernatural state during these first three days. They are extraordinarily subject to evil influences and the function of the special ritual is to protect them. They are secluded. Their heads are protected from evil eyes. Magically potent steel is by their side. They are fed by others, their own hands being ritually unclean. This restriction is not unlike the Arab taboo against eating with the left hand, the one with which he cleanses himself after defecating.

During the first day there is a ceremonial fight between the kinsmen of the two families—a battle I hesitate to call "sham," considering the saber scar on the head of my Arab informant. The relatives of the groom, mounted on horses

and carrying a white and a red flag, storm the house of
the bride and try to force an entrance. The house is defended by the girl's kinsmen with swords and clubs. The
battle continues until the red flag is forced into the house.
If the flag is thrown in, the encounter is normally terminated, but if it is thrown out again, the siege continues
until someone gains entry by forcing the door or scaling
the wall. Then all attackers are permitted to enter chanting, "We got in, we got in!" While the defense is stout, it
is all good-natured and no one holds a grudge for the
blows he has received. There are never any serious cas-
ualties and the defenders have never been known to carry
the day. This ritual battle is of the sort sometimes referred
to as a survival of bride-stealing. Whatever its historical
origin, functionally it portrays the inherent friction between the families, one of which gains a member at the
other's expense. Much of the marriage ceremony can be
understood in terms of the marriage constituting an act of
aggression of family against family and sex against sex.

The storming of the bride's home is followed in the late
afternoon by drum entertainment, during which the bride's
hands and feet are hennaed. She dons her cheap white
robe and a pair of cheap slippers. The guests receive gifts
of kola or food and move on to the groom's house to dance
and receive further donations. The hands and feet of the
groom are covered with henna and he dons old sandals
and robe. For the consummation of his marriage, he slips
an inexpensive ring on his left little finger. This ring he
must purchase himself. It is discarded after the marriage
and, like the marriage clothes, would greatly embarrass
the groom should his mother or particularly his father see
him wearing it.

In the evening the male relatives who have access to
the bride go to bring her to the house in which the couple will live or which has been provided for the wedding
week. The men are accompanied by the girl's mother, female relatives, and her girl companions. The men take
the bride and carry her to the new home. She weeps and
struggles against them and the women belabor the men.

She may even break out of their arms, only to be retaken. This struggle is "to show the purity of the girl." Once she is installed in the house the men go off to escort the more willing groom to his marriage bed.

The groom wears a black burnoose with the hood or a turban down over his eyes. Carrying a spear, he walks to his new house with the sword-bearing smith at his side. He is preceded by one or two marabouts and his older kinsmen. Beside him are his comrades. Behind him are the slave and serf women of both families, beating drums, singing, and clapping their hands. The men chant the Moslem writ as they proceed through the streets. Arriving at the house, all partake of a feast prepared by the groom's family. Then the guests disperse, the man's comrades being the last to leave except for the smith and his wife. These two are finally told to leave and the bride and groom are alone with their dowry blanket and leather cushions.

The smiths return in a couple of hours to ascertain if the bride was a virgin. The groom informs the smith but the latter's wife examines the bed or even the bride for the evidence. If she was a virgin, there is great rejoicing at the ensuing dance. The groom gives his bride a gold ring or provides a cow to be slaughtered for the smiths and the celebrants. If, in spite of all the girl's struggles en route to the marriage bed, the evidence is against the bride, her father and husband are highly indignant. The husband has good material for future tongue lashings. If he was never pleased with the marriage his family arranged, he may even use this as an excuse to divorce his new wife after the wedding ceremonies have been concluded, several days hence.

The morning following the consummation of the marriage, the couple separate, each going to the house of a grandparent, uncle, or aunt. They are still accompanied by their respective smiths. This day the groom is joined by his comrades and visited by those of his parents' generation. The guests are served tea and on departure given a kola nut. The young men each bring five francs and ten kola for the groom. He takes tea with his comrades but still may not converse. The kola which remain, after the guests have departed, are sent to the bride's house. Half of these and an accompanying ten francs go to the smith's wife. The other half of the kola are for the relatives of the bride's mother.

At her house the bride is having a new coiffure, including gold ornaments, arranged by her smith. The bride gives the cheap robe and slippers of the bridal night to her menial companion and dons her embroidered slippers and the black and white robes. The white garment is worn over the black. The two remaining pairs of common slippers, which the groom provided, are given to the mother-in-law and her sister. After the bride has been coifed and dressed for her second marital encounter she may entertain a few of her companions. In the evening she walks to her husband's house, accompanied by women relatives, slaves, and serfs of the family. There is the usual rhythmic clapping and chanting en route. Leaving the bride with some of her relatives, the party proceeds to the home of the groom and conducts him in procession to the bride as on the previous evening. While the bride remains retired from view, the men chant sections from the Koran before they leave. This night even the smiths leave the couple to their own devices.

The low class companions are back again the next morning bright and early to conduct the pair to separate abodes once again. If the bride has no local relatives with whom she has not stayed, she may remain in the nuptial house. The groom leaves, however, even if he must stay with the same relative twice. It is essential that the groom be away to permit some further byplay. As in the battle at the bride's house and her struggling protest as she is forcibly taken to her marriage bed, the values and social groupings of the culture are emphasized in the ceremonial dramas attendant upon the change of role effected by the rites of marriage.

This day the companions of the girl, both married and unmarried, converge on her house. The older women in the bride's home try to keep the young women out of the house but, overcome by their numbers, the dames retire. The bride's companions then proceed to steal the bride, substituting someone else in her place and in her bridal clothes. The substitute is an Arab; she should be unmarried. When the stand-in has been dressed, the girls take the bride to a hiding place, which may be anywhere from a mud house in the center of town to a grass hut in the suburbs. There the bride is left with a few friends while her other companions disperse.

Back at the residence of the bride, the impostor has been "discovered" by the unsurprised matrons and has returned the bridal finery. When she departs, she is seized by the waiting age-mates of the groom. If she is a slave or serf she is beaten by the men. For her pains she receives ten francs from the girls. If the impostor is an unmarried Arab girl she is seized and incarcerated until the bride is found. If the substitute were a married Arab woman, she would have to be released or her husband would interfere with the proceedings. While a married Arab would thus obviously be the best choice for a bridal replacement, a married woman is rarely selected as it would spoil the ceremonial play.

The young men search all over town for the bride. Any of her comrades whom they encounter are playfully beaten and interrogated as to the whereabouts of the bride. None, of course, tells where she is. The bride is rarely found. The competition of the ceremonial dramas, while providing good-natured sport, has a predetermined outcome. In the evening the companions of the bride and groom reassemble at the house from which she was "abducted." Here the elders leave them together with the serfs and slaves. The men are told that the bride was stolen and that she will not be returned until a ransom is paid. The amount of the ransom is a bolt of Guinea cloth or its money equivalent, forty francs. The men claim they are unable to pay. The girls reply that not only must they pay to secure the bride's return but they must sing and dance as well. Amid joking, teasing, and cajolery, each man performs. Then the ransom is paid, but the men may try to trick the girls by giving only half a bolt of cloth. Not easily deluded, the girls usually measure the cloth, discover the ruse, and secure full payment. Ony then is the wife of the smith sent to fetch the bride from hiding. The bride may refuse to return until she has seen the ransom or some of her companions to verify the payment. Upon her return the day's festivities are over.[6]

The next morning the groom has his head shaved and, for the first time, dresses in his best clothes. Those of the past three days are given to the smith. Then, with his comrades, he mounts and rides out to the saints' tombs to pray. He returns to pay his formal respects to his parents-in-law and their brothers and sisters. He then proceeds to greet his own relatives. During this series of visits, the relatives promise gifts to the new couple. These gifts are usually not of a domestic sort but are things of value, particularly bars of salt. They are brought to the couple's house that evening where the smith receives them and is remunerated for his service. The visits and family celebrations often continue for two or three days. Thereafter, the bride may live with her father for one year, visiting her husband nightly. But a husband who is able to support his wife keeps her in his house after the marriage.

The ritual attendant upon an Arab marriage finds close counterparts in North Africa.[7] The only really distinctive Sudanese traits are the employment of kola nuts and the postponing of the dowry discussion from the engagement ritual to the marriage.

[6] The pagan Hausa also use a substitute for the bride during the marriage ceremony, but the purpose is explicitly to protect the bride from supernatural harm (Greenberg, 1946:24).

[7] Westermarck, 1914. Nowhere in this book is the whole marriage complex as described for Timbuctoo found intact. However, identical or similar traits are found scattered in North Africa. Even in Timbuctoo there would probably be variations dependent upon the particular Arab peoples involved. The description is that of shereef marriage.

Gabibi Marriage

Before concluding anything as serious as a marriage
agreement, the Gabibi consult a *kambu* and several marabouts with "Fortune Books." If the prognostications are
favorable, preparations continue. The Arma "master" is
consulted by his Gabibi serf concerning the offer of marriage. The Arma receives all money gifts given by the
groom to the bride's family. In return, he provides food
for the marriage feasts.

On the first day of the marriage, meat, rice, millet, and
condiments are sent to the bride's parents by the groom
or his relatives. On the third day the mother-in-law sends
a return gift of mutton and couscous used to feast the
groom's comrades and the bride's younger brothers. The
Songhoi overcome the stresses between families upon marriage by ceremonial food exchange instead of expressing
them in ritual conflict. The Arab custom of storming the
bride's house and that of hiding the bride and holding her
for ransom are entirely lacking among the Gabibi. Non-
Arab and distinctively Songhoi is the practice of outlining
the doorway of the marriage house with the bright yellow
"Bourem clay."[8] The comrades of the bride also bring
water to the marriage house for the bathing of the bride
and one jug is broken at the threshold.[9] The bride is
bathed in her new house by her mother but henna is not
used on either the bride or the groom. Charms are hung
from the rafters over the door to avert sickness by dis-
pelling the genii which are drawn to the house by the
marriage. The prophylactic ritual which the Arabs practice in the isolation of the bride and groom with their
smith companions is entirely lacking.

As the Gabibi are low class themselves, there are no
slaves or serf roles in their ceremonies. Relatives and
friends are the celebrants. Before the marriage is consum-

[8] From the Songhoi village of Bourem on the Niger, to the
east between Timbuctoo and Gao.

[9] Water is ritually thrown on the ground during the marriage
ceremony in Dahomey (Herskovits, 1938:1, 307).

mated the groom is given advice by his father's brother. He is admonished to give up philandering and to work hard to support his family. The moral lecture over, the groom is left with an old woman to assist him in overcoming his biting, scratching bride. It is the crone who bears witness to the girl's virginity—or more frequently, lack thereof. Some non-virgin brides may try to deceive the public by substituting chicken's blood for the hymeneal evidence but such practice is greatly frowned upon.

After the physical consummation of the marriage, the bride remains in her new home. In fact, she is not supposed to leave it until she has borne a child or at least for a whole year. The wedding festivities last three days instead of the week which wealthier Arabs, Arma, and Alfa devote to them.

Arma and Alfa Marriage

The Arma, quite naturally, show mixed Arab and Songhoi backgrounds in their marriage ceremony. A young man's first marriage normally follows about two years after his engagement. During the period of engagement, on the eve of the Birthday of Mohammed, *Ramadān* and *Tabaski*, the fiancé sends a dress, slippers, and kerchief to his prospective bride and a small money gift to his future mother-in-law and her elder sister. On the feast day itself he receives from his prospective mother-in-law enough bread and sauce to entertain his age-mates. For the actual ceremony, as with the Arabs, there is the sham battle and the stealing of the bride for ransom. The Bourem clay doorway and the water purification of the house and bride have been adopted from the Songhoi. The Arab smith roles and the use of henna are absent. A possibly distinctive feature occurs during the purification of the new house. The age-mates of the bride and Gabibi girls parade through the streets drumming, clapping, and singing. They go to the tomb of a saint and bring back sand from the tomb which is scattered on the floor of the new house, bringing it the protection and benediction of the saint.

Needless to say, the protection of Arma womanhood is accompanied by high value placed on virginity. Brides give quite a good account of themselves in the defense thereof, even on the marriage bed. It is not surprising that young grooms are apt to dread this encounter. Sometimes they are unable to consummate the marriage on the first night, even with the assistance of one or two slave women who are there as witnesses to virginity. An unsuccessful groom is the butt of his comrades' jokes.

One such case of a frustrated groom occurred during the period of this study. The son of the Imam of Sidi Yahya mosque married his cross-cousin. Her family is very wealthy. On the day following the first nuptial night, it is the custom for the Songhoi to present their wedding gifts. When a bride is found to be non-virgin, elaborate presents are not given. In this particular instance, the groom received three houses, two slaves, two horses, sixty bars of salt, cash equal to fifty dollars, seven embroidered robes, twenty-six blankets, and much jewelry and dress material for his wife. The Imam's son had failed to have relations with his wife and evil tongues said he was just covering up for her lack of virginity.[10]

Alfa marriage is essentially like that of the Arma. Marabouts chant the Koran for four days in the groom's presence and the bride is brought to her new home by four slaves instead of on horseback but otherwise the ceremonies are the same. The Bela, on the other hand, being neither Arab nor Songhoi, have distinctive customs. A combination of patrilineal Moslem and matrilineal Tuareg traits is exhibited in the following account of marriage.

Bela Marriage

A young man may choose a wife for himself and ask his father's approval of the match or the father may find a wife for his son. If the father is meeting all expenses of the marriage, the son must follow his father's will in the choice of a bride. The father

---

[10] In North Africa the evidence of virginity must be produced whenever the groom does succeed in having intercourse with his bride, but not so here.

of the young man gets a friend of recognized character and a good speaker to go to the father of the girl and ask her hand. When he goes he takes fifteen to twenty-five francs as a present for the girl's parents. The acceptance of the amount indicates the willingness of the parents to accede to the match. Afterwards forty kola and possibly a sheep are sent to be divided among all of the older relatives of the girl. Later, the dowry of two sheep and fifty to one hundred and fifty francs are paid to the family of the girl. The amount to be given is not discussed previously, it being well known that a girl of a particular family must bring a dowry equal to that of her sisters and her aunts. If the amount offered is less, the father may refuse to give his daughter in marriage.

The adult relatives and friends of both families meet at the girl's home. Unmarried girls who are present hide in the dark recesses of the house. The personal marabout of the groom officiates and asks the girl's mother, "Does it please you to marry your daughter to my son?" The mother responds that she gives her daughter to his son and that she is satisfied with the arrangement. The girl's father gives his hand to the father of the boy and concludes the agreement.

This ceremony constitutes the formal joining of the two. They do not live together until a year or two later. During the delay the husband is not supposed to be given any liberties with the girl. However, he must send robes and sandals to her and her mother on all feast days. He is also obliged to help her father in his fields or with his herds. After the couple takes up residence together, presents to the in-laws are not obligatory. The girl's mother is supposed to provide, in the meanwhile, a house, mats, cushions, beds, and all necessary utensils and vessels. The year's delay is intended to give her time to collect these materials. If the husband asks that the house be built, he may be put off, saying that the necessary materials are not yet gathered. If he gets tired of waiting he may start visiting his wife.

After the house is built, the man is led there by his comrades and they walk around it three times. The resisting bride is carried to the house by her comrades and old women. Her companions circle the house three times and the bride follows her husband into the house. That evening an old woman is present to bear witness to the bride's virginity. The bride resists her husband this first night but rarely to protect her virginity. Attempts to establish virginity, when it is non-existent, are never made. The marriage celebration may continue for as long as a week with feasts and the reading of the Koran by the groom's family marabout.

Slave Intermarriage

When slaves intermarry the children of the union belong, as slaves, to the master of the woman. For the intermarriage of household slaves the permission of their masters is required. Non-household slaves live in separate communities, subservient to particular tribes, who are their masters. The local Bela have a desert tribe of Tuareg nobles as their masters. Marriage between Bela is thus uncomplicated by their slavery. When they marry slaves belonging to other tribes, however, the rule of children following the master of the mother adheres. In this rule is the rationale of freemen only "marrying" slaves they have bought—their concubines. Only thus can a freeman recognize the children of a slave as his own. The French have forbidden slave sales and have permitted any slave to become free who so desires. Most slaves retain their old status but rare marriage of Bela women to Gabibi and Arabs indicates that freeman-slave marriages do occur. It is impossible to say, in these instances, if the Bela were actually purchased. They could have been married, with French sanction, without purchase.

Divorce

A man may divorce his wife at any time, for any reason or even without cause. The procedure is quite simple, consisting solely of a statement before witnesses that he no longer wants his wife. Upon divorce the children belong to the father. Infants too small to leave their mother are supported by the father until they are old enough to join him. A woman may not remarry for three months after being divorced unless she is past child-bearing age. The delay permits the partners to ascertain if the woman is pregnant, in which case she may not remarry until delivered of the child. A child *in utero* is considered as belonging to the father who pays all expenses entailed by its birth and naming and care through infancy. When the divorce is initiated by the husband, the wife is not required to return any of the marriage gifts or dowry.

Even a wife's adultery is not considered sufficient cause for return of the marriage gifts, if the husband decides to cast off his wife because of her illicit behavior. If four witnesses of good character testify before the cadi to the woman's adultery, the cadi will sentence her to one hundred lashes. The testimony of a husband who has found his wife in adultery is insufficient evidence for punishment. The cadi's advice in such a case is for the man to leave his wife. Not only is the woman protected by this necessity for witnesses but it is said that, if one witness contradicts the charges of adultery made by the others, the witnesses charging adultery and the husband receive the lashes.

Having recourse to the cadi in order to beat a wife for adultery illustrates the limited extent to which a husband can exert physical force over his wife.[11] If a woman is beaten by her husband "until she befouls herself or her clothes are torn off," she can secure a divorce by stating her case to the cadi. As long as a woman remains with her husband she must be fed. If he fails to provide food, she can secure a divorce. These and impotence are the only causes for which a woman may leave her husband with no return of the marriage costs.

A woman may appear before the cadi and demand a divorce even without these legal grounds. In such a case, she must return double the amount of the marriage gifts and dowry. The law declares that her head should be shaved and she should never marry again. Any man marrying her should be subject to trial and punishment by beating and stoning. Actually only the commercial aspect of the broken contract is enforced. Double indemnity must be paid. The stigma of head shaving and enforced celibacy does not find sufficient support to be made effective. Such

---

[11] Moderate chastisement of a wife is permitted by the Koran (IV:34).

separations always involve family quarrels, from which the community at large remains so aloof that the cadi cannot force humiliation on one of the quarreling families. In times past, the cadi himself has been known to give his blessing to the remarriage of a wilful divorcee a few years after her separation.

Some younger Arabs have a distinctive attitude toward divorce. Either sex may place positive value on the rupture of marriage. After some years of marriage, a man's friends may begin to tease him about keeping one woman so long. In mock commiseration they will express their regret that he is too poor to divorce his wife and marry again. Among his tormentors there is sometimes a comrade with ulterior motives. He wants to marry the woman himself. There are also wives who feel that they can "do better." A wife may upbraid her spouse, telling him that he should divorce her, that it reflects adversely upon them to be married so long. Divorce becomes a mechanism for gaining prestige by demonstrating the opulence of the man and the pulchritude of the woman.

The prevalence of divorce among the Arabs is also related to mobility. Many transients in Timbuctoo marry local women during their stay and leave them upon departure from the city. When the caravans come to town, the caravaneers settle in the quarter of Abaradyu while they conduct their trade, and their camels recuperate for another trip. Many short-lived marriages are contracted in the quarter in addition to the increased activity of the prostitutes. Strangers in town can actually arrange marriages for a lower dowry than can local men. The reason for this is that the stranger is apt to leave and may want to take his wife with him. Rather than leave the city and accompany her husband into the bush, the woman will pay the double dowry to secure her freedom.[12]

[12] Marriages-of-passage by transients are frequent in Djenné also. It is the custom that women of Djenné are not forced to follow these husbands when they leave the city (Monteil, 1932:126–127).

Frequency of Intercourse

It is held in Timbuctoo that Moslem law sets the standard for frequency of intercourse at one union during the
day and two at night. This number may be exceeded or
reduced by mutual accord. If such accord is lacking, either partner may take up the matter with the cadi. Songhoi women keep such matters to themselves. Their unsatisfied husbands may, through an intermediary, ask their
mothers-in-law to intervene. Arab wives are embarrassed
to bring the matter directly to the cadi's attention but if
they air the situation to their friends and it reaches the
cadi's ear, he calls in the couple. If the husband cannot
satisfy his wife, he is advised to divorce her. If he is too
demanding he is advised to marry additional women until
his spouses "are his equal."

If a wife is denying her Arab husband the legal amount
of intercourse, he may go to the cadi. The advice in this
case is likely to be to win the wife's favor with gifts. If the
presents do not bring about the desired change, the husband may divorce the woman and secure the return of the
gifts. In actuality, there is little recourse to the cadi concerning matters of sexual satisfaction, except by the Arabs
who, being closer to Islamic culture, are more likely to
bring family problems before the native judge.

Subsequent Marriages

The ceremonial aspects of the marriage, the involvement of kin and comrades, the granting of the large dowry,
and the giving of rich presents, are characteristic of first
marriages. Parents obtain only the first spouse for their
children. After first marriage even the woman is her own
mistress with respect to subsequent marriages. If widowed
or divorced, she may return to the parental home for protection, shelter, and sustenance, but any new suitor approaches her directly and she herself determines the
dowry. The amount, as well as the number of wedding
gifts, is much reduced if the woman has been previously
married. The ceremony is limited to the contractual as-

pects. The family and community participation is apt to be quite restricted, with the consequent elimination of those aspects of ceremony requiring activities of the marriage guests.

Double Standard and Secret Marriage

Moslem law permits a man to be simultaneously married to four women and to possess any number of concubines. Any young female slave is a potential concubine. If the concubine conceives by her master, her status changes. She may no longer be called a slave, may not be disposed of as a chattel, and cannot be expected to perform tasks not expected of wives.[13] Her child is legitimate and free. Upon the death of the father, the concubine is free but linked to the family through blood and interacting obligations. Concubinage is still common in spite of restrictions on slave traffic.

Polygamy is condemned by Songhoi and Arab women. A slave concubine cannot object to her master's having other concubines but a wife often refuses to live with a husband who has another wife or a concubine. Most women will leave a husband who refuses to give up his second spouse. Wives who are sterile or without independent means or family connections, tolerate polygamy. Sometimes a woman, for economic and status reasons, knowingly enters into marriage with a rich man who already has a concubine but not a wife. Even in such cases, the woman refuses to share a house with the concubine with whom she must share her husband's bed. The astonishing fact is that the wife has no legal backing for her stand against polygamy and the men have no comparable monogamistic values. Yet a woman's father will harbor her from a husband who insists on being polygamous,[14] even when the

13 The pagan Hausa also free a concubine from slavery when she bears a child (Greenberg, 1946:16). See also Trimingham, 1959:133–134.

14 Some Arab fathers "give" their daughters to shereef husbands, i.e., they require no dowry because they want the sacred benefits of a shereef in the family. Such fathers would not harbor their runaway daughters.

cadi orders the father to return the woman to her husband. Obviously, women exert very effective power within a system which is formally patriarchal.

The origin of the women's monogamistic values poses an interesting problem. Their dislike for polygamy is not limited to Timbuctoo. Trimingham cites the fact that to the east, in the Songhoi region of Bamba, less than one per cent of the men are polygynous because of the women's refusal to accept such multiple marriage.[15] He implies that this preference derives from intermarriage with the Tuareg, who prefer monogamy. This could not be the case in Timbuctoo, for the Bela are the only resident carriers of Tuareg culture, and they are not averse to polygyny. Among the Bela, the first wife has recognized rights over subsequent wives. This is contrary to Islamic law, under which co-wives have equal rights. In Timbuctoo the status of an Arab or Songhoi woman is threatened if her husband takes another wife, for the first wife must share her prerogatives without acquiring any new ones. In less Islamized Songhoi areas, however, the first wife in a polygynous family has special prerogatives.[16] It is probably for this reason that, much farther east than Bamba, the rate of polygynous marriage rises to ten per cent. The conflict in Timbuctoo does not result from sex differentiated diffusion of monogamistic values. Rather, it seems to stem from the imposition of the Islamic code regarding equality of wives. Husbands have little to lose under that code, but wives have much to lose.[17]

The dilemma of Arab men in Timbuctoo is solved by various ruses and devices which allow expression of values favoring polygamy. Frequent divorce provides one solution. A man gains prestige through successive marriages to numerous wives much as he does through the posses-

[15] Trimingham, 1959:176.

[16] Rouch, 1954:37.

[17] The same conflict was found in Algeria, where Arab husbands are forced to be monogamous because of the violent quarrels which occur between co-wives (Miner and DeVos, 1960:77).

sion of many wives simultaneously in a polygamous system. There is also a marriage trick employed by Arabs, to approximate polygamy, which operates as follows: A married Arab sees an unmarried woman whom he desires sexually, but at the same time he does not wish to lose his wife. He publicly marries the second woman and his wife indignantly returns to her parents. The Arab knows that his first wife is legally forbidden to remarry for three months following their separation. He can count on her waiting at least that long for him to divorce her. Later she might assume the initiative and expense of divorcing him. Fully conscious of this pattern, the Arab keeps his new wife just three months and then divorces her, whereupon his first wife returns.

An even more prevalent Arab solution to the double marriage standard has been secret marriage. A man may marry numerous wives as long as each is ignorant of the others. Men who travel marry women in the villages which they frequent, in addition to the wife at home in Timbuctoo. While the chance of discovery is greater, many other Arabs have secret wives or concubines in the city itself. Among men there is common knowledge as to the true marital condition of other men. The secret must only be kept from women who are friends or relatives of the "public" wife, as they are certain to inform her.

There are class and ethnic qualities to the secret wife system which are of interest. As has been indicated, the Arabs have access to women only through marriage and prostitution. When their wives deny them polygamy, they take wives in secret so that their first wife will not leave them. Local secret marriage must be with lower class people. Any reputable Arab woman could only be married publicly, which would spoil the whole endeavor. The secret marriages are therefore with Arab slaves, Gabibi, and Bela. Gabibi women do not knowingly enter into secret marriages. Bela women have no feeling against polygamy although the taking of multiple wives by the Bela is unusual. They recognize the Arab custom of secret liaison but their interpretation is that the union is secret because the Arab is ashamed of his low status spouse.

Songhoi men, unlike the Arabs, do not resort to secret marriage. Instead, premarital sexual freedom with Gabibi girls is carried over into marriage in the form of adultery. While adultery is recognized as wrong, the men say, "I have a beard; I have to get around a bit." The cloak of anonymity covers these liaisons just as efficiently as it does the secret marriages.

[13] Dyingerey Ber—The Great Mosque

[14]   Donations for the Muezzin

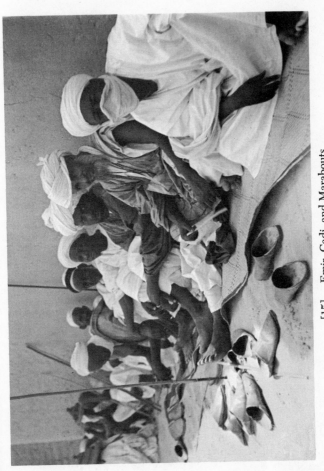

[15]   Emir, Cadi, and Marabouts

[16] Students with Their Writing Boards

[17]   Interquarter Fight at New Year's

[18] Songhoi Baking Bread

[19]   Grinding Grain outside a Bela Hut

[20]   Bela Wife, Spinning

CHAPTER 11

Birth—A Family Focus

Conception

While the general biology of conception is understood, pregnancy also finds sacred explanation in the belief that the child is formed in the mother's womb by two angels which accompany her. The Bela, however, hold that a woman can also be made pregnant by sorcery, even though she has not had intercourse. Under such circumstances the unfortunate woman seeks to abort. The foetus is believed to be abnormal—"just a mass of flesh and bones." It appears likely that the foetal form is not anomalous but results from the process of achieving abortion.

Sterility is believed to be the result of the will of Allah. The initial presumption of responsibility for sterility in a childless union is against the woman. She is often left for this reason. The fertility and non-fertility of subsequent marriages by the previous partners determines which is actually sterile. Many a father, desiring grandchildren, would refuse to permit his daughter to marry a man who was known to be sterile. A sterile woman, however, is sought by Arabs for secret marriage, for it is childbirth which usually exposes such unions. In addition to complete sterility, the natives note that couples often have one or two children and then no more. This again is considered foreordained. Between the effects of syphilis and abortion it is the rare woman in Timbuctoo who bears six or seven children. Judging from genealogies, three or four live births is closer to the norm.

Prenatal Care

There is universal belief in Timbuctoo that a pregnant woman develops possessive obsessions which must be satisfied by the husband to avert evil consequences. One young Songhoi husband was greatly upset over his wife's insistence that he buy her a particularly expensive skirt. "You would say that the baby itself wanted it," he wailed, as he went to spend most of his money to purchase the garment. The desired objects may not always be utilitarian. A Bela woman took a fancy to a pair of men's breeches which she insisted upon keeping beside her. Another woman, an Arab, demanded that she be brought the fecal matter she had seen another woman drop. She smelled it and was satisfied.

The desire for a new skirt is the most commonly voiced. The pregnant wife of a Bela saw a tradesman passing by with skirt material piled on his head, as is the custom of such peddlers. She had him show her one of the most attractive pieces, which her husband priced. The woman said it was too expensive and the trader left. One of the husband's comrades who had witnessed the episode warned the husband that he had better watch out, as his wife was obviously greatly taken with the cloth. An hour and a half later the wife fainted while doing her housework. The distraught husband dashed cold water in her face. When that failed to revive her, he rushed forth to find the merchant. He succeeded in doing this and purchased the material. Returning home, he placed the cloth about his wife's head and she was quickly revived. Such episodes need not be interpreted as representing female cunning. The seizures are probably real but suppressed desires do find expression through this culturally patterned outlet.[1]

The tradesmen who hawk their wares through the city do not hesitate to take advantage of this culture trait. They make a practice of showing their goods to pregnant women, knowing full well that their husbands will have to

---

[1] The obsession of a pregnant woman for a skirt finds a psychological parallel among Haitian Negroes. In Haiti a woman possessed by a deity and speaking as the deity may demand that she be given jewelry (Herskovits, 1937:147).

purchase anything the wife wants. With this advantage, the merchant can keep his final price high.

A woman with child is expected to be shrewish at times. The husband should simply leave her alone and not argue with her when she is in a bad humor. A young husband, who was unaware of what to expect during his wife's pregnancy, complained of her ill temper to his comrades. They laughed at him and called him "a little boy" because of his ignorance of the inevitability of his difficulty. They told him that it was not really his wife who was cross with him but *wisiwisi*, the unborn child. It is likewise held that it is the child who wants the objects for which the mother expresses such strong desires. These facts of life are customarily explained to the uninitiated father by his more mature friends.

Failure to observe these precautions toward expectant mothers results either in severe illness of the mother or miscarriage. As a Bela expressed it, "A pregnant woman is like a small child on a camel. A slight incident may cause it to be thrown off and killed." For this reason the Bela, who normally strike a shrewish wife, restrain the impulse. Otherwise they know the woman is apt to die of the blow or at the very least the child will bear the mark of the blow.

The Bela, being pure Negro types, are marked only by the rare blotches of partial albinism. Arab children may have either light or dark birthmarks, depending upon their racial background. The Arabs, like the Arma, do not strike their wives. They believe that birthmarks are allied to the possessive desires of the pregnant women. An unrequited desire will find expression in a mark on the child. One man told me of a large black mark on the leg of his baby. Immediately after its birth, the mother had confessed that she had wanted a *bazin* robe shaped identically like the birthmark but had not made her desire known to her husband. He avers that even the pattern of the *bazin* is visible in the child's mark.[2] The Arabs are particularly con-

2 For comparable beliefs among Egyptian Arabs, see Blackman, 1927:62.

cerned about objects which pass quickly through the mother's field of vision without her being able to see them clearly. Care is taken with objects which a pregnant woman sees and they are left in her presence for several days "so that they may pass out of her heart." Deformations are attributed either to the above, to the breaking of *kabi* restrictions, or to natural causes such as a mother's fall. Blindness falls in a special category of belief concerning the *baraka* of the blind and concepts concerning the evil eye. The affliction may simply be considered to be the will of Allah.

An expectant mother is not only deferred to but also shielded from unpleasant or startling experiences. The sickness or death of a member of her family or other bad news is never made known to her directly until after she is safely delivered of her child. She is, however, made aware of the death of close kin. A marabout is called who gives her some "Koran water"[3] to drink and who washes her head and abdomen with more of this holy water. The same treatment may be used for illness, but if she is well the ritual informs her of a tragedy in her family. Anxiety replaces the possible shock. It is then up to her, through conversation and visits, to determine who has died.[4]

A pregnant woman is not awakened from her sleep or frightened playfully. She is not allowed to leave the house alone at night for fear of meeting a frightening genie. Expectant Gabibi mothers wear *tira* about their necks or string charms about their abdomens to protect them from frights which would kill the unborn child. Beliefs concerning prenatal influences are limited to physical effects upon the child. The personality of the child is not believed to be shaped by prenatal occurrences.

Women are under few other restrictions during pregnancy. Arab women leave their homes for ceremonial oc-

[3] Water with which a Koranic passage has been washed off of a writing board.

[4] This procedure for informing a pregnant woman of the death of close kin was given by a Bela informant but may be more general to the population.

casions as usual, even during first pregnancies. Women of other groups, however, show a strong aversion to leaving their houses the first time they are with child. The Bela wife continues her heavy housework, but it appears that other women avoid work if possible. Meat, milk, and butter, if available, are included in the mother's diet. Sexual relations may be continued up to the accouchement, although some husbands may not desire intercourse as their wives' pregnancy advances. Only the Arabs consider intercourse after the sixth month as improper, but admit this restriction is not always observed. Everyone counts the period of pregnancy as being nine lunar months from the first menstrual period which is missed.

Arab Birth and Naming

There is the same reticence between parents and their daughter with regard to her pregnancy and delivery as the Arabs exhibit between parents and a son concerning his marriage. When a woman has passed her menstrual period by two weeks, she informs her husband of her pregnancy. The husband may or may not tell his wife's mother of the fact through an intermediary. A mother never inquires of her daughter about such a matter or comments about it even when the condition becomes obvious. The daughter never mentions her pregnancy to any of the older generation but she confides in her age-comrades, even as to the month she expects the baby to be born.

The first accouchement of an Arab woman takes place at her father's home if possible; otherwise she goes to the home of some other paternal relative. In this connection, it should be recalled that the Arab wife often does not take up permanent residence with her husband until after her first child is born. Thus, she may still be living in her father's home. The custom certainly reflects the fact that marriage alone does not transfer an Arab woman to her new household. The birth of a child does so and subsequent children are born in their father's home.

When labor pains begin during daylight, the woman

goes to her father's house in the company of her husband's sister or one of his other female relatives. At night, however, the husband accompanies her. Delivery is assisted only by an Arab or Gabibi midwife, preferably the former. The midwives are all older women. Parturition takes place with the mother on her knees and elbows.[5] The mother is not supposed to cry out during her first delivery "as she would be ashamed to have her parents hear her." If it is not the first parturition, the woman is free to scream and her cries punctuate her rantings against her husband "for having done this to me."

When the baby is born, it is laid on the ground a few minutes so that dirt gets in its eyes, nose, and ears. This contact with the earth is considered to be beneficial for its body. The umbilical cord is tied and cut with a knife. Then the baby is washed and laid upon some of its father's old clothes. If the child is stillborn or dies during the first day, it is buried inside the house. If twins are born, the mother experiences an increase in *baraka*. It is said that a woman who has thrice borne twins cannot go to hell. Twin boys are held to be very difficult to rear alive; a boy and girl not so hard. This reflects a Moroccan belief in greater danger to twin boys from the evil eye.[6] Human triplets were unknown to my informants who volunteered the opinion that such a multiple birth would be very bad.[7]

The birth of the first child and that of each subsequent boy is marked by special ritual. Only a very rich man celebrates the birth of any subsequent daughters. The patriarchal emphasis of the Arabs finds marked expression in the attitudes toward the birth of girls and the lack of associated ritual unless the girl is the first child born. As we

[5] The exact position of the mother during childbirth in Morocco is not clear in Westermarck, 1926:II, 372, but it is definitely not like that in Timbuctoo. Algerian Arab women are delivered in a squatting position (Miner and DeVos, 1960).

[6] Westermarck, 1926:II, 402–404.

[7] An Arab informant credited the Tuareg with killing one triplet when such births occurred in their herds. The Arabs transfer one of such multiple animal births to another lactating female.

have seen, the ceremony at the birth of a first child functions as a sort of final marriage ritual for the parents themselves. Arab preference for boys is evidenced in their numeration of offspring, for the number of male children is stated initially. They definitely want their first child to be a boy. The woman who carries the glad tidings of a male birth to the Arab father is richly rewarded. But the bearer of the news of the birth of a girl goes unrewarded. "Dirty like its mother," is often the disappointed father's comment under these circumstances.

It is said that some Arabs have even divorced their wives for not bearing a male child first. I found no evidence to substantiate this claim and it probably only emphasizes the preference for boys. There are a few beliefs which weakly counterbalance the situation when a girl is born. Even Arab men will admit that if the first child is a girl, the marriage will be a happy one, the contrary being true if the child is a boy. Likewise, the initial birth of a girl indicates future riches for the father, while a boy means hard times from forty days to a year.

In the case of a birth which is to be ceremonially noted, the father's female relatives are informed of the baby's arrival.[8] Each sends a woven grass tray, some old cloth and two francs to the mother. The money is given to the midwife. The baskets are piled up, with the cloth on top, and the baby lies on this improvised bed for the next week.[9] Thus, the sequence of resting places for the newborn child consists of a series of symbolic associations: first with nature, then with the father, and then with his family. The mother's parents are notified of the birth but they have no ritual role until the naming ceremony.

Immediately following the birth, the child's father purchases one or more sheep, slaughters them and provides a portion for his wife, who should have mutton broth, butter and meat as a recuperative diet. The remaining

[8] Informing the father's mother, his sisters, and his paternal aunts is mandatory, if they can be reached.

[9] "Eight days," including the birthday, is the usual manner of stating the period.

meat is sent to the father's close female relatives. They, in turn, distribute it to other kin along with the news of the birth. After two or three days, those thus notified send donations of money to the woman who sent the announcement to them. These gifts are then sent to the child's mother. The father's comrades contribute up to three francs apiece to assist the man in meeting the unusual expenses associated with the birth and naming of a first or male child.

The mother-in-law of the delivered woman comes to see the child a day or two after its birth. But the child's father as well as older men in his patrilineal family are not permitted to see the child until after forty days have elapsed. This restriction is imposed only when the woman is delivered in her father's house. Her husband's younger brothers may visit her and see the child under any circumstances.

Four days after the child's birth, food and money are sent by the father and his family to the mother's parents. Her relatives prepare a feast during the next two days and on the seventh day following the birth the festal foods are sent to the home of the patriarchal head of their son-in-law's family, i.e., his father, paternal uncle, or elder brother. Here the friends and relatives of the baby's father gather for the sacrifice of a sheep, the feast, and the naming of the child. The baby's maternal kin are not present for the ceremony. The fact that they prepared the food for the feast expresses the solidarity of the extended family. Their absence from the feast denotes the patriarchal emphasis in the Arab family.

The guests partake of the feast and then the paternal kinsmen of the baby informally discuss possible names for the child. The usual practice is to select the names of deceased members of the family. As the child is believed to acquire the qualities of the person whose name he assumes, the lack of illustrious forebears may result in the selection of the name of an important marabout or some other outstanding person who died during the preceding year. Obviously *baraka* lies in personal names. Following this same principle, names from the Koran may be considered. The name Mulai, or a variant such as Mullali, is popular for shereef boys and Siti for girls of this group.

After three names have been agreed upon, each is identified with a particular string of prayer beads. The three strings of beads are then sent to the mother of the child who selects and returns one immediately.[10] The name which was associated with that string of beads is announced and the guests pray for the child's welfare. The maternal kin are then notified of the child's name.

The child's head is subsequently shaved by a barber. If the baby's eyes are believed to be weak or diseased, three, parallel, vertical lines are cut in the skin beside each of the eyes which are bathed with blood from the incisions.[11] Each of the father's close kinswomen sends two robes for the baby. The midwife, who has been acting as nurse and housekeeper for the mother during the week, is given the cloth which constituted the baby's bed, half of the sheep sacrificed for the naming, and five francs.

At the expiration of forty days after the birth, the husband sends new clothes for his wife and child. A wife will refuse to come to her husband's house until these gifts are received. When she and the child do join him, the baby's head is again shaved. The paternal kin now visit the home to see their new kinsman.

The ceremony as described above is carried out upon the birth of each male child. The birth of a subsequent daughter, however, is not even announced to the grandparents. The father simply selects a name for the girl and informs his wife of the choice.

[10] The Fellahin similarly fortuitously select names identified with candles (Blackman, 1927:80–81).

[11] Another Arab informant stated that the cuts beside the eyes were always made at this time. Three similar cuts, filled with antimony to make a tattoo, are made beside the eyes and in the middle of the forehead of young Gabibi girls. These are considered "beauty marks" and are made by a barber on the Feast of the Naming of Mohammed.

Gabibi Baby

The Gabibi make no ceremonial distinction between male and female births. The naming feast for a first child, however, is more elaborate and is considered to be as expensive as the marriage ceremony itself. The expectant woman always goes to her mother's house for the delivery. Parturition is assisted by a midwife, the woman's mother, and aged kinswomen from both sides of her family. Those present assist by holding the parturient woman or sit around giving advice.

Immediately after the baby is born, the midwife says, "*Bismillahi*" to keep genii from exchanging the newborn child for one of their own. This they have been known to do just at birth. The child they leave has a big head, prominent eyes, and long hair. When it grows to adulthood, it retains some physical deformation but is usually taken for a normal human being. "Only in anger will someone call him the son of a genie that he really is."

After the child is washed it is further protected by the midwife who cries the muezzin's call into its ear.[12] Both mother and child are very subject to attack by witches and genii in the period shortly following birth. An additional precaution is taken by subsequently bathing the baby in "Koran water" which protects it from witchcraft until it is old enough to talk.[13] Also shortly after the delivery, one of the old women chews up small pieces of dates and kola nut and gives them to the baby to eat.

The mother is given milk to drink "so that she may nurse her child." If she has difficulty with lactation, a charm is obtained to make the milk come. If she is still unable to nurse the child, a wet-nurse is sought among the relatives on either side of the family. Mother's sister is preferred as a wet-nurse. Nursing creates an extension of kinship

[12] For similar customs in Morocco and Arabia see Westermarck, 1926:II, 378.

[13] The Arma lay a knife in the baby's bed until the naming ceremony. It is probable that the Arabs do likewise. In this connection see Westermarck, 1926:II, 373, 378, 382.

such that "children of the same milk" may not intermarry.
Mother's sister is therefore a preferable wet-nurse to father's sister because in the first instance wet-nursing does
not create a block to marriage between cross-cousins who
are the preferred marriage partners. If no wet-nurse can
be found, a sheep is bought to provide milk for the child.
The Arabs are said to secure a goat, even in preference to
a wet-nurse, if the mother cannot nurse the child.

If a nursing baby dies and the mother continues to lac-
tate, sand from the child's grave is rubbed on her breasts
to dry them. The mother's feet are heated by an open fire
to the same purpose. If the child is stillborn or dies the
first day, it is buried inside the house under a wall. If it
dies later, it is buried in the cemetery. The afterbirth is
always buried in the house. When the child's umbilical
cord falls off, it is either used to make a fertility charm
for the mother or it too is buried in the house.

Following parturition, the birth is announced to the
child's paternal grandmother and paternal aunts, who, like
the Arabs, send woven grass trays and cloth. Unlike them,
however, the paternal great-aunts do not send these gifts.
On the following day the age-set of the father sends one
or two sheep and about twenty francs[14] for condiments
to the baby's maternal grandmother. The sheep are slaughtered and cooked and then the meat is shown to the child's
paternal aunt. She, in turn, shows it to her age-mates.
They each donate a franc to the aunt who uses the money
to purchase shea butter and millet which she keeps for
later presentation. The mutton is returned to the maternal
grandmother and is eaten by the women who assisted at
the birth.

During the week following the birth, the father accumulates the provisions necessary for the naming feast. He
is assisted financially by his father who donates rice and
flour and fifty francs. Each of the *kondey* of the child's
father donates two and a half francs to him for the pur-

[14] This amount, and subsequent ones named by informants,
are probably not mandatory. The amount donated by each
age-mate (*kondey*) is fixed, however.

chase of a sheep for the ceremony. The father makes the necessary purchases and takes the provisions to his mother-in-law's house.

The naming feast takes place there a week after the birth.[15] Both paternal and maternal relatives attend the feast, which begins in the morning. Some of the father's age-group comrades are present but not those of the mother. The guests are separated in various rooms so that the women are segregated and the men are grouped on the basis of age and kinship. The platters of food are distributed among the groups. The paternal grandfather of the newborn announces the name he has selected for it.[16] The guests give their benediction; kola is distributed and the feast is terminated. That evening the child's paternal aunts and their age-mates come to see the child and present the mother with the shea butter, millet, and the remaining money from their donations. The mother, who has remained in bed until the naming ceremony, gets up on this day.

The mother does not leave the house, however, until forty days have elapsed. Then she returns to her husband's home. He welcomes her and gives her robes, skirts, and slippers as rich as he can afford. He is very generous at this time "because he wants to have more children" and it is not unusual for the wife to deny him sexual relations for long periods following the birth of a child. The supernatural sanction supporting this behavior is the belief that "the taste of intercourse will kill a nursing baby." Thus the father frequently has to content himself with sexual relations every fortnight. If this is not allowed him, the matter is taken up through a go-between with the mother-in-law.

[15] This may be seven days including or excluding the day of birth itself. The Gabibi favor the former, the Arabs the latter. The Bela hold the ceremony "the evening of the seventh day," which, according to our reckoning, is the evening of the sixth day. A "day" begins with sunset in Timbuctoo. Similar variation in the time for the ceremony is found in Morocco (Westermarck, 1926:II, 386–397).

[16] If circumstances do not permit this, the father gives the name.

It is also thought that a man's adultery at this time will have bad effects upon the child. These beliefs are particularly striking when it is realized that the child may be nursed for two years.

On the day that the wife arrives home, her husband invites all of his age-mates to a feast at which he announces the child's name. All of his sisters come to visit his wife this same day and each presents her with two robes for the baby, one black and one white. These may be worn separately or together with the white robe outside. The baby's paternal aunts also bring charms for the child.

On the forty-second day after the birth, the midwife who attended the wife at parturition and during the following week returns and takes the baby to the home of each of its father's siblings. At each house she receives food, clothes, and money. This payment is in addition to the robe and skirt doffed by the mother at the time of birth and given to the midwife. She also receives food from the naming feast.

Upon the birth of the child, its father's brother may have indicated his intention to adopt it and sent the appropriate two meters of cloth and a large platter of rice to his brother. Other Gabibi say that it is at the time of the baby's visit to its father's siblings that they decide who shall adopt the child. Some families give the father's brothers prior choice; others give priority to father's sisters. If twins were born, one child is adopted by the paternal kin and the other by a maternal relative. This is said to be the only condition under which a child is adopted by its maternal kinsfolk. Mother's sister is the preferable choice in this case, for then the adopted child will not be living in the same household with its maternal cross-cousins, who might eventually be spouses. After the adoption is decided, the child is taken every morning for a short visit at the home of its foster parents. After two or three years the child makes the change of residence to its foster home and only visits his actual parents every Friday thereafter.

Bela Baby

Bela women are delivered in their own huts, not those of kinsmen. When parturition starts, all the men of the household must not only leave the hut but the yard enclosure as well. Old women, who are neighbors or kin, come to assist with the birth. No professional midwife is employed. The parturient woman lies on the floor with her knees drawn up under her. Her arms and legs are held by some of the women, while others massage her sides and abdomen and still another delivers her. When the baby is born, the umbilical cord is cut with a knife and hot butter and ground charcoal put on the cut end of the cord.

The child's head is shaped and its eyes, ears, and nose cleaned out. Then the baby is bathed in warm water. The mother is given hot butter to drink. A heated and buttered wooden platter is used to pound and massage the thigh muscles of the delivered woman. The afterbirth is buried in a deep hole in the hut floor. Another hole is dug alongside of this and is kept covered with a mat. During the week the mother remains in bed and uses a pottery or calabash vessel as a sort of bed pan. This container is emptied into the hole, which continues to serve the woman as a latrine during daylight until forty days have passed. When the baby's umbilical cord falls off, it is buried in the hut.

The burial of these human products in the hut is closely associated with the belief that the danger of evil from supernatural causes is very great following birth. "A witch who saw a newly delivered woman or a new baby would thirst after its blood as though it were fresh water." Likewise, genii like the smell of blood and are attracted to the hut. If a woman should leave her hut before seven days after her delivery, the comments of people seeing her leave so early would be very bad for her. Because of these dangers, the woman remains secluded and the hut and yard are incensed for forty days to drive away the genii.

The family marabout is called in immediately after the child's birth to protect it by crying the muezzin's call into each of its ears. A book of Koranic writings is placed in the calabash crib beside the head of the baby and is not removed for forty days. During the first seven days, relatives come to greet the mother, but not even the father is allowed to examine the child closely until after the naming ceremony.

The baby is given its mother's breast the same day it is born. In the rare instances that a mother does not produce milk or enough of it, a goat's teat is placed in the baby's mouth and the goat milked. But if the mother of a nursing child dies, a wet-nurse is sought among kin. Maternal and paternal aunts and the wives of uncles are not acceptable wet-nurses, for such nursing would create a block to marriage between the cousins who become "siblings of the same milk." A child is nursed until it is two years old unless the mother becomes pregnant, in which case the child is weaned.[17]

The recuperating mother is urged to eat heartily to regain her strength. Her diet includes much mutton, mutton broth, milk, millet beer, and millet cakes with butter. The wife's age-mates contribute one franc apiece to purchase butter. The man's comrades provide a leg of lamb and mutton cutlets during the first three days. They also each pay two or three francs to purchase other foods for the new mother. The woman remains inactive for six days.

On the evening of the seventh day a large sheep is brought to the hut for the naming sacrifice. Relatives who are of the parents' generation assemble in the yard enclosure, along with the members of the child's father's age-set. The father holds a knife against the sheep's throat and announces, "He (she) is called ——!"[18] As the name is pronounced, the knife is driven into the animal's throat. The name selected is frequently that of a dead relative, but not necessarily one recently deceased. The sheep is cooked and a feast ensues. Parts of the sheep are sent to the paternal and maternal grandparents of the

[17] There is a widespread Moslem taboo against a pregnant woman nursing a child. (Westermarck, 1926:II, 401).

[18] Rodd states that for the Tuareg a holy man gives the name but its selection is influenced by the mother (*ibid.*, 181).

baby and to the members of its mother's age-set. The head is given to a cross-cousin of the newborn.

After the naming ceremony, the parents order charms from the marabout to make the child intelligent and well liked. Forty days after the birth, the mother receives new sandals, a skirt, and a robe from her husband. She has a new hairdress arranged and appears publicly for the first time. Only after her isolation is ended does she resume sexual relations with her husband.

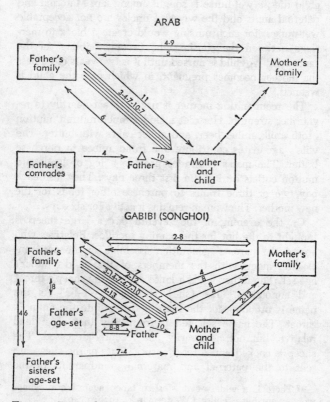

Fig. 14 Personal Contacts Associated with Birth and Naming

Analysis of Birth and Naming Customs

The birth and naming customs of the three dominant population elements show a marked similarity based on Moslem practice. While the variations evidenced by the different groups appear superficially to be unimportant, they actually reflect three quite distinct social patterns. The differences become very apparent when we compare the graphic representations of the flow of personal contacts required by custom in each of the three groups.

The squares in the diagrams represent the interacting units: father, mother-child, maternal kin, paternal kin, and comrades (*kondey*) of the child's father, mother, and fa-

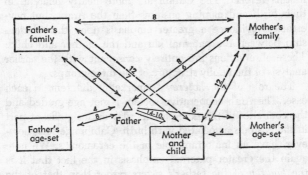

BELA (TUÁREG)

SYMBOLS

```
◄─── Customary act having direction
◄──► Customary interaction
───── Occasionally associated contact
```

1. Locale sought for parturition
2. Assist in parturition
3. Give cloth and baskets
4. Give money, sheep, or produce
5. Send prepared food for feast
6. Send mutton
7. Visit

8. Participation in ceremony or feast
9. Send notification of child's name
10. Give clothes
11. Send prayer beads to determine name
12. Act as wet nurse
13. Indicate desire to adopt child
14. Decide name of child

Fig. 14   (*cont'd*)

ther's sister. Each line between two squares indicates that some customary birth or naming practice involves interaction between the two units. When the interaction had definite direction, as the *giving* of a gift *to* someone or *going* to visit someone, the arrow point indicates this direction. Some interrelations lack specific direction, such as the wet-nurse/child relationship or joint participation in a feast. In such cases, arrows are pointed in both directions. Although paternal kin are represented as a unit, only segments of that unit, such as father's sisters, may be involved in a particular relationship. Similar simplification is found in most of the units.

Even a cursory inspection of the diagrams reveals the strong patriarchal emphasis of the Arabs in the thick group of arrows between the paternal kin and the mother and child. In contrast, the Bela diagram is completely bilateral in this respect. The Gabibi are more nearly bilateral in their birth and naming customs than the Arabs, but nevertheless evidence a greater emphasis upon the relationship between the paternal kin and the mother and child. These observations are entirely consonant with the earlier analysis of the family structure of the three groups.

The role of the *koterey* is markedly different in each case. The Arab cooperative society is not age-graded and the comrades of the new parents play an insignificant part in the customs associated with birth. Gabibi age-sets, however, have an important role in the ceremonies. We note again the greater paternal emphasis in the fact that it is the *koterey* of the father's sisters rather than that of the mother which is ceremonially important. Of course the mother's *koterey* may be identical with that of father's sisters, but this is not necessarily so, and custom explicitly dictates the role for the latter. For the Bela, the age-set of each parent is important. The only limitation on complete bilaterality is the fact that the mother's age-set does not attend the naming feast, as the father's age-set does, but is sent meat from the feast.

Another distinctive feature of the Gabibi age-set participation is the direct interaction of the *koterey* with the maternal and the paternal kin. The age-sets are a more integral part of the total ceremonial complex. In the other ethnic groups, the age-set interacts only with the parents of the newborn child.

The Bela household into which the child is born is clearly the focal point of all interaction. Groups important to the child's parents are drawn to the household. The structure seems atomistic when compared with that of the Gabibi who require a great deal of interaction among all of the units. For the Arabs, the ceremonies are almost entirely a patrilineal family affair. There is a small amount of interaction between the family of the husband and that of the wife, but none between the husband and his wife's family.

Comparing the three diagrams, that for the Gabibi ceremonies shows the most complete pattern of social integration. Either Bela parental group may be entirely missing without appreciable effect upon the ceremonies. The maternal kin are not at all vital to the Arab rituals. The Songhoi, on the other hand, require participation of both kin groups or there is a definite loss to the ceremonies. The internal solidarity of any particular Songhoi unit or pair of units may be less than that of comparable units in the other culture groups. The solidarity of the whole group, however, is greater for the Songhoi. The Arab system is perfectly adapted to a culture which for a millennium has been carried and spread by men who have often found their wives among non-Arabs. A final observation is that there is little or nothing in the birth and naming ceremonies which brings the community as a whole together.

CHAPTER 12

Death and Afterlife

Cemeteries

There are numerous burial grounds around the city, practically encircling it, except to the south where the ground is low and sometimes flooded by the Niger. Even within the city the mud tombs of saints are common near the mosques, but they are relics of earlier days. The various cemeteries have definite ethnic and quarter identities. These identities are not generally known, however, each population group being familiar with its own burial ground and few others.

Every quarter of the city has a special cemetery and two quarters have children's cemeteries as well. Arma and Gabibi are buried together in the town quarter cemeteries. The Bela graveyard is completely separate. Arabs tend to be buried apart from other people and even different Arab groups are buried separately. Thus shereef, Kunta, Moroccans, Araouan Arabs, and Berabich have special areas for burial, although some cemeteries may contain more than one Arab group. Sometimes Arabs and Songhoi are buried in the same cemetery, as is the case in the graveyard for the town quarter of Sankore.

The ecological pattern of the dead strongly reflects that of the living. The Bela are the only group that lives and buries entirely apart from the rest of the population. The city quarters are units of burial and Arma and Gabibi are intermingled in death as in life. The Arabs alone show greater solidarity in their burial pattern than in their living pattern. The cultural mechanism through which the unity of the living is perpetuated among the dead is quite simple. A man is buried near his paternal kin. If none of these relatives is interred in the locale, he is buried with others of his ethnic group. A woman who dies and is survived by her husband is buried with his paternal kindred, otherwise near her paternal relatives.

Ethnic variation finds more detailed expression, of course, in the funeral customs themselves. Moslem ritual is all-pervading but each group also has distinctive rites and beliefs associated with the dead.

The Funeral of an Arab

A dying Arab is placed so that his head is to the south with his face turned to the east. This orientation is like that of the corpse in the grave and it is held that all Moslems should pass from the world in this position. When the person dies, his brothers, sisters, and children are notified and they quickly join any surviving spouse. It is mandatory that the funeral and interment be conducted as rapidly as possible. There seems to be no explicit fear of the dead but the cultural imperative of speed is such that the pall-bearers carry the body to the cemetery at a fast walk. The elapsed time between the occurrence of death and the closure of the grave is normally less than two hours.

Rapid interment along with limited medical knowledge may result in the burial of still living persons. Yakouba tells of one such case which was frustrated by the "corpse" rising up from the bier while being carried to the cemetery.[1] It is said that the "dead" man in question subsequently had a robe made of his shroud.

There is a relevant story told concerning an Arma who lived in the early days and who had a unique system for exploiting the population. Whenever anyone of means died, this Arma would accost the relatives of the deceased, as they started to the cemetery with the body, and would demand payment of a false debt from the estate. He would refuse to permit the funeral to continue until the claim

[1] As will be seen from the subsequent description of the handling of the corpse, it would be impossible for anyone thus tied to "rise up." It would be possible, however, before and after being on the bier.

was paid. This practice continued until one day the Arma claimed a debt from the family of a saint who was about to be buried. The saint rose up from his bier and denied the debt, whereupon the Arma fled in terror and never bothered bereaved families again. The story concludes appropriately, "The saint was then persuaded by his brother to return to the dead and submit to decent burial."

The first step in the rapid sequence of rites which remove an individual from the world of the living is the washing of the corpse. The kinsmen of a dead man, or kinswomen of a deceased woman, assemble in the room where the corpse lies. One of them disrobes the body and washes it with a little water. When this initial washing has been completed, the corpse is removed from the wet bed, laid upon boards on the floor of the same room, and covered with a white cloth.

The secular lavation is followed immediately by a ritual washing of the body. While any relative of appropriate sex who knows the proper procedure may officiate, it is usual to call in a marabout, if the deceased is a man, or the wife or daughter or a marabout, if the deceased is a woman. Notification of the death has by this time gone out to all relatives, friends, and important Arabs of the city. As these people assemble at the house of the deceased, the women enter the house and the men remain outside.

The ceremonial lavation is conducted by the holy man or woman, assisted by three of the bereaved relatives of the same sex. Brothers, sisters or children of the deceased are the preferred kin for this function. One of these assistants pours water over the body, while the other two turn the body as the ritual expert washes the corpse with a white cloth. During the ablution the women in the house chant the profession of faith. One of them grinds myrrh and cotton seed in a small metal mortar. She beats the pestle from side to side, making a cross in her grinding movements and taking care not to strike the center of the mortar. She thus avoids the secular manner of grinding. She beats first with her right hand while the right side of

the corpse is being washed. At a signal from the washers
to "change hands," the grinding hand is shifted to correspond with the side of the body then being washed. The
tempo of the chanting and the pestle beat increases and
reaches a crescendo as the washing is concluded. All of
this noise is said to "chase the noise of the city from the
ears of the dead." The myrrh and cotton seed oil are placed
in the ears, nose, eyes, and mouth of the corpse. The
stated purpose of this is to keep the eyes closed and the
body fluids contained.[2]

Meanwhile a length of white cloth has been purchased
from which to make the graveclothes. If the death occurs
at night there are particular merchants who are known to
sell cloth in such emergencies. Gravecloth is not bought
in advance of death. The amount of cloth depends upon
the opulence of the deceased. The minimum is enough
for a shroud—two meters, or one in the case of a child.
As much as fifteen meters may be secured. With the exception of the practical minimum of two meters, the preferable lengths are odd numbers of units. Seven meters is
considered the proper amount for decent burial.

While the body is being washed in the house, the men
sit quietly outside, some of them occupied in cutting and
sewing the graveclothes. The proper graveclothes are
drawers, a short robe, a turban, and a shroud. The very
rich may have two shrouds. A large, ordinary grass mat is
also purchased and the completed graveclothes are laid on
this mat. The clothes are sprinkled with "Koran water,"
which not only softens the cloth and makes it more "comfortable," but also imparts a spiritual benefit to the deceased as the ablution does. The clothes and mat are then
incensed and the mat rolled up to hold the incense in the
clothes. The lavation completed, those who washed the

---

[2] Westermarck, 1926:II, 447, reports that in Fez and Tangier
cotton is similarly employed and is also inserted in the anus
and vulva. It is possible that reticence may have limited my
informant's account in these particulars. Also in Dahomey,
which is not Moslem, cotton cloth is inserted in the ears and
nostrils of the corpse. (Herskovits, 1938:I, 353).

body now dress it, put it in the shroud, and tie it in the mat. Some of the men then carry the body, feet first, from the house. Outside, it is laid on a crude, stretcher-like litter made of poles. Such biers are available to the public at all of the mosques and some of the tombs of saints. The body is covered with a white cloth and four men take up the bier and move off toward the cemetery. The charitable act of carrying the corpse brings divine favor on the pall-bearers. They are continually changed on the way to the cemetery and their number may be increased so that more men may profit spiritually thereby. The initial bearers are usually kin of the deceased, but stand in no particular relationship.

If the deceased leaves a widow, she is brought by the women mourners to the spot where the ablution took place. There she is disrobed and her hair is taken down. Some of the water left over from the washing of the corpse is poured over her three times. The widow then dons her husband's robe and sandals and puts his white turban cloth over her head. In her hand she takes his sword or dagger. She and the other women remain in the house and do not accompany the cortege to the cemetery.

While the body is being prepared for burial, a mason is sent to the cemetery to dig the grave. If, in digging, he soon strikes a previously buried body, he refills the grave and tries another spot among the gravestones. If the burial he encounters is deep enough, the new interment is made above the old. The Arabs consider proper burial depth to be about three feet, but the existence of deeper burials indicates considerable variability in this regard. If the grave is too deep, the deceased can not hear the cry of the muezzin from the mosque, and the weight of superincumbent earth on the body is also undesirable.

The grave is given a north-south orientation and is dug somewhat shorter than the stature of the deceased. A hole is scooped out of each end wall, at the bottom of the grave, to lengthen it so that it will correspond to the length of the corpse. These depressions and the shallow grave are the only evidence of practices intended to protect the corpse from contact with and pressure from the sand and earth used to fill the grave.

The funeral cortege proceeds to a mosque for the funeral prayers or moves directly toward the cemetery from the house of the deceased. In the latter case, when the funeral party gets to the edge of the city, beyond the perimeter of the masonry houses, the bier is set down. The mourners, facing east, form several rows which run north and south. Before them is the bier and a marabout who leads them in the prayer for the dead, chanted without prostration. The more rows of mourners there are, the more the deceased benefits from their prayers. Thus, in the case of a funeral held at the time of the sunset prayer, the mourners gathered at the edge of the city and formed three lines. There they were led in their evening prayer by the marabout. The bier arrived during their prayers and the body was set down behind them. After the prayer was finished, the worshippers formed five rows, the body was placed before them, and the prayer for the dead began.

The bier is taken up again and carried to the cemetery. The body is removed from the mat which envelops it. It is then lowered into the grave by two men, who should be close relatives of the deceased. The father, brothers or sons of a man place his body in the grave. For a woman, her husband, brothers, or the sons of her siblings bury her. The omission of father and sons in the case of women is entirely consistent with the Arab aversion to anything even vaguely suggestive of carnal contact between parents and children of opposite sex. If a deceased woman has no kin, three men are selected to carry out the interment. Two actually lower her into the grave and the third is a witness to attest to the fact that the deceased was handled as little as possible and that those interring her did not look at her. It is bad for both the deceased and the observer, if non-kin look on the body.

While the two men take up the body and step down into the grave, two other men take the white cloth which covered the bier and hold it over the grave so that the interment cannot be observed by the mourners. The cloth is gently waved "to expel flies from the grave." Under this cover the body is lowered, feet first, into the grave. Placed with its head to the south, the corpse is laid on its right side so that it faces east. Sufficient sand is shoveled in to hide the deceased from view and the cloth is raised. Some of the mourners throw three handfuls of sand into the grave, saying as they do so, "Of this you are made, to this you return and of this you will rise again." This pious act, like praying for the deceased and carrying the bier, brings blessings to the person who performs it. As soon as a mourner executes this little ritual, he leaves the cemetery and goes to the house of the deceased. He must not look back, a restriction which all must observe. The men who secured the litter, on which the body was carried, return it to the mosque.

The mason remains behind to fill in the grave but no markers are set up until after the prayers at the house. Sometimes no gravestones are used. The marabouts differ among themselves as to whether or not the grave should be marked. Some say that the grave should be unknown; others contend that people should know where to pray for their dead. If markers are used, they are usually undressed stones placed at either end of the grave. If one is inscribed, it gives the name of the deceased and that of his father, and possibly also the date of death and tribal identity. In some cases a low, rectangular, mud tomb is erected over the grave. The way in which the grave is marked is an indication of the opulence of the deceased or of his family. Through the charity of a wealthy man, the saintliness of the deceased may be indicated by a more elaborate tomb. The poor pay for the grave-digging by giving the mason the mat in which the body was wrapped. They expect no grave markers in return.

Death is but the death of the body. The soul continues to exist and through it the deceased sees, feels, hears, and speaks. After a person is buried, the two Questioners

of God come and ask the deceased if he belongs to them.[3]
If God does not want him to see Paradise, the response is
affirmative. Thereupon the Questioners beat the deceased
until he descends ten meters into the ground. He is allowed to rise to his normal resting place again and then
the process is repeated twice more. After this, the Questioners open a door to a passage to Hell. The flames sweep
up into the grave and torment the dead sinner until Judgment Day.

On the other hand, if the deceased answers the Questioners saying that he belongs to Allah and follows his
prophet Mohammed, then a door to a passageway to
Heaven is opened. Heaven is a great house of God in the
sky and the deceased can regard its wonders and see his
place therein until the Final Judgment when he will enter there.

Allah, through the holy word of the Koran, has laid
down regulations concerning the widow and goods left by
the deceased. The widow may not remarry for four months
and ten days. The proportionate distribution of the estate
to various types of kindred is quite explicitly stated.
However, there is wide misbelief among all groups in
Timbuctoo concerning the details of inheritance distribution. This doubtless contributes to the general suspicion
of the cadi or marabout who divides the estate according
to the law. The division of a large estate almost inevitably
causes friction among relatives.

The practice of the levirate, which is fairly common
among the Arabs, is particularly likely to be followed,
when there is a sizeable inheritance. An older or younger
brother of the deceased, by marrying the widow, gains
control of her part of the estate, as an agent for her and
her children. Except for the fact that the brother is forced
to divorce any wife he already has, the arrangement is
advantageous to him. Upon his death, however, the inheritance problems resulting from his service as trustee

---

[3] Dr. Raphael Patai identified the "Questioners" for me as
local variants of Munkir and Nakīr, widely known angels who
examine the souls of the dead.

are very critical, for the wealth held in trust is usually mixed with the personal wealth of the trustee.

Death and Burial of a Gabibi

When a Gabibi is seriously ill, a Gabibi sorcerer is called in. He diagnoses the illness and then returns home to consult his fetish and determine if he can effect a cure. If the *kambu* agrees to help, the practitioner returns and receives a small down payment and the price of the medicine which he has to buy. The complete price of the treatment is fixed at this time, but the remainder is paid only if the patient is cured. The practitioner visits the sick person every morning and evening. In the morning an herbal powder (*turi hamni*) is either rubbed on the body of the patient or he drinks it in water or milk. In the evening he drinks an infusion of a diuretic herb (*turi ferro*) sweetened with a little sugar. If this treatment and the power of the *kambu* effect no cure, the aid of a marabout is sought.

Gabibi prefer a marabout of Songhoi rather than Arab background. As any really educated marabout disapproves of fetish practice as a matter of dogma, the holy man whose assistance is sought is not informed of the earlier treatment. For a small initial fee, the marabout sleeps on his "Fortune Book" to learn the nature of the illness and its cure. The family of the patient procures a new, earthenware pot and incense (*dugu*) is put in it. Every morning the marabout washes into this pot the charcoal-written words of the holy passage revealed as a curative. The patient drinks some of this "Koran water" three times in the morning and washes with it every morning and night. The marabout may also incant his powerful phrases over the patient.

If the holy man decides that the case is hopeless, this information is relayed to the relatives of the patient through a friend of the family, who transmits the opinion that the sick person is "God's slave." Then they know that the illness is beyond treatment and that the outcome depends on God's will alone. Relatives also are advised, adds an informant, that they might as well save their money and not seek further aid. At this juncture, if at all, the gratuitous aid of the French dispensary is sought.

When death comes, the Songhoi believe that the dying person inevitably passes some fecal matter. It is felt that the corpse should be cleaned by a sibling of the deceased before others see it. If there are no siblings, anyone of the appropriate sex can perform this washing, known as the "bad water." The clothes of the deceased are removed, the loins washed, the bed covering hidden, and the corpse covered. The death is announced to the family by the phrase, "Allah has done his will." Other relatives, the quarter chief and other city leaders learn the news through the traditional announcement, "That which comes to us all has come to ———." While these statements are made in Songhoi, the usual response, "Allah is great," is in Arabic.

The six meters[4] of cloth required for burial may have been procured in advance, if the deceased was aged or knew he was dying. If, under such circumstances, the person does not die, but recovers, the cloth is given to the poor. On the other hand, if a man dies and the gravecloth has not been procured in advance, the purchase price is taken from his personal money. If he was destitute, the cloth is donated by relatives or even by an unrelated rich man, as an act of charity. As women mourners gather in the house, the men assemble outside, where some men crudely tailor the four pieces of graveclothes.

The family marabout comes to the house to direct the ritual washing of the corpse—the "good water." The body is laid out just inside the threshold of the house and there washed by four persons of the same sex as the deceased. The three who assist the marabout, or one of his women relatives, should be siblings or cross-cousins (*basey*) of the deceased. The eldest full sibling should assist with the bathing and clothing of the top of the body, the others taking the lower body. A metal mortar, brought by the marabout, is beaten with the pestle during the washing

[4] According to one informant.

"so that the deceased cannot hear what is said." When the ablution is completed, incense is passed around the body three times "to chase away the flies." The censing of the graveclothes is referred to as "perfuming" them. The Bela belief that genii are attracted to the dead is strongly denied by both Arabs and Songhoi.

As with the washing of the corpse, the remaining funeral rituals vary from those of the Arabs only in peripheral details and in the meanings attributed to the acts. Thus the initial pall-bearers should include not only brothers of the deceased, but also male cross-cousins, a category of relatives which the Arabs do not even recognize. The similarity in the rites of the Songhoi and Arabs stems not only from their common basis in Islamic practice but also from the fact that members of each group usually participate in funerals of the other. There is no such interchange with the Bela. Both Songhoi and Arabs use Gabibi masons as grave diggers and their graves are comparable.

At the grave, the Songhoi include sons of the deceased among appropriate relatives to inter the corpse after taking it out of the enveloping mat.[5] Some one of the mourners may roll on the mat, after its removal from around the corpse. Such an act is held to cure a sore back or, if the deceased was very old, rolling on the mat can impart longevity. A person may wash in the "good water" of the ablution for the same reason.

Relatives and age-comrades of the deceased each throw three handfuls of sand into the grave. The rewards for this act, like those for participating in the funeral itself, are perceived as being more explicitly social and less supernatural than among the Arabs. These acts of piety for

[5] At one funeral, two sons of a Gabibi woman failed to remove the mat when they placed her in the grave. When this was discovered, general discussion led to the conclusion that the body must be taken out of the grave, removed from the mat, and laid to rest again. My Arab companion on the occasion had no feeling whatever that this breach of ritual had supernatural consequences.

the Arab, the Gabibi tends to interpret as acts of respect. A Gabibi also takes part in funerals so that others will come to his own funeral. "If there are few mourners, people will say that the deceased was bad and not to be respected."[6] God, however, is unimpressed by the size of a cortege.

The grave is filled by the mason and sand is mounded up over it. A stick of brush wood is stuck upright in the sand at each end of the grave. The mourners return quietly to the home of the deceased where the marabout leads them in the triple repetition of the *fātihah*. Then, before the group breaks up, everyone shakes hands with those around him, asking divine blessing for the deceased and the mourners.

A widow is bathed, dressed in old clothes and her head covered with a black cap. She either remains in her husband's house or returns to that of her parents. If the widow has intercourse before the expiration of four months and ten days, she will be crippled in her arms or legs.[7]

For three nights following the death, sons of the deceased must sleep in his house. If the family is well-off, several marabouts will be invited to the house to read the Koran during these days. A feast terminates the period. A poor family can afford none of this and will owe the marabout who conducted the funeral only a few francs and the clothes of the deceased.

It is usual to return to the cemetery, particularly on Fridays, to pray at the grave of relatives. Whereas such acts bring divine benediction to an Arab or Alfa, the Gabibi perceive the benediction as coming from the forebears themselves. It is fruitless to pray at the grave of a sibling, but the benediction of a father, and particularly of a grandfather, is well worth seeking.

[6] Infidels are buried without ceremony. The cadi paid four Bela to inter a pagan Bambara in the bush.
[7] Moslem law forbidding remarriage for this length of time is respected by the Gabibi. A Gabibi woman made the interesting observation, of dubious validity, that this period was six months and ten days for Arma women and two weeks for slaves.

The spirit image of a dead husband may haunt the mind of a widow with visions of past episodes. One widow is known to have been driven mad by the spirit of her husband the first night after his burial. All widows run this danger and must be ritually protected. During the mourning period, knives are stuck in the floor, to the right and left of the widow's feet, while she sits or sleeps. If the spirit of the husband still comes to her, she pulls up the knives and hits the blades together to chase the image away. There are also special maraboutic charms employed against persistent spirit images.

The Passing of a Bela

When a man feels that he is going to die, he calls in his relatives and announces his debts, his credits, his wishes as to his funeral ceremony and the division of his goods. He also gives testimony as to whether his wife and children have been good to him. He may indicate that certain of his small children are to be taken into the homes of some of his older relatives. The deathbed distribution of goods has its limitations, for bequests which diverge greatly from Moslem inheritance patterns, such as cutting off a son, would be disregarded in the final settlement of the estate.[8]

Upon a person's death, the family marabout is called in to take charge. The corpse is never touched by relatives for fear of the evil spirits which are known to lurk about the dead. The marabout lays out the body on a mat, on the floor of the house, head to the south. Persons of the opposite sex to the deceased leave the house and the door is closed. The ritual washing of the corpse ensues while the graveclothes are being prepared.

Meanwhile, three or four men, preferably maternal or paternal uncles of the deceased, have gone to the cemetery to dig the grave. First a round hole is dug about half a meter deep, the diameter being roughly equivalent

[8] The property of a noble Tuareg woman is said to be divided according to Moslem law unless otherwise disposed of in satisfaction of her expressed wish (Rodd, 1926:168).

to the stature of the deceased. From the floor of this pit, an oblong trench is sunk another half meter. The trench is oriented north and south.[9]

The envelopment of the corpse and the bearing of it to the cemetery follow the pattern already described with only minor exceptions. Cross-cousins of the deceased are expected to strike the body on the bier and failure to do so would be interpreted as lack of respect for the kinsman. The prayer, en route to the cemetery, is conducted in a clean courtyard. At the grave the corpse is handled by the grave-diggers, who lower the body, head to the south,[10] into the trench at the bottom of the circular grave. A cloth-covered Koranic charm is tied to a stick which is stuck in the sand near the head of the corpse. Mourners pick up a handful of sand, murmur in Arabic, "Praise be to Allah,"[11] spit in the sand, and throw it onto the body. Then a few pieces of wood are laid at intervals across the grave trench, the ends of the wood resting on the bottom of the circular pit. The mat in which the corpse was wrapped is cut in two and the halves laid over the wood supports. A layer of straw is placed on top of this. The mourners fill the grave by scooping sand into it with their hands. Sand is mounded up over the grave and a stick is placed upright at its head and at its foot.

Sometimes a flat gravestone is set up, on which the marabout scratches, in Arabic characters, the name of the

[9] *Ibid.*, 259–260. Rodd contends that the older Tuareg graves in the Air district are round or elliptical, the latter showing no fixed orientation. Graves from the Moslem period are oblong and oriented in the Moslem fashion. He has no data on the subterranean structure of the round graves. The change of form in the Air and the composite type at Timbuctoo suggests that the Bela may have combined the ancient grave type with Moslem form. However, in Morocco also, the grave has a narrow trench in the bottom to contain the body and provide ledges of earth to support the ends of the stones or boards used to cover the trench. (Westermarck, 1926:II, 458).

[10] Rodd, 1926:181, describes the head of a Tuareg burial as being to the north.

[11] In this case, as in the daily prayers, the Arabic is purely ritual, its meaning not being known to the Bela.

deceased and that of his mother.[12] Seven of the assembled group say a final prayer at the grave and the burial party leaves the cemetery. There is no taboo against looking back but the grave is never visited by kin or friends. In fact, the Bela are mortally afraid to enter cemeteries because of the genii which surround the dead. A marabout can enter with immunity because "he knows the words to say." A burial party can enter a cemetery because it is under the protection of the accompanying marabout.

While the men are gone to inter the body, the women's activities are focused on getting rid of the evil influences left by the corpse. The wet sand is collected from the floor where the corpse was washed and is carried far out of town and thrown away. The entire house of the deceased is filled with incense, for evil spirits do not like the odor of incense. Fresh water is brought to the house and the widow is disrobed and bathed. The widow's hair is arranged in a distinctive and "unattractive" way. She is dressed in black and a string is tied around each wrist and ankle, and around her neck and her forehead. She may wear no jewelry. The widow remains thus in mourning for four months and ten days, during which time she may not speak to any man. A widower and children of the deceased are under no restrictions and wear no special dress. Strictly speaking, a widower can remarry the same day as his wife's funeral. If he did so, however, people would say that he was "too fond of women."

After the interment, many members of the funeral cortege return to the house of the deceased to pray for him, commiserate with the women, and urge the widow "not to cry." She acknowledges their words by lowering her head. Similar visits continue for seven days after the funeral. Ground millet, mixed with milk, salt and honey, is prepared for guests during this period. After this a sheep, and later a cow, must be sacrificed for funeral feasts. These are required, irrespective of the sex of the de-

---

[12] The Tuareg of the Air district occasionally inscribe on a stone, in Arabic or T'ifinagh, simply the name of the deceased (Rodd, 1926:260).

ceased. The cost of these feasts is, if possible, paid out of the estate left by a man. The poorest family must make these sacrifices, even if it requires a year or more to accumulate the means. The sacrifice is not only essential to the feast but it is felt to be beneficial to the deceased. In addition to the meat for the feast, there are also great platters of rice balls covered with butter. Three hundred and sixty-six balls are prepared, each the size of a fist. There are also three larger balls of rice which are said to represent the head of the deceased. These large balls are eaten by his maternal and paternal cross-cousins.

At the end of a widow's mourning period, a marabout is called in to read from the Koran and prepare "Koran water." The widow is bathed in this water as a final purification.

Souls and Afterlife of the Bela

A person's shadow is like a part of his body. No one ever sees all of his shadow at once, however, for when the shadow falls to one's right, it is only the shadow of that side of the body. Because of its intimate attachment to a person, the shadow must always do as he does. It sleeps when he sleeps, dies when he dies, and rests in the tomb with him. The shadow is always present, even when there is no light, but then, of course, it cannot be seen. The shadow moves from west to east as the sun crosses the sky, but when the sun sets, the shadow moves to the west again and there it is found when the full moon appears or the morning sun rises. No one can hurt a person through his shadow and no particular attention need be paid to where it falls.

The image of a person which another sees in his dreams is called *teli*. Although this word refers both to the shadow and to the dream-image, the two are quite different. The latter is not a partial image but is complete in all detail.[13]

[13] It was this *teli* which natives feared was being taken away when photography was introduced into Timbuctoo. The fear that the *teli* would be used to harm its personification ultimately proved groundless.

This personal image continues its wanderings even after the individual is dead. It may leave the tomb, pass unseen through the streets, go through doors, and enter the dream of a sleeper. As soon as the sleeping person awakes, the image becomes invisible, although it is still present. Such images are impotent and can do neither good nor harm.[14]

The quality which departs from the body at death is the breath. A man near death will feel his breath leave his lungs and rise to his throat. At death the angels of God come and take the breath away. The dying man sees the approach of the angels and for this reason may die staring wide-eyed into space. When there are people with a dying man, they will close his eyes so that he will not die open-eyed "like a jackass."

When a man dies, his conscious state continues for eternity. The corpse is aware of all the funeral rites and what everyone does for him. This continued consciousness is the reason for placing the dead man near his relatives in the graveyard. Thus the dead kinsmen can all see one another. Immediately after a man is buried and the funeral party leaves the cemetery, the corpse tries to rise from his tomb and follow those who have left. But the tomb tells him he must stay in this, his new home, which is much better than the one he has just left. It is better because all work is finished and family dissensions and problems are over.

After a man is buried, angels of God, carrying iron rods, as big around as a man's arms, come and stand by the tomb. They are fearsome to behold, with their bushy hair,

[14] The concepts of shadow and dream-image resemble beliefs among pagan Negroes to the south and west, among whom multiple souls are prevalent. The Ashanti 'kra leaves the body only at death but the sunsum may wander about in sleep (Rattray, 1927:153–154). Lay opinion in Dahomey is that each person has two shadows and one of these is buried with the body (Herskovits, 1938:II, 232). In Liberia there is a dream soul, zu, which wanders about while the body sleeps. Another soul substance is the shadow, which accompanies the body to the grave. A living person is susceptible to attack through his shadow, however (Schwab, 1947:320–322).

big moustaches, long beards, heavy eyebrows, protruding eyes, and huge chests. These creatures demand of the corpse, "Are you one of us or do you belong to God?" On the merits of the man's life, God answers through the mouth of the deceased. If he belongs to God, having led a good life, he will remain quietly in his tomb until Judgment Day and his body will not putrefy. An evil-doer, on the other hand, becomes bloated, his body is eaten by beetles and other insects, his grave is filled with snakes, and the grave itself shrinks so as to squeeze him. Even when nothing remains of the deceased but his conscious state, his misery continues.

An evil-doer is unwanted by the other dead and may even be rejected by the cemetery itself. When a newcomer is buried in the cemetery, the other dead may say, "We have a stranger among us who is a good man," or "We have a rotten man with us who is not good." There is a known case of a Tuareg who had been very wicked and who had killed many men, including many of his own slaves. When this man died, he was taken to the cemetery in the bush and as soon as a grave for him was dug, its walls would collapse. Several graves were attempted and finally the sons of the man had to buy an old pirogue and put him in it in the shade of a large tree. Sometimes when wicked men die, God even moves the cemetery so that it cannot be found for their burial. In contrast, if a worthy native of Timbuctoo dies in some foreign land, God will have him brought by angels to the Timbuctoo cemetery where his relatives lie.

There are seven levels of the earth, one below the other, that of living men being the first. When the punishing angels of God appear and ask the corpse if he is a man of God and receive a negative answer, they beat the deceased with their iron rods and drag him down to the seventh hell. The grave itself sinks with him to this seventh level, which is full of black serpents, fires, and furious demons. When the sinner has suffered sufficiently to be pardoned by God, the grave mounts to its original position and there the deceased remains tranquil until the end of the world.

There are also seven levels in the sky. God and his angels live in the seventh heaven. This paradise and the seventh hell are unimportant after the Last Judgment. At the end of the world, all the dead will arise and their sins will be weighed against their good deeds in a pair of scales. After the final Judgment, those who are condemned to eternal punishment will be thrown into a burning hole which is probably near Mecca. All of the trees, rocks, and mountains of the world are the fuel for this fire. Those who are saved will go to a land of unknown location, where oranges, dates, rice beer, and foods of all sorts are plentiful and where every man has a two-story house, good rooms, good beds, and as many wives as he wants. This is not a land of complete equality, however, for the marabouts and shereefs will have better houses, clothes, and drink than other people.

Ancestors can be of direct supernatural aid to their descendants. If a man, at the time of his death, is well satisfied with the way his children have treated him, he can bless them. If a person thus blessed should die the next day, he would rest tranquilly in his grave until Doomsday. The blessings of deceased ancestors may also be sought. A frequent form of prayer is to profess belief in God and then say, "If my parents forgive me, may I have ———." Then the dead may help the living regain health or achieve happiness, wealth, or prestige.

Comparison

The mortuary customs which are common to all groups in Timbuctoo are shared, in large part, with other Moslem peoples as well. The Koran provides the content of most of the oral ritual, as well as the law regarding remarriage of widows and the basic inheritance regulations. Mohammed's revelations concerning afterlife are recognizable in local beliefs, but only in much altered and variable form. The other common elements of custom stem not from the Koran but from tradition.

The common core of funeral practice consists of the necessity for speed; the separation of the sexes; the ritual washing of the corpse; the use of incense, graveclothes, mat, and bier; the mourners' participation in carrying the corpse, in saying the prayer for the dead, and in throwing earth into the grave; the orientation of the grave and corpse; and the washing of the widow.

The three ethnic groups differ in the matrix of cultural detail which surrounds, in each group, this common core of rites. Some of these specific differences reflect general distinctions between Arab, Songhoi, and Bela. Thus, the Arabs, who were the original bearers of Islam in Africa, adhere most closely to Moslem practice and belief. They seem the most matter-of-fact about death. The supernatural aspects of death center primarily around Allah, his agents, and the soul of the deceased. In addition, the fulfillment of the religious obligations of the survivors toward the deceased is believed to affect the state of grace of the survivors. Otherwise funeral and mourning practices are simply customary and socially appropriate.

The Songhoi Gabibi are, on the one hand, less inclined to recognize the supernatural effects explicit in Moslem dogma, but are, on the other hand, more inclined to hold to non-Islamic supernatural beliefs. On the whole, Arabs and Songhoi are not markedly or even consistently distinct in these matters. They have been in close interaction for too long. The Bela, however, stand in marked contrast to them both. The Negro slaves of the Tuareg are terrified by death and anything having to do with the dead. Bela funeral rites, in spite of their outward Moslem form, serve primarily as means of eliminating the dangerous contamination of death. This distinctive attitude illustrates how subtly culture traits may be reinterpreted in the process of diffusion.

CHAPTER 13

Patterns of Conflict

Rain Hockey

Timbuctoo shows evidence of its mixed background in an almost ceremonial game of hockey called *alkura*. As the name indicates, the game is an introduction from North Africa. In Timbuctoo *alkura* is played on the sands outside of town by two teams, each consisting of young men and boys. The number of players on each team is not fixed, nor do they have to be equal. The game consists of driving a cowhide ball, by means of sticks, over one or the other of two goal lines. The ball cannot be touched with the hands and the sticks cannot be used to hit opposing players unless they are trying to secure possession of the ball. The game is played for two or three hours in the late afternoon, until halted by sunset. If neither team has succeeded in crossing the goal defended by the other, the contest is resumed on the following evening, starting the ball in the center of the field. The struggle has been known to continue thus for ten days before one side emerged victorious.

In addition to the organized game, children play it in the streets as a Timbuctoo version of shinny. But the real *alkura* is played following the short, seasonal, heavy rainfall. The game in no way represents thanks for the rain but is said to be played at this time because the ball will only roll well on rain-packed sand. In North Africa the game is played either to bring the rain or to stop overabundant rains.[1] When introduced into Timbuctoo these sacred functions were dropped. It could not be

---

[1] Westermarck, 1926:II, 271.

played satisfactorily on the soft sands to induce rain, and there is never an overabundance of rain. There still remains a vestige of the old magic, however. When the parched city was waiting for its overdue rains in 1940, the Emir announced by crier that if any children were caught playing *alkura* before the rains came, both they and their parents would be thrown in prison. The reason for the edict was that the playing of the game would keep the rain from falling.

The most interesting aspect of *alkura* is the composition of the teams which belabor one another with sticks. The four main quarters of the city play against one another. Inter-quarter antagonisms, based on cultural differences, have been noted earlier, as have the New Year's fights between gangs of boys from the different quarters. *Alkura* provides further opportunity for hostilities to be expressed. During the rough and tumble of the game, a slave may hit a noble with impunity. Personal grudges developed during the year have been known to result in particularly rough stick work between the personal enemies. Custom decrees that blows received in the game should be taken without ill will and fights never develop during the playing of the game. True to type, however, the players often harbor a grudge after the game and many fights result in the ensuing days.

The game is always played between traditional rivals —the quarter of Sara Keyna versus Badyinde and Sankore versus Dyingerey Ber. The latter two play on the area to the west of town and the others to the east. There is also an all-city game in which Sankore and Sara Keyna, together, oppose the combined players of Dyingerey Ber and Badyinde. This arrangement keeps traditional rivals on opposite sides. When one studies the basis of these inter-quarter rivalries, as expressed in the traditional sets of opponents, it is found that the Arab-dominated quarters fight it out with the quarters where most of the Songhoi live. This is true both in the games between two quarters and in the all-city contest.

The satisfaction of beating one another with sticks is

limited to the players but the whole quarter enters into the spirit of the contest. When the game is halted inconclusively because of darkness, the players are taunted in their own quarters, particularly by the women who tell the men that they are weak and will surely lose the next day. When one side is finally victorious, the families of the winning players give a big dance that same night and the ball is painted with henna. On the ball are drawn four circles, each with a central dot—the evil eye symbol of the Arabs, but symbolic only of *alkura* victory to the Songhoi. The following night there is an inter-quarter feast of rice and mutton which is paid for by all of the players. The losing players are not permitted to attend the feast. Guests from the losing quarter, or quarters, are taunted by the victors and the losing players are insulted, *in absentia,* by the women.

Alkura obviously functions as a social instrument to allow interethnic hostilities to express themselves in a socially acceptable form and, by so doing, to unify the population. Historically fortuitous, but functionally important, is the fact that the post-rain games follow the dry period of agricultural shortages and cornered markets when interclass hostility is at its highest. The games also contribute to the social solidarity of the various quarters.

Economic Conflicts

One of the most common areas of conflict is that of commercial trickery and dishonesty. Honesty is universally recognized as the "right" thing, but between strangers there are no effective sanctions to maintain the practice of honesty. The religious sanctions are disregarded. On the other hand, there is considerable economic reward to be gained through dishonesty. The greatest chicanery takes place between transients and local entrepreneurs. Cheating between these persons must be only subtle enough to avoid detection until the transient has left the city. Between local residents, the irregularities must be of such a nature as to avoid detection. While dishonest trading among natives is not punished if discovered, local sentiment and authority hold the dishonest transaction as invalid. Even a reputation for being dishonest does not ruin a man commercially. Each new buyer is always free to satisfy himself that the deal *he* is making is honest.

There is a very old trick occasionally played on visiting traders. Victims for this trick must be selected from persons utterly unfamiliar with the city, to whom the mud-walled streets are novel and confusing. A pagan from the forest is an ideal choice. A resident of the city finds such a stranger who has goods to sell. A sale is agreed upon and then, on the pretext of lacking money, the buyer, now in possession of the goods, asks the seller to accompany him home for payment. The buyer stops at the door of a mud-walled mosque, indicating that it is his home, and asks the vendor to wait while he goes in to get the money. The buyer then enters the door, exits by another, and leaves the credulous stranger cooling his heels.

Frequently it is the stranger who cheats the city resident. Produce often comes to the city in matting sacks which are sewn shut. Wholesale purchases are usually made without opening all of the sacks. Because of this fact, wet grain is often sold for dry; heavy Guinea corn is mixed with more expensive and lighter millet; dirt is sprinkled through grain to increase its weight; small straw packages of tobacco are sacked together so that the packaging is weighed as tobacco; honey is watered. Local produce is handled similarly. Rotten grass is sold for good if the grass sheath still is unspoiled; butter is adulterated; milk watered. In livestock transactions, sterile, aged, or decrepit beasts are sold as fertile, young, or healthy, if the buyer is not an expert.

The guild craftsmen are no different. It is normal to provide the requisite materials to a jeweler, tailor, or slipper-maker. Rarely do all of the materials go into the product. The jewelers, who are said to cheat their own mothers, adulterate gold with silver, and silver with copper, keeping the surplus of precious metal thus created. Tailors, who, it will be recalled, are maraboutic holy men, are suspected of taking up to a tenth of the yardage provided for a large flowing robe. Although not all of the silk thread provided for its embroidery ever seems to be used, there is no way of checking on the amount stolen by the tailor short of tearing out the embroidery. Slipper-makers withhold part of the good leather which is supplied and fill the inner layers of laminated soles with scraps. The butchers mix good meat with bad. The masons, unless constantly watched by the builder, delight in making walls out of plumb or in leaving spaces between the bricks where water can enter. When the wall collapses they have a new job, for the owner cannot get another mason to touch the house. The type of clay used in the protective, covering wash on the walls is important. Yellow clay, which washes off in one season, will be used by the unwatched mason instead of white clay which will last several years.

The slabs of salt mined at Taodeni are sometimes covered with a thin coat of mud to protect them against wear and against the elements in the more humid southland. The mud dries very hard during the desert trek to Timbuctoo and the bars are not broken until they go on the retail market. Bars of poor quality can thus be covered and sold as good quality salt. Even better, thin bars can be built out with mud until they are almost twice their original size! By the time the trick is discovered, such bars are thousands of miles and numerous transactions removed from the perpetrators of the hoax.

Dishonest weight and measure are still common despite attempts of the French to control them. At Djenné, Timbuctoo's sister city, Ahmadou, the Tukulor king in the early nineteenth century, instituted an official measurer in the market who still functions. That city also had a set of standard weights, against which the merchants' weights could be checked. Actually the *karui* weight unit had three standards, known locally by distinctive terms. The heaviest was employed in purchasing from traveling merchants.[2] Even the standards were established for fraud! Timbuctoo also had, at one time, standard weights which

[2] Monteil, 1932:283–285.

were kept by the Arma. There is no evidence that they were more effective than French control.

The Koran teaches that hospitality shall be extended to strangers.[3] Timbuctoo follows this precept and lodges the itinerant merchant—for a price. Some residents specialize in this service and lodge travelers who address themselves to the emir, seeking shelter. Most of the traveling traders stay with persons with whom they have trade connections or who have been recommended by friends. Arabs, Tuareg, and Songhoi stay with local residents of their own ethnic background. The host acts as commercial agent for his guest, except in the case of the Bela, whose guests are largely Tuareg herders.

In the case of the Tuareg, the system works reciprocally, the Bela staying with the herders while on commercial trips. When the nomads have produce which the Bela is known to want, he is informed. A Bela in Timbuctoo, who is commercially active, may have as many as fifty such guests during a single month at the height of the trading season. But even this traditional system has limits which indicate its secular character. One Bela was burdened with what he considered to be too many guests, who had been directed to him by friends in the bush. He met the situation by having no meals prepared in his house for ten days. He would go to the market and eat what he could purchase there. His wife would likewise leave home to eat at the homes of friends. How the guests fared, no one knows.

The Arab and Songhoi traders turn their goods over to their hosts who may buy them outright if they can get the right price. Otherwise, by acting as middleman, the host secures, at a fixed rate, a ten to fifteen per cent commission on the sale price of the produce or goods. In addition, the guest is expected to give the host a present, frequently a bolt of Guinea cloth, upon departure. The host will try to cheat his guest by misquoting the market and sale prices. The guest will cheat his host by selling him

3 Koran, IV:36.

adulterated produce. One host rationalized his cheating by saying that he did not think his guest was going to give him the traditional present on departure. When you cannot count on tradition, then it is every man for himself. But even if the commercial boarding system is not entirely based on personal bonds, it serves two important city functions—it provides shelter for the transient and some degree of protection to the outsider in the local market.

People who discover that they have been cheated are naturally furious. If possible, they seek rectification. But even if the perpetrator can be found, it is often difficult to prove anything against him except in the most flagrant irregularities. Even when restitution is made, the seller has lost nothing. He is just back where he started. Even his good name is hardly sullied. Commercial dishonesty is an accepted pattern as long as you are not the one who has been duped. Tricks of the sort described above are a constant topic of conversation. The gullible purchaser complains to friends about the perpetrator of a dishonest transaction. The shrewd tricks which a man plays on strangers, enemies, or those from other ethnic groups are detailed proudly to his intimates. Timbuctoo expects such impersonal dealings outside of the family and ethnic group.

The populace cannot be counted on to behave any differently in their intra-ethnic and familial dealings. The Arabs show the greatest contrasts in this regard for they sometimes give strong evidence of ethnic solidarity. A much respected Arab merchant found himself unable to pay a very large debt which he owed to the local Syrian trader. Out of sympathy for the previously rich Arab merchant and in order to maintain status before the disliked, Christian Syrian, most of the influential Arabs contributed from their wealth, over a period of years, to pay off two-thirds of the debt. One Arab alone gave a hundred bars of salt from each *azalai*. The Syrian himself accepted the loss on the remaining third of the debt and kept the "good will" of the rich Arabs. The only thing which spoils this picture of brotherly love and solidarity has been the ensuing miserly behavior of the Arab merchant. Compensating for the loss of status which he feels, he has been very harsh in the collection of the smallest debts, even beating those who cannot pay him the pittance they owe. The Arabs decry this behavior.

In contrast to economic relations of a personal nature is the Arab practice of cheating one's father. The young sons of a wealthy Arab take over the arduous duties of accompanying the caravans to the Taodeni salt mines. As long as the camels and capital belong to the father, the son is supposed to work for his board and clothes and his eventual share in the inheritance and a parentally arranged marriage. After a man is married and has a child, he can work for himself, but many prefer to continue working for the father and accepting support. The exceedingly prevalent but uncondoned practice is for the sons of camel owners, on an *azalai* for their fathers, to overload each camel with one bar of salt. These bars are secured through the barter of goods obtained on credit without the father's knowledge. If the son is married and has a separate house in Timbuctoo, he can hide the additional salt in his house, when the caravan arrives, and sell it later. If no such repository is available, the son will load one camel with his own bars and leave it with the desert Berabich several days before he arrives at Timbuctoo. Upon arrival he tells his father that one of the camels was sick and could not keep up, so he transferred its load to the other camels and continued his trek. Subsequently the son goes back to the Berabich, brings in and sells his salt and informs his father that the camel has finally arrived.

Another version of this performance is to leave only the extra salt with the Berabich. It is then secured at a later date under the pretext of visiting the camel herd in the bush. Fathers, probably having indulged in similar irregularities themselves, are highly suspicious. Some meet the caravan at the edge of Timbuctoo to count the bars and question the caravaneers. Others even go a whole day's journey into the desert to meet the caravan. The net effect is only to push the depots of withheld salt farther out into the desert.

The same unfilial behavior often characterizes the handling of other commercial matters. Fathers who can no longer make the necessary trips associated with trade in the bush send their sons out with the goods and produce. The sons are instructed as to the price at which to sell and the price to be paid for the foreign produce to be brought back. This procedure does not indicate lack of confidence in the son's acumen as much as lack of confidence in his honesty. These set prices are minimal guarantees to the father. Any profit which the son derives by more shrewd trading should, it is universally agreed, be turned over to the parent. It is common practice, however, for the Arab son to withhold this additional profit from his father. Many young men even withhold more, telling their fathers that the market was such that selling prices were lower and buying prices higher than those set in advance. This always leads to a quarrel but fathers will usually continue to prefer their sons to unrelated agents.

There is a significant variation in these patterns. An only son is very apt "to work for his father as for himself"—i.e., not to cheat. Where there are several sons, each will get as much as he can from his share of his father's transactions. The competition is thus really between sons, who will all inherit equally in the estate. Each son concludes that if he is honest, he eventually shares with his brothers the profit he could have kept by being dishonest. Thus the competition between the sons results in conflict between father and sons. The Arabs have only one legitimate solution to this problem. Married sons, who have already benefited from the paternal estate in their marriage, may work on their own, securing credit from their fathers. This solution is employed by "conscientious" sons when there are several male offspring. The extension of credit, for interest, within the family characterizes one aspect of internal familial relations. The contrasting aspect is illustrated by the fact that the sons of the poor always have to work for themselves but feel an obligation to care for their parents. Likewise the respectable poor can count on public assistance from other Arabs in securing the funds necessary to marry.

The Bela likewise believe that a son should work entirely to his father's account until he is married. At least since the arrival of the French, some sons have been able to profit personally while trading for their fathers and thus hasten their marriage by accumulating the necessary funds themselves. There seems to be little doubt that in the old days father and elder brothers would have seized any such personal profit and applied it to the family community of property.

Family solidarity characterizes many aspects of trade relations between relatives. Arab and Songhoi alike feel that a close relative's request for goods or produce is best met by giving the goods outright. If one is not in a financial position to do this, the sale price should be lower than the market price. The Bela concur in this latter practice, saying that one is assured of reciprocity. If, on the other hand, the relative desires to sell something, rather than buy, he is dealt with strictly in terms of commercial ethics. If he is known to be in economic straits, his asking price will be beaten down, as is the case with non-relatives under such circumstances. Alternatively, his goods may be held as security against an extension of credit—again casting the transaction in commercial terms.

There is clearly a marked contrast between this personal reaction to a relative's request for goods and the impersonal reaction to a relative's desire to sell goods. The clue to understanding this contrast lies in the preference for donation of the requested article in the first instance. Such a gift or, alternatively, a patently low asking price creates an obligation to the donor or seller. But if the relative wants to sell something, the payment of an asking price equal to or more than the market value is not clearly generous and does not establish an obligation to the buyer. Hence the transaction is cast in impersonal, nonfamilial terms.

What are the life values of the native which are reflected in this economic struggle? We saw earlier that to have many sons was desirable, for it provided security. The other dominant desire is to accumulate wealth. Wealth can bring one almost everything in life. Wealthy Songhoi women, both Arma and Gabibi, have even secured husbands by assuming all of the marriage costs and paying men to espouse them. Obviously, the men involved also had faith in the power of money. Aside from these exceptional opportunities to secure money, it is generally believed that one must work to achieve wealth. Such work may consist of physical labor or it may only involve the effort expended in trade and commerce. Yet it is recognized that conscientious work does not always lead to the accumulation of wealth. This fact is explained in terms of fate. In this insecure situation supernatural charms are employed to influence fate. People's success is most often attributed to their potent magical powers.

Being a good Moslem has no bearing on success. For some, increased religiosity seems to offset their poverty. Others lose their religion with their fortunes. Still others become more religious when Allah assigns them a wealthy fate. Even the marabouts must work to prosper and even they may fail. Nor does knowledge or intelligence determine the outcome in the economic struggle. To illustrate this point, one informant cited the case of a rich man who could count only to two. He would count by pairs, saying, "this and that are comrades" but he never knew how many pairs there were. "If he had been robbed of two of anything, he would never have known they were gone!"

Work values are not the same for all groups. The Gabibi and Bela believe in work for its own sake. It is only through continued work that capital is not exhausted. They consider it derogatory to say of a man that he is so rich that he does not want to work, even when the comment is made about Arabs or Arma. These work values are entirely in accord with the greater necessity for work in the lower class groups. The Arabs and Arma believe in the value of work until one accumulates enough wealth to live by extending credit or until one can turn the active commerce over to sons, hirelings, serfs, or slaves.

From rags to riches and back again in two generations is a well recognized phenomenon in Timbuctoo. The sons of the wealthy are notorious spendthrifts. Cases of such inheritors exhausting their fathers' fortunes are common. The Arabs say that a man must have had to work and to have experienced hunger in order to appreciate the value of money. Some rich Arab fathers have turned a ne'er-do-well son out of the house, forcing him to work so that he would later be fit to inherit. There is virtue in the discipline of work even for those whose ultimate aim is to escape it.

Crime

Timbuctoo not only produces its own undesirable elements but it draws them from the hinterland as well. The halt and the blind from the bush come to live in the city. The natives recognize this phenomenon and attribute it to the genii who drive the physical dregs of society to Timbuctoo. The moral dregs follow the same current. The misfits from the bush can find a niche in the city.

Thievery is very common. The houses and even the huts are kept locked when unoccupied. In the market, produce must be under constant surveillance to keep it from being stolen. French criminal justice has to deal most frequently with thieves. Armed robbery, on the other hand, is rare except for the molestation of travelers by the Tuareg. Thieves come from the poor classes, particularly the Bela and Gabibi, who constitute the majority of the prisoners who daily clean the market. Arma and Arab are not above stealing but only poor men from these groups would do so. Even a poor man of the upper classes is more likely to be able to secure financial aid and not have to resort to thievery. The relationship between poverty and stealing is clear-cut in the native mind.

A thief is usually known as such by his intimates, either in his age-set or ethnic group. A man's friends know his family means and the amount of commerce he carries on. If a man who is known to be poor suddenly appears with signs of wealth, he is naturally suspected of stealing. Once a thief is caught, his lack of integrity becomes common knowledge among his acquaintances. No one condones theft, although the robbery of a miserly, rich man may be a source of amusement. Respectable people withdraw from intimacy with thieves, who tend to find comradeship among their own kind. But this natural unity of the dishonest is not organized in any way. It is said that the bush Bela have organized bands which prey on other tribes. Under the protection of some Arma, there were organized bands of brigands in the old days but today crime is individualized.

An age-set might remonstrate with a thieving member but it would not exclude him from the society unless he began to reflect on the whole group. Pressure from other *koterey* sometimes arises. All of the age-mates of the thief may be accused of being dishonest because they are willing to retain a thief in their midst. Under such criticism the *koterey* would act to expel its member—who, of course, simply goes his way like those who leave the *koterey* voluntarily. There is some evidence that in the quarter of Sankore, with its concentration of marabouts, public opinion can become strong enough to force a known thief to leave the quarter. But even then the miscreant just moves to another part of the city.

There is general consensus that theft is more prevalent now than it was before French occupation. One reason is apparent. Today a thief is put in prison for a few months, is adequately fed, and required to do a small amount of menial labor. In the old days a thief lost his hands and feet, one at a time, for successive offenses. There are still those who recall seeing the amputated stump of a thief's limb cauterized in boiling shea butter in the market place. One ingenious Arma chief conceived the following punishment for prisoners in the native jail which existed before the French arrived. The prisoner was hung up by his hands and a cat was placed in his baggy oriental pants. The trousers were then tightened about the victim's waist and the cat was beaten into a frenzy. This punishment is said to have been greatly feared.

Stealing is by no means confined to the city. The bush nomads steal cattle or camels from one another or pillage sedentary agricultural settlements. But such robbery occurs only between separate and distinct communities and not within the bush community. The use of different values in dealing with the out-group is a well-recognized social phenomenon, expressive of solidarity of the in-group. The significant point with reference to Timbuctoo is that the city does not constitute an in-group in this sense. Further, even the ethnic units within the urban community do not show the same solidarity as the bush communities. A thief in Timbuctoo will steal from anyone.

One implication of stealing within one's own community is that discovery leads to punishment. In stealing from other communities, successful robbery may give the thief status in his own locale. In Timbuctoo, he must be surreptitious in disposing of stolen property. As a result, the "fence" appears, quite probably as a uniquely urban role. The impersonal and intensely competitive economy of the city readily produces commercial agents who will dispose of stolen goods. The profit possibilities are great, for the "fence" possesses that most useful bit of knowledge—he knows that the seller must dispose of the goods. One need hardly add that there are numerous "fences" in Timbuctoo.

One further word should be said with respect to robbery. Before the *paix française*, armed robbery was a common thing. Robbers even stole children and sold them into slavery. This brigandage was indulged in only by those who were powerful enough to avoid reprisal. The Tuareg nobles looted the city almost at will and met resistance with murder. Banditry was not confined to out-group victims. Arma robbed Arma and Arab alike. Victims were selected on the basis of their wealth and weakness. Now that the French have made such appropriation of goods impossible, the upper class must live from commerce.

An instance of mass resort to violence occurred just before my arrival in Timbuctoo. The difficulties arose between the Bela, or slaves of the Tuareg tribe of the Kel Inerkunder, and another slave group, Alkhali Sidali, who live in Abaradyu. It should be recalled that this latter group speaks Temajegh as well as Arabic and has a mixed Arab-Tuareg culture. Each slave group tries to lord it over the other. Youths often find the women of the other group attractive and mixed marriages occur, most frequently between Sidali men and Bela women. As a result of one of these marriages, agricultural land in a Sidali area passed into the hands of a son who identified himself with the Bela. The crop land was in grain and it is customary for all of the Alkhali Sidali to harvest their grain at the same time. Thus the damage inflicted by birds and insects is not concentrated on a few fields left for later harvest. The Bela farmer decided his crop was ripe and that, as the insects were ruining it, he would harvest it immediately. The Sidali protested that the insects would then devour their less mature crops. Undaunted, the Bela set out with his harvesting knife and dared the Sidali to prevent him from harvesting. A vicious fight ensued and someone ran to the Bela chief to secure his aid in stopping the fracas. Instead, the chief rallied a group of Bela men and led them, armed with clubs and knives, into the fray. The fight lasted over two hours before it was broken up by the French. One man was left dead, stabbed in the heart, and twenty-five others were treated for cuts and skull fractures.

This conflict is far from unique. In another instance, the mistreatment of a Bela wife by a Sidali husband led to a general free-for-all. The source of this conflict was eventually removed by the cadi who gave the mistreated Bela wife a divorce. There is constant strife resulting from sexual competition. Individual Bela who came to Abaradyu to court Alkhali Sidali girls were assaulted by Sidali men. The Bela resorted to coming in groups of ten or twenty on their amorous missions. Such groups were likewise attacked, beaten, and stripped. These events led up to the harvest riot just described.

But Bela men find favor in the eyes of Alkhali Sidali girls. Such a girl was bringing a gift of tobacco to her

Bela lover, who was participating in communal work on the mosque. A jealous Sidali slave knocked the tobacco from her hand and another interethnic fight ensued. This case is mentioned to point up the fact that the conflict does not exist between the ethnic groups as units. The women of each group apparently welcome attention from the men of the other. It is the men who express their ethnic solidarity in conflict over the women. There is no shortage of women in either group. The status structure in Timbuctoo decrees that a woman cannot marry a man of lower status than herself. At the bottom of the status ladder we find two slave classes of very similar ethnic background, but the men of each claim status superiority and try to enforce a status differentiating pattern on their own women and on the men of the opposing group. The frustrations of low status position find expression in the scapegoating of the other low status group.

Insanity

Timbuctoo evidences a high frequency of insanity.[4] This is probably not a product of the insecurity of city life but rather the result of syphilis.[5] The extreme prevalence of this disease makes paresis a likely diagnosis. Nevertheless, the psychoses bear on the urban problem in two ways. The content of the delusions and the natives' views as to the causes of insanity constitute relevant cultural data. In them we may find expressed the values and conflicts of the city.

[4] The French census is said to have found "a hundred" cases of insanity. There are probably many more. Cases of extreme withdrawal and depression (Songhoi—*bine*) are not even considered to be insanity by the natives. In my own search for insane, it was largely cases with delusions and stereotyped behavior patterns which were uncovered. Sixteen of these were very incompletely documented but correspond with the eleven here presented. One feeble-minded case was classified with the insane by the natives.

[5] The first record of syphilis in Timbuctoo occurs in Es-Sadi, 1900:178, and was recorded for 1570. It is referred to as "the sickness called the ulcers of Masar." The term "Masar" is current in Timbuctoo today. The French doctor says that Masar is syphilis and not yaws.

Descriptions of the background, symptoms, and "causes" of twenty-seven psychotic cases were obtained from native informants. In analyzing the more detailed cases it should be remembered that the common explanation of insanity in the Moslem world is that it results from divine benediction—producing saints, or from a divine curse, the malevolence of genii, or from the evil eye. In other words, the cause is supernatural. Only four of the Timbuctoo cases were attributed to such sources. The story of one of these cases reveals the background of his hallucinations.

Almuctar Badu's insanity first appeared when he was twenty-two. He is a Gabibi but had learned to read Arabic and was following the trade of tailor. These facts indicate that he was trying to achieve the status of an Alfa by becoming a marabout, a very rare accomplishment for a Gabibi. He now has hallucinations that he is a great savant and marabout and even flaunts his status in the face of the emir. Badu carries a stick to protect himself from the genii who bedevil him. He is said to have become insane from fear after he conjured up the genii by reading magical passages from the Koran. He had learned the passages from a marabout but "it was forbidden for any but Alfa to read them."[6] The status strivings of Badu, of course, did not produce his insanity. But both his hallucination and the popular explanation of the cause of his condition emphasize the inherent conflict between his actual status and his desire for higher social position.

In another of the supernaturally caused cases, the victim was a butcher, Berma, whose great economic success is said to have made his guild brothers so jealous that they used magic to drive him crazy. Here the conflict is economic and is expressed less symbolically. In still another instance, supernatural causation was cited by one informant but another stated that social conflict had caused the

[6] This causal explanation was given by a young Arma. The "cause" of Badu's insanity given by an old Arab was that it was a divine curse visited upon him when he refused to stop frequenting the wife of an Alfa after swearing to do so. Note the conflict with an Alfa in this version also.

loss of reason. The case involves Nana, an Arma woman, whose husband took a lower-status Gabibi woman as a second wife. The latter flaunted herself and her new jewelry before Nana and told her that if she did not like it, she could leave her husband. Nana went mad, either from the magic worked by the Gabibi wife, according to one version, or because of the intolerable situation in which she found herself, according to the other informant. This conflict situation, which the natives recognize as causal, certainly patterns Nana's demented behavior. Now living with her parents, she sometimes plays and sings soft music "for her husband" or mournfully tells the story of the second wife, saying that she would rather kill herself than meet the other woman again. When asked if she is going to marry, she responds that she does not want the men who desire to marry her and that she is going to marry a jackass.

Sarmahamane, a Gabibi, went insane at sixteen when he encountered a spirit one night while returning from having intercourse with his sweetheart. He was much afraid of his father. Worried over paternal disapproval of his amours, he returned to his grandfather's house this night, told him of his demonic encounter and went crazy that same night. He now says that Timbuctoo belongs to his grandfather and he has told the French commandant that the native troops are his slaves.

Yousouf is another Gabibi who had learned to follow the status trade of tailoring. At one time he also owned a horse, a definite symbol of status in Timbuctoo. Because of poverty he had to sell the horse. His insanity is said to have first struck him when he saw a rich man riding by on this horse. Thereupon Yousouf stripped and went running down the street naked, crying, "Have you seen my slave? He stole my horse and I shall kill him!"

Mixed delusions of grandeur and persecution of this sort are not unusual. Bamasudu worked for a European trading house in Timbuctoo until it closed. He took some of the goods at that time to sell on commission. A part was stolen and the remainder was taken back by the proprietor. Bamasudu tried everywhere, even in other cities, to find employment but failed. This sequence of events "caused" his loss of reason. He now plays store with bits of rock, claims to be wealthy, and threatens to go to the French authorities to collect the huge debts which people "owe" him but refuse to pay when he accosts them.

One Bela was a man of some wealth, with flocks and two wives. He had the reputation of being a miser but is known to have converted his flocks to cash, probably to sustain his family. Finally impoverished, he lost his wives. This poverty is said to have driven him mad. He now goes about telling his woes; how he hid his wealth in a hole in the desert and urinated on the spot "so as not to forget it"; how he was observed and the money stolen so that now all his money is lost. Freudians will certainly link the hole in the sand, the urination, money, and wives.[7]

The real or threatened loss of a spouse, when associated with loss of status or economic privation, is a conflict situation which is often reflected in the explanations for insanity and the behavior of the afflicted person. Nana and the Bela, just mentioned, show this pattern. The conflict is not conceived as resulting from an amorous attachment to the spouse but from the fact that the loss of the spouse reflects the loss of status or wealth. An Arab, Baba, once had wealth as well as six consecutive wives. His money gone, the last wife constantly berated him for his poverty and threatened to leave him. This "resulted" in his loss of reason and he is now obsessed with the idea that people

[7] Public or symbolic urination, self-exposure, and the eating or handling of fecal matter are commonly associated with the behavior of the insane in Timbuctoo. Two instances have been noted in the text. That of the Bela is the only one in which the background is sufficiently detailed to suggest the meaning of the symbol. Fragmentary case descriptions show the same tendency. Of the eleven more complete cases, the following showed one of these traits: Disrobing in public—Almuctar Badu, Nana, Yousouf, Sabane, Hamel. Urination—Bela and Sabane. Eating of feces—Berma. Among the Hausa, the eating of feces is characteristic behavior of persons possessed by Nakada or driven mad by this god (Greenberg, 1946:39).

are all talking about his poverty, even telling the French commandant about him.

The three remaining cases show conflicts of a non-economic nature. One is that of Sabane, an Arab slave from a family of moderate means. He has some relatives who are marabouts. Presumably this relationship is through concubinage. Sabane studied awhile with marabouts at Araouan before coming to Timbuctoo. There he married a beautiful, light-skinned woman of a non-Songhoi tribe. He was generally disliked, even by those who had been his friends, for having married a girl who everyone thought should have married a rich man. Sabane's status strivings are obvious. His wife's death is said to have caused his insanity. Now he engages in exhibitionism and repeats incessantly, "I am going to dig up my wife to see her once more."[8] The status symbol, for which he sacrificed his local friendships, is gone.

A Gabibi barber went insane when the parents of the girl he desired to marry refused to agree to the match. A year later they agreed to the marriage and his sanity returned. The occurrence of long lucid intervals in the early stages of this mental deterioration is not unusual. Hamel, an Arab, lost his mind at thirty "because" one of his comrades married his mother and became his father. The form of Hamel's insanity, however, bears no relation to this episode, except possibly his exhibitionism. He collects burnt matches which he "sells" in the market and plans to export to Morocco. When people refuse to buy, he becomes very angry, insults and strikes them, shouting that his slaves refuse to purchase.

Noteworthy is the frequent association of French symbolism in these cases—the trading house in one case and the commandant in three instances, and French-introduced matches. It is likely that the highest authority would be involved in persecution and grandeur delusions simply be-

[8] When urged to give a "cause," an Arab informant attributed the insanity to the fact that Sabane killed and ate an oriole. Most birds have supernatural qualities for the Arab. See Westermarck, 1926:II, 329–341.

cause it symbolizes power and wealth. However, this explanation is not entirely satisfactory. There is at least the suggestion that the French are somehow involved in the conflicts which the people experience. This also finds overt expression, often fallacious, as when increased bastardy is attributed to French influence. One old informant said that when the French conquered Timbuctoo many people went insane as a result. It is certain that these case histories have a disproportionate amount of reference to the French, who touch the life of the native very indirectly and who are only infrequently mentioned in conversation.

The principal thing which the insane of the city have to tell us is that the native has definite conflicts in his life which result from his inability to retain or to achieve wealth and status. In a way, if these insanity cases derive from syphilis, they have an advantage, as data, over purely psychically induced aberrations. The Timbuctoo cases may be accepted as expressing typical conflicts within the population. Practically everyone has syphilis. The cases are unselected and represent both sexes and all major ethnic groups. A physically healthy person who loses his mental health is atypical and must be taken to represent the extreme of social and personal conflict. The native of Timbuctoo who becomes insane because of syphilis is a typical citizen expressing common social stresses in his pattern of insanity.

Suicide

Self-destruction has long been recognized as a symptom of conflict in the social order.[9] Suicides occur in Timbuctoo but it is not possible to compare their frequency with that in villages for lack of data of the latter sort.[10] Eliminating suicide by the insane, seven cases were found, all involving men. There is a strong taboo against suicide. The Koran warns, "Neither slay yourselves, for God is merciful toward you, and whoever doth this maliciously

[9] Durkheim, 1897. Cavan, 1928.
[10] Bohannan, 1960, provides a comparative study of African suicide.

and wickedly, He will surely cast him to be broiled in *hell* fire."[11] This interdiction finds support in the practice of throwing the corpse of a suicide into the desert to be picked by the birds and beasts. Nevertheless, suicides occur.

One suicide did not fall under this taboo. He was a pagan Mossi who had settled in Timbuctoo and married a slave woman there. He possessed a single cow which he intended to sell to secure working capital. The cow died and the Mossi hanged himself. He was a poor, low-status stranger in the city, who had responsibilities but no one to turn to when in financial difficulties.

There are several remarkable things about the remaining suicides. They consist of four Arabs and two men of low status—a Bela and a Gabibi. The latter two hanged themselves, like the miserable Mossi. Hanging is an African pattern. The Arabs, on the other hand, shot themselves in two cases and two others stabbed themselves. While Arab culture includes a taboo against suicide, it also includes patterns for breaking the taboo. Notable also is the fact that four of the suicides derived from familial difficulties.

One Arab, the father of two children, stabbed himself when his wife appealed to the cadi for a divorce on the grounds of brutality and the cadi told the man that he must let her go. Before the French conquest, a Berabich settled in the city and married his father's brother's daughter—an ideal marriage. Finally, however, he divorced her at her insistence. When his brother married her, the former husband shot himself. More recently, a third Arab found his wife in adultery, killed the couple with one shot and himself with another. A desire to escape punishment may have been involved in the suicide.

We note, that, while adultery is lightly punished by the law, offended husbands not infrequently resort to violence. One such outraged Arab cut off the noses of the

11 Koran, IV:29, 30. Some commentaries do not construe these verses to mean suicide.

offending pair. Moslem marriage is not based on a sacrament or romantic love but on contract. An outraged husband should divorce an adulterous wife. But when strong attachments to a wife are present, no matter whether they are based on status, love, or property concepts, the husband is in a situation fraught with conflict. The loss appears worse to him than the culture considers it. Suicide offers a solution, either with or without murder. This whole complex is quite clear in the case of the frustrated suicide of a Bela.

This man was married to a beautiful wife, but he was poor and could not provide her with the things which she desired. He was much in love with her—"too much," says the informant. She started going into town and prostituting herself to obtain the things she wanted. He would follow her about or search for her in the city in an attempt to stop her adultery. One night she stayed all night in the house of her paramour. The husband looked for her unsuccessfully and in the morning he hanged himself in their hut. He was soon found, cut down, and revived. "Then his comrades laughed at him and said that he was silly; that if he had died, his wife would not have been to blame but only himself." His wife eventually left him, married a wealthier man, and was forced by the cadi to repay double the Bela's marriage expenses.

In a recent case, a Gabibi was caught stealing. The man from whom he stole was compassionate and did not want to see him go to prison, so he was released. The French authorities, however, had heard of the matter and were expected to imprison the man. With this prospect, the Gabibi went home and asked a neighbor for a knife but was refused. The thief then entered his own house, locked the door, and hanged himself. The fact that stabbing and hanging appeared as possible alternatives is noteworthy. The Gabibi are more influenced by Arab culture than are the Bela or the Mossi.

The seventh suicide was that of an Arab who murdered the local French commandant and then eviscerated himself. The murder of the commandant was entirely consonant with values of the native population. The conflict, resolved by the suicide, resulted from the inability to escape the consequences of the murder, as the French conceived them.

In résumé, three of the seven suicides occurred under conditions where suicide seemed to provide an escape from punishment for an act which would have gone unpunished or which would have led to lighter punishment in the days before the French conquest. The French obviously introduced the conflicting values in these cases. In three other instances the suicide resulted directly from family conflicts involving adultery or the loss of a wife. One of the possible suicides-to-escape-punishment was initiated by the same sort of family difficulty. Finally, two of the suicides were of relative strangers in town and three were at least indirectly the result of poverty.[12]

The large number of Arab suicides is striking in spite of the small total number of cases, particularly when it is realized that the Arabs make up only about a quarter of the population.[13] The Arab cultural disposition toward violence tends to lead to aggravated conflicts, but it is the Arab family system in Timbuctoo which creates the situations leading to violence and suicide. Three of the Arab suicides stem from divorce or adultery situations. In contrast, the entire lack of suicides stemming from family difficulties among the largest population group—the Songhoi —corresponds with their more stable family pattern.

Marginal Men

The concept of "marginal man" includes the personality type[14] which results from a dual cultural background. He is thus the product of culture contact and the victim of a

[12] For material on primitive suicide see Wisse, 1933, which also contains an excellent bibliography.

[13] Westermarck's encyclopaedic *Ritual and Belief in Morocco* makes only one reference (1, 281) to suicide. In the Berber tribes there have been suicides resulting from inadvertent public flatulation, which is under very great taboo.

[14] Park, Robert, 1928.

welter of conflicts resulting from the incompatible beliefs and loyalties of his double heritage. The cultural diversity present in Timbuctoo would seem to provide a potential breeding ground for marginal men.

In some ways the social structure of Timbuctoo has precluded the development of these conflicted personalities. Most of the natives grow up with loyalties to their own ethnic group. Contacts with people from other groups are impersonal and, while they may result in interpersonal conflict, they do not produce conflicting loyalties within the individual. It is among the children of mixed ethnic marriages that we are most likely to find marginality. In general, however, each ethnic group tends strongly toward endogamy. Arma frequently marry Gabibi, but both are basically Songhoi. Bela men usually marry Bela women. It is only the Arabs, with their great mobility and heritage of polygamy, who often take wives from other culture groups. The strongly patriarchal nature of the Arab family and the likelihood of divorce leading to the separation of mother and child are factors which operate against the development of marginal men in Arab mixed marriages. Nevertheless, there is definite evidence that the conflicts inherent in these families of mixed culture are not always resolved or even suppressed.

Arab culture dictates that the children of Arabs, born to wives or slave women of the father, should all be accepted equally as Arabs irrespective of the race, culture, or condition of servitude of the mother.[15] These values hold true in broad outline. The child of a slave is not believed to have any inferior social or physical qualities but, when the mother is not an Arab, definite tensions result. These strains find expression in the general belief among

[15] This Moslem principle was recognized in the fifteenth century by the Songhoi Askia El Hadj Mohammed (Askia the Great) on his return from Mecca and as a result of advice of a sheikh of Cairo. This Askia specifically exempted the Moslems from the old Sudanese rule which forbade marriage into artisan serf castes. The edict further established the fact that the children of such marriages would be "of the same condition as their fathers" (Kâti, 1913:15).

Arab men that an Arab household with Bela concubines will quickly go to ruin while a house with Arab concubines will prosper. Bela concubines are "evil roots in the house" and the master is doomed to see his fortune dissipated before his death. The mechanism by which this evil influence operates is conceived in supernatural terms —disasters divinely visited upon the master. Only eight Arab freemen have Bela consorts while Gabibi wives are much more prevalent.

Arab family patterns are designed to reduce the conflicts of mixed marriage to a minimum. An Arab's first marriage is almost always with an Arab. Any subsequent marriages with non-Arabs are with women who have been previously married. As first marriage is the ceremonial union, this system avoids conflicts resulting from ethnic differences in marriage ceremonies. Marriage to a non-Arab is now considered by Arabs as the equivalent of purchase of a concubine, even though this is not legally true. The Arab man approaches the parents of the girl directly, not through an intermediary. He considers the dowry as purchase price and, after espousing the girl, he observes no in-law taboos with her parents. The parents are not permitted to visit their daughter except on ceremonial occasions. She is confined to the house like Arab women. This confinement would be natural for an Arma girl and would be considered "upper class" and hence of merit to a Gabibi. A Bela simply does not agree and this is a source of continual conflict in Arab-Bela unions. The threat of divorce is all that is held over the Bela woman to make her conform.

In the setting of an Arab household, a non-Arab wife or concubine naturally imparts her own culture to her offspring. This process, operating over three hundred years, has made the descendants of the Moroccan invaders, the Arma, more Songhoi than Arab. One observes the process at work in all Arab families, the amount of change depending upon the length of residence in the Sudan. Songhoi quickly becomes the language of the home and Arabic is used as a second language for contact with other Arabs, particularly those of the desert and bush.

This acculturation process does not take place without conflicts between the cultures of the father and mother. Some fathers have even divorced non-Arab wives when they found the maternal influence becoming too strong. In any case, an attempt is made to force the child to follow Arab custom until after marriage and the birth of the first child. Thereafter, cultural identification is an individual matter. Violent quarrels result over differences of opinion between paternal kin and a son who follows maternal custom. These quarrels tend to drive the son completely into the non-Arab group. Even then bitterness may develop upon the death of the father. The son determines the nature of his father's burial rites and the brothers of the deceased may object strenuously to non-Arab interment.

In the Arab household there is almost always friction between the offspring of Arab mothers and those of non-Arab mothers. The children of Arab mothers are domineering to their half-brothers and sisters, telling them that they "have only one foot" and that "if it were not for my father, I could sell you." The children with "one foot" frequently speak Arabic badly. They are teased about this deficiency and, as a result, often become ashamed to associate with Arabs. The more they are seen with the Songhoi, the more they are jeered by the Arabs for not associating with their own kind. They frequently experience difficulties in connection with their paternal inheritance. They have identified with the culture of the mother, as do the children of inter-slave marriages. Their half-brothers often contest their paternity in an attempt to stop their inheritance. In the case of "secret marriages" to non-Arabs, the children are most apt to follow the culture of the mother and their paternity is most open to question.

The Arabs liken the child of a mixed cultural marriage to "a piece of gold wrapped in cloth." The ideal is to "take the gold and throw away the cloth," i.e., the maternal heritage. Not infrequently it is the "gold" which is thrown away. An Arab shereef of Timbuctoo married a rich Tuareg woman. She and their son remained in the desert and he in town. The son was unusually old, ten years, when he was brought to join his father. The father would find the boy braiding his hair in the Tuareg fashion and drag him to the barber to have his head shaved. On other occasions, the irate father would jerk the Tuareg veil from his son's face or tear off great bundles of charms from around his neck. In less than two years the boy ran away to join his mother's people. He was brought back but eventually returned to the desert and married a Tuareg woman.

In another instance, a much-married Kunta had only one son, and that by a Gabibi wife. The boy spoke no Arabic and dressed as a Gabibi. This continually infuriated his father who would threaten to send him to an Arab bush community for a few years to learn the paternal ways. But the father could never bring himself to be so harsh with his only child, so the bickering continued. Another Kunta had a Kunta wife and a Gabibi "secret wife." The latter bore him a daughter, Kadidye. Then the Kunta wife learned of the marriage and forced her husband to divorce the Gabibi. Kadidye remained with her mother until she was three, when she joined her father. The latter died when she was ten and she begged to go back to her mother because she had been so unhappy with her half-siblings and stepmother. This was violently opposed by the Arabs who did not want the girl to become a Gabibi. Distant Arab relatives of her father took the matter to the cadi who let the child join her mother "because the Arab litigants were not brothers of the deceased." Kadidye eventually married a Gabibi.

Still another Arab, of poor means, married a wealthy Alfa woman, who bore him a daughter. The difference in their economic status led to the dominance of the maternal family over the child. The Arab divorced his wife and contrary to all rules, the daughter was left with the prosperous maternal family. She now dresses and circulates in the city like other Songhoi girls.

Such difficulties are not entirely restricted to the Arabs. An Alfa of the city had a daughter by a Bela concubine. He shortly divorced the slave wife. The daughter, from the age of three to fifteen, was forced to remain with the father. But in spite of urging and beating she was always running away to Bela Farandi. She is now entirely Bela, married to one, living in a grass hut, and taking no part in Songhoi age-set activities.

Strained Bonds

We have seen that there do exist basic attachments to ethnic group, to family and to individuals. But this web of bonds is continually under strain. Various groups have different and often opposed beliefs. No ethnic unit is self-contained and interrelations are inevitable. While cultural differences make it difficult for a person to leave one group and identify with another, it is possible to live as a Songhoi, Arab, or Bela without the cooperation of others of the same culture. One can always escape from the family into this loosely structured ethnic group. Wealth and status constitute the cultural values understandable to all individuals, families, and cultures in Timbuctoo.

CHAPTER 14

City-Folk

Timbuctoo is a city. It has a stable population of over six thousand persons, living in a community roughly a square mile in area and patterning their lives after three distinct cultural heritages. The size, density, and heterogeneity of the city are all evident. Timbuctoo became a city without drawing upon the Euro-American tradition of the Industrial Revolution, without benefit of the Western capitalistic system, and outside of the sweep of democratic ethos. Having seen in some detail the way of life of this Sudanese city, we return to the question which took us to Timbuctoo. Is life in such a city secular and impersonal and does it show disorganization?[1]

Before attempting to draw any theoretical implications from the data, it is important that we outline some methodological limitations of the study. The most serious of these is that of measurement. Basic to the whole idea of the folk-urban continuum is the valid proposition that the difference between the poles is a difference in the degree to which the definitive traits are evident. Yet aside from population size, there exist no adequate measurement scales for the traits. As long as comparisons are made between societal types which are extreme contrasts, this is not serious. The difficulty is also fairly well controlled when comparisons are made between communities sharing the same basic culture. Thus, Redfield was able to report from Yucatan that customs relating to marriage

[1] See discussion of this problem in the Introduction. The whole folk-urban continuum is also discussed elsewhere (Miner, 1952).

and the selection of godparents varied in specific respects from the tribal village to the city. The nature of this variation could then be appraised with regard to the critical characteristics of the continuum—sacredness, degree of individualization, etc.

Cross-cultural comparison, however, necessitates more definite operationalization of the definitions of the polar traits. Beyond the simple expedient of noting the presence of non-folk traits in Timbuctoo, this study can say nothing as to the degree of urbanism present there. A contingent and hitherto ignored aspect of the folk-urban problem, which became important in the field, was the obvious fact that different aspects of life in the same community vary in their degree of "folkness." So the problem of measurement exists not only among communities, but also within them.

The crucial nature of this whole consideration becomes apparent even if one considers only the basic characteristic of homogeneity. The heterogeneity of Timbuctoo is clearcut in the presence of three diverse cultures. Yet the different culture groups are woven into a system of diverse economic and status groups which constitute elements in the division of labor. Compared to Western cities, the heterogeneity of Timbuctoo appears to the writer to be more a product of diverse cultural origin and less a result of elaborate division of labor. It is significant that anthropologists have tended to think of heterogeneity in terms of different cultural origins, while sociologists are more inclined to concern themselves with heterogeneity stemming from elaborations of the division of labor. This, of course, reflects differences in the groups which these social scientists have traditionally studied and does not deny the fact that the two kinds of heterogeneity are but special cases of the broader category of cultural differentiation.[2]

The lack of any concise benchmark from which to appraise the degree of homogeneity can be illustrated from

[2] Ralph Beals, 1951, points this out clearly.

research in Guatemala. Dr. Sol Tax characterizes Guatemalan Indian culture as homogeneous, yet he finds life is secularized and relationships are impersonal.[3] Redfield and Tax attribute these latter traits to the importance of commerce and a money economy.[4] It would appear just as reasonable to attribute secularization and impersonalization to the heterogeneity upon which the ancient intervillage commercial life is based. It is true that the Indians are homogeneous in that they are all Mayans, but village specialization in economic production, as well as in dress and other local custom, is very marked.[5] Whether Guatemala is more homogeneous than heterogeneous is beside the point which concerns us here. The disturbing question is whether this author and Dr. Tax, or this author and his readers, use the same benchmarks in judging homogeneity and the other characteristics under investigation.

Another caution must be mentioned because remarks concerning it are strikingly rare in the anthropological literature. The concern here is with the typicality of informants. There are several pressures which incline the ethnographer to use the atypical or marginal native as an informant. One of these pressures is linguistic. The native who speaks the field worker's language or some third language common to both, as was the case in this study, is almost always a native who is, in some degree, peripheral to his own culture. While every ethnographer tries to learn as much as possible of the language of the people he is studying, the degree of facility required for detailed interrogation is achieved during limited field periods by only the most gifted. The use of bilingual natives as informants or interpreters is common practice.

Quite aside from blocks to communication, informants are apt to be marginal unless the ethnographer has achieved a role which demands general respect, attention, and time from the natives. The vital question is why any

[3] Tax, 1937; 1939; 1941.
[4] Redfield, 1939:48–49. Tax, 1939:467.
[5] Redfield, 1939.

individual should be willing to share his time with an inquisitive stranger rather than pass his time in traditional ways. Those natives most thoroughly engrossed in the life of the community will be least inclined to work with the stranger, unless the latter has something of special interest to offer. It is, of course, the ethnographer's job to devise methods for making himself attractive to the typical natives but, in this, the marginality of his interpreter is again a hindrance. In sum, the Western origins of the ethnographer naturally make him most attractive to those natives who already have some knowledge of Western ways and this knowledge tends to make such natives useful to the field worker.

There are recognized techniques which are employed to offset the danger of distortion by the informant. The simplest of these is the use of at least two informants to cross-check each other. It seems probable that even this device is not used for all data but only for material in particularly important or difficult areas of inquiry. The same is true for validation through observation. The internal consistency of the material collected is a good check against misinformation, but does not reveal consistent bias such as that which a single interpreter might introduce.

The above hazards of field observation are well known to ethnologists. Depending upon the situation and the skills involved, such distortion is controlled to varying degrees. Rarely does the reader of a monograph know to what degree, for obviously every anthropologist eliminates all distortion of which he is aware. The bulk of ethnographic material concerning custom is based on such commonly recognized and observable facts as to cause us no real concern as to its validity. It is only when we approach the more subtle aspects of culture, such as the native's *Weltanschauung*, that we run into real danger.

While this author, also, conscientiously tried to get a "true picture" of Timbuctoo, possible sources of uncontrolled bias should be indicated. As stated earlier, all work was done through bilingual informants and interpreters, with French the common language. Such double translation certainly has obvious drawbacks. Its use can be defended only as a practical necessity. There is probably no one who speaks all three of the native languages nor is perfect control of any one of the languages an open sesame. The amount of Songhoi known, as the lingua franca, to other groups is too limited to be generally useful. Leland Hall's account of Timbuctoo[6] greatly underrepresents the non-Arab elements of the population, apparently because he knew Arabic so well that his contacts were limited to that language group.

During the field work here reported, native words for distinctively different native concepts were used whenever possible. In that most of the data are derived from bilingual informants, communication was at least direct and subject to greater control than it would have been had intermediary interpreters been generally employed. This advantage was gained at a price—that price being the fact that the informants were clearly marginal to the groups for which they spoke, though none had ever been in a Western city. Through continued association, I came to know each informant well and to recognize many of his personal biases. What he had to say sometimes required evaluation in the light of the sort of person he was. Obviously, my sample of the population was biased—more urban than the rest. On the other hand, it was chosen from all four of the major population elements and included an Arma, two Gabibi, two Arabs (first and fourth generation Sudanese), and a Bela. The last named was possibly the only French-speaking Bela in town. No French-speaking women were found. The sorts of customs and incidents which the informants reported were not preponderantly autobiographic. The details they gave referred to the general population and agreed with my personal observation. It may be that these informants were more interested in the sorts of data which we here call urban, but this raises no question as to the accuracy of what is reported.

In an age of indices and attitude scales, and in the light

[6] Hall, 1927.

of all the aforementioned hazards, it may seem presumptuous to attempt to state what life in Timbuctoo is like. Still, if life appears thus to the author and, if the discipline of training in social science has not lost all meaning, Timbuctoo should seem much the same to others who might try to see its pattern. It is then at this rather global level of analysis that the following generalizations are made.

Our problem does not imply that if urban traits are present in Timbuctoo, they will exist to the exclusion of the contrasting traits of sacred and personal behavior and social organization. Our knowledge of the American metropolis tells us that many aspects of urban life do show these latter traits. We ask, rather, can we characterize any aspects of the community life by non-folk traits and, if so, what sort of relationships do they typify?

Cultures in Contact

Reviewing what we have seen of life in Timbuctoo, it is apparent that the family and ethnic group constitute social spheres of great importance. Leaving aside for the moment those recent innovations traceable to French influence, a person's occupation, status, marriage arrangements, and supernatural beliefs are patterned by his family and ethnic origins. While the customs differ among the ethnic groups, the traditions of each are in large part sacred to its members. The extended kinship pattern is important in determining the nature of relations with local co-ethnics. Birth and marriage ceremonies, religious and magical beliefs and practices, circumcision and age-set rituals and duties, even occupations and especially crafts are traditionally defined for the various culture groups of the city and even for status groups within these ethnic units. Relations with kin are preponderantly personal in character, as are those with co-ethnics, the only marked exception being the frequently impersonal nature of economic relations.

In spite of the exceptions, the Songhoi, Arabs, and Bela, taken as separate groups and considered only with regard to their internal relationships, are strikingly folk in character. They are, however, a city folk. Their lives are not limited to contacts with their own kind. Commerce, age-sets, worship, government and law, marriage, and amusement—all draw together in interaction the peoples of different cultural backgrounds. It is in this interaction between the different population elements that behavior is the most secular and impersonal and the society shows the greatest disorganization.

The Songhoi call themselves "townsmen" and dislike the greedy "outsiders" who live in Badyinde. The rough play of *alkura* and subsequent fights reflect interethnic hostility. The Alkhali Sidali and Bela battle out their antagonisms. The Arab and Songhoi marabouts degrade and discriminate against one another. The age-set system is weakened by the introduction of *koterey* for each of the different ethnic stocks. The children of mixed cultural marriages are made to feel they are social misfits.

Commerce, of course, was the activity which drew the heterogeneous population of Timbuctoo together and functioned to maintain the community for centuries. In the market relations between the culturally diverse people, profit motives appear to be paramount. They are not mitigated by the cultural patterns of prerogatives and obligations which typify economic relations within a homogeneous culture. Cultural values as to what is fair, honest, or humane are effective within a folk culture because faith in these values is supported by strong sanctions and each individual can see for himself that conformity is to his advantage as well as that of the whole "we-group" with which he identifies. Between people of a folk culture, economic relations are but one aspect, even a minor one, of a totality of social relations of all sorts. But when the ethnocentric individual relates himself commercially to an unknown person of another culture, he feels little unity with the stranger and the primary sanctions which operate are the economic sanctions of the market; the only motives are those of profit. We have seen the similarity between such market relations and the ethnocentric behavior of nomadic, bush folk who feel free to cheat or pillage outsiders. In market relations between two people of different cultures, the economic relation is often the only kind of interaction. The specificity of their relationship is reflected in their impersonal behavior. The anonymity of the market relationship is also important. When the other person is not known personally and his customs are strange, not understood, or even repellent, it is not difficult to treat him impersonally—to wring all the profit possible from the situation.

The market is an aspect of division of labor which relates diverse people to one another. Structurally, the peoples of Timbuctoo and its hinterland are as necessary to one another as are the people of a small, homogeneous folk society. There is a need for the heterogeneous market community to find or develop values consistent with their broad interrelations. Community-wide government and law are such developments. It is noteworthy, however, that such new social structures arise with difficulty. Community government did not develop independently in Timbuctoo. It was imposed from without by the power of a homogeneous society. As soon as that power was removed, the local organization began to fall apart. Even the universally accepted system of Koranic law was not generally operative except under outside control. The community failed to defend itself against outside aggression, when it could have done so. Some attempt was made to extend the *koterey* system to include non-Songhoi, but all of the Bela and most Arabs are still excluded.

Not only was there resistance to the development of a body of community-wide culture, but the distinct culture units show internal disorganization traceable to life in the city. The secular, impersonal attitude of the market invaded intra-ethnic and intrafamilial relationships as the interdependence of individuals within each ethnic group became less necessary, less obvious to its members. The folk culture was no longer a closed system. Essential, everyday functions continually took one out of one's own group. While the necessity for interrelations with one's own kind diminished, the possibility of escaping its sanctions increased. In Timbuctoo it was possible to abandon one's family and still marry and make a living.

The city provides a social milieu in which economic success may be achieved with less regard for activities which are not primarily economic in nature. In the folk community, because of the close-knit functional organization of its culture, religious and family behavior have definite economic implications. In fact, it is exceedingly difficult, if not impossible, to say what is economic behavior and what is familial. In Timbuctoo it is often easy to make such a distinction. A market economy requires specialized and individualized activity. In these activities the market rewards secular and impersonal behavior. This fact, plus the inherent conflict between different traits of cultures in contact, results in interrelations of a non-folk type. The obvious need for community-wide organization is smothered in the lack of mutual understanding bred of heterogeneity and the obvious rewards attainable by disregard for tradition. Traditional behavior is operative when it is conceived as the only legitimate method of achieving success. Changes in economic structure and weakened sanctions may make it apparent that the traditional ways of life are not so successful as other forms of behavior and that the traditional ways may be successfully questioned. Then secular behavior challenges the sacred traditions.

The Gradient in Urban Behavior

Throughout our study of this primitive city, when we have found urban traits exemplified in relationships between kinsmen, the same sort of behavior has been found between unrelated co-ethnics and in interethnic relations as well. But urban traits evident in interethnic relations do not seem to show the same prevalence in intra-ethnic contacts and, in turn, the extended family is least marked by them. Conversely, folk behavior appears to be most typical of family relationships, next most common in intra-ethnic behavior and least evident in interethnic relations. It is true that these statements are based upon the comparison of data which are not expressed in metric terms. Yet it has seemed possible to discover certain basic relationships by simply examining extreme contrasts, which we shall now consider.

Islamic dogma provides the focus of much of the traditional belief in terms of which all residents of the city can relate themselves to one another in an organized and personal manner. The whole religious dogma is not thus shared, but everyone is a Moslem. The importance of this identification to group life is to be seen in the refusal of the community to admit non-Moslems before the French conquest. The Koran, the marabouts, the mosques, the obligations of prayer, alms, *Ramadān*, and the Pilgrimage are symbols which are common knowledge. Koranic laws find universal acceptance and the role of the cadi as arbiter and judge is recognized by all. The basic contract of marriage and the laws of divorce and inheritance are thus universal to the community.

Public participation in the work of repairing the mosques is markedly folk in character. People of different ethnic groups work shoulder to shoulder. Even the rich, who escape the labor through money donations, participate in the activities as honored spectators. The raids by small boys on the market are a special and authorized sanction against merchants who may try to compete with the communal mosque work.

At other times, the functioning of the market and of general commerce demonstrates additional factors of city-wide organization. Currency units were standardized long before the arrival of the French. Legitimate methods of price determination, payment, measurement, and transfer of goods are known to all.

The *alkura* games and victory feast are another organizing factor in the city. It is true that interethnic hostilities find expression in the games, which become extremely impersonal and rough. However, the fact that teammates come from the same city quarter contributes to quarter solidarity. The victory feast is a warmer, more personal occasion, financially supported by all of the players and attended by all but the losers. Thus *alkura* contributes to community solidarity by providing catharsis for tensions as well as being a focus for cooperative action.

Two types of what is essentially intra-ethnic organization were so generally recognized and respected that they should be considered factors of community-wide structure. One is the guild system. In pre-French days the monopolies of the guilds within particular ethnic groups were accepted by all groups. Likewise the internal status structure of the different ethnic groups is generally recognized, as are certain types of status equivalence. This equivalence finds common agreement only with regard to classes higher and lower than one's own. Freemen and slaves agree that slaves of any group are of lower status than freemen. Slaves of different groups, however, do not agree that they are of equal status. The same situation adheres between nobles and between serfs. Both class and guild traditionally pattern the legitimate expectations of personal relations.

In contrast to the city as a whole, each ethnic group possesses a much larger body of common customs. The life crisis rites of each are in many ways distinctive. These characteristics both separate the groups from one another and provide a basis of common understanding and cohesion within each. The factor of common language facilitates effective relations within the ethnic unit. Even strangers are housed with co-ethnics. Contacts with people of one's own group are naturally more frequent than with others. Such contacts result not only from the linguistic situation but also from group-limited institutions and rituals.

The Songhoi age-sets came to include the descendants of the Moroccan army through the acculturation process which drew both into a common ethnic unit. The Bela have their separate system and the Arabs possess mutual cooperation societies. Within each group, this sort of organization provides a strong basis for well-ordered relationships of a personal character.

Except for the Arabs, with whom circumcision is a family ritual, the circumcision ceremony is another focus of activity for the whole ethnic group. The sociograms of birth and naming customs illustrate the manner in which the subgroups of each ethnic unit are also organized around the event of birth. The different ceremonies vary in such a fashion that their cohesive effects are most widespread among the Songhoi and the least extensive for the Arabs. We note also the special custom of New Year's gift giving, which further contributes to the unity of the Songhoi.

The members of each ethnic unit are in considerable agreement with regard to supernatural beliefs. This operates to obviate some types of friction within the group. Differences in belief become the point around which marabouts and their followers in one group are organized in power conflicts with those of other groups. From the point of view of intra-ethnic structure the effect is cohesive.

Most important to ethnic organization is the fact that marriages are preponderantly within the ethnic group. This functions to keep the totality of life crisis rituals and family connections as elements of structure which strengthen ethnic unity. By the same token, of course, these organizational factors tend to maintain the pattern of endogamy. Even some non-kin patterns of a folk sort are cast in kin terms, such as the relation of the circumcision "father" to the initiates, or the Arma to their Gabibi "cross-cousins."

This brings us to family organization itself. In the family, the patterns of ethnic solidarity are reinforced by kinship systems which define mutual rights and obligations in the greatest detail. The potentiality of withdrawal of the rights provides strong sanctions for the maintenance of the obligations. These obligations of kinship preclude impersonal behavior.

A folk aspect of family life which is most distinctive is the extent to which economic behavior is sacred and personal. In contrast to the profit motivated transactions of the market, the sharing of wealth within the elementary family of children and parents, and even their siblings, is striking. Traditional behavior associated with circumcision,

[21]   Bela Beauty Parlor

[22]   Wedding Dance of Bela Age-Mates

[23] Gabibi Wedding Guests and the Marriage Bed

[24]   Bela Mother

courtship, engagement, marriage, and annual religious ceremonies is full of gift-giving patterns between relatives. The economic responsibility of children for parents continues after the offspring have families of their own. Even more distant relatives are assisted when in need. Adoption customs transfer potentially productive and desired offspring from one household to another purely on the claim of kinship. The patterns of expected behavior among kin clearly order their interrelations. Behavior oriented around these expectations is personal in nature. The legitimacy of the patterns seems rarely to be questioned.

The foregoing material seems to substantiate the observation that there is a gradient in the degree of "folkness," which increases from the community unit to the family. The polar concepts of "folk" and "urban" are drawn in such a way that a relative decrease in the characteristics of one is by definition an increase in the importance of the other. What evidence have we that the logically expectable reverse gradient in the occurrence of urban traits actually exists?

While kinship organization is strong, it is not free of disorganization, impersonal acts, and challenges to the sacred order of things. Most noteworthy is the conflict and deception which occurs over the question of polygyny. The marked difference of values between husbands and wives on this issue is a common source of strife. Men may take secret wives, but the deception is ultimately discovered and divorce ensues. Another device, employed by Arabs, uses the wife impersonally and uses the law secularly. An Arab can publicly take a second wife and divorce his first, with the intention of divorcing the second before the end of three months, and taking back the first wife who cannot legally remarry before that time.[7]

[7] It should be emphasized that we are not citing the frequency of divorce as evidence of disorganization, as contended by Hansen (1954) and Sjoberg (1955). It is the nature of the conflicts leading to divorce which seems urban. A sex difference in the perception of the structure of the family can hardly be other than disorganizing. Similarly, it is the *abuse* of Islamic divorce law, not its *use*, which is urban in character.

The impersonal economic behavior of the market even invades the family of extended kin. Arabs must be urged to aid starving, out-of-town relatives. Arab sons cheat their rich fathers. All groups demand interest on loans to their relations. A kinsman is not favored commercially unless he is in dire need.

Clearly the Arab family is less folk in character than the other family types. The African Arabs have experienced centuries of heterogeneous culture contact. Both on the basis of the hypothesis and on the evidence from the Sudan, it would therefore seem probable that this group was urbanized before its arrival in Timbuctoo. Yet the Arab family is much more urban in Timbuctoo than I found it to be in a homogeneous Arab oasis of comparable size in North Africa. The primitive city seems to have affected the Arab immigrants in ways comparable to the manner in which such a Western city as Algiers alters them.

Impersonal and secular market behavior, which is not generally typical of family economics in Timbuctoo, characterizes commercial relations with non-kin. In this regard, little distinction can be made between interethnic and intra-ethnic behavior. It may be easier to deceive a person of different background, but dishonesty and trickery are common practice. The stranger is housed with a co-ethnic. The latter may try to escape his obligations as host. Host and guest must both be alert for the other's chicanery.

Outright robbery is common and dealers in stolen goods prosper. The grain merchant who has cornered the market will let non-relatives starve if they cannot pay his inflated price. It is normal to take advantage of a man who is known to need money. The market vendor saves her goods for no one and extends no credit. Merchants capitalize on the local belief that the whims of a pregnant woman must be satisfied, to the consternation of the husbands who must buy the things their wives select from the merchant's wares.

Even the age-sets, which operate as cohesive factors in

each group, are secularized. Their power to apply sanctions to their members for misbehavior is sometimes used only after outside pressures force such action. Thus a known thief may be retained in the group as long as he fulfills his obligations of cooperation. *Koterey* membership is open to other ethnics who participate economically but not personally.

Among the various ethnic units, sexual relations are primarily organized through prostitution—a strikingly impersonal occupation. Courting and marriage between members of different groups of equivalent status results in open conflict between the groups. Co-wives of different ethnic origin are in greater disaccord than are other co-wives. The children of such marriages are obviously marginal, torn between their two cultural heritages.

Ethnic differences in supernatural belief result in conflict between the Arab and the Songhoi marabouts and between the marabouts and sorcerers. The fear of the supernatural power of strangers and of the genii of strange ethnic quarters expresses the same inherent conflict. Even marabouts of the same belief compete for the trade in charms and for students in the manner of the market.

Within the framework of the sacred ideologies, the people's behavior is strikingly secular. The money evaluation and impersonal trading of the market permeate religion and magic. One bargains with God, the saints, and the marabouts. Supernatural services are either on a C.O.D. basis or the efficacy of charms is conceived as being proportionate to the amount paid for them. Some of the religious values are disregarded. Usury is common practice; the marabouts charge for their services; impostors use the sacred title of shereef; the rich fail to make their pilgrimage; non-public daily prayers are slighted; and false oaths are sworn on the Koran.

Post-Conquest Changes

Forty-five years of French occupation in Timbuctoo have brought about still further changes away from folk beliefs and practice. The coming of the French, of course, added to the cultural heterogeneity of the community. Yet the French have been present in small numbers and for a relatively short time. They have done little to alter native customs, aside from attempts to stop sorcery and the sale of slaves. New institutions of the French—the colonial administration and court, the French school and doctor, and the Army—have touched relatively few of the native citizens directly. French trading houses have had direct contact with a wider range of people and French currency has replaced cowries. These commercial innovations have resulted in little basic change for they fall almost completely within the old trading patterns of the people. As we have seen, the natives are sometimes more secular, impersonal, and shrewd than the French when it comes to dealing in credit and interest. Fixed price is the principal new commercial trait, but it has shown little tendency to spread beyond the trait complex of store trading. Commercial dealing with Christians, both French and the Syrian, is something which could never have occurred before the occupation. It is certainly evidence of secularization, considering the fact that no known Christian could have survived in Timbuctoo earlier.

Among other departures from traditional patterns, we have noted lower status people building themselves houses or dressing in clothes previously reserved for higher classes. We find Bela who cheat their fathers as they could not have done before. Marriages are concluded between low status men and higher status women. Even the crafts, hitherto limited to upper class people, are invaded by persons from lower classes, in utter disregard for tradition and the supernatural sanctions which protected the class-craft system. None of these changes is the direct result of French action and design. The fact that they have occurred following French conquest certainly indicates they are indirect effects of the contact.

We can attack the problem of these recent changes by posing the question, "What would have happened before the French conquest if the craft-guilds had been invaded; if a Bela had dressed as a noble; if a Bela son had stolen from his father; if a Gabibi man had tried to marry an Arma?" The answer is that the individual who behaved in this manner would have been severely beaten or killed outright by the individual or group whose rights and prerogatives had been infringed.

While the French have not tried to change native culture, they have assumed complete control of all major physical punishment. The French do not use such punishment to enforce all of the native culture patterns of Timbuctoo. It is used to protect the persons and property of the residents of the city and to enforce French administration and much of Islamic law. With the sanction of physical punishment no longer in native hands, social forces which have long been present can now make themselves felt. Other sanctions of the ethnic groups and families, such as ostracism, supernatural punishment, or disinheritance, cannot make an individual conform when he can gain a better livelihood by ignoring them and finding his social contacts with those who will judge him on the basis of his improved condition.

Some Further Considerations

Since the preceding pages were first published, our conclusions have been subject to the sort of friendly discussion and controversy which advances the understanding of society. A new edition of the study, therefore, provides an opportunity to review and summarize the most relevant aspects of this growth of knowledge.

There is still a lack of consensus as to what constitutes the essence of the city and this lack bids fair to continue until we have a generally acceptable theory of urbanism. William Bascom, a long-time student of the Yoruba in southern Nigeria, prefers a demographic definition of urbanism. He suggests that Timbuctoo is not a very good example of an indigenous African city. "Contrasted to Timbuctoo's 6,000 inhabitants," he writes, "the Yoruba have six cities of more than 100,000."[8] Most of this strik-

[8] Bascom, 1955:446.

ing contrast in size is, however, due to differential European impact. Early European trade along the Guinea Coast drew commerce away from Timbuctoo. In contrast, more than two centuries of slave trading along that coast was a great stimulus to warfare and the growth of large states and population clusters back of the coast. We find that, even a century ago, the population of traditional Yoruba cities was estimated to be only around 20,000 while that of Timbuctoo was given as 13,000, with seasonal increments of 5,000 to 10,000.[9] It is worthy of passing note that population concentrations of this general size also characterized the earliest urban centers of Mesopotamia, the birthplace of cities. Even in medieval Europe, such dominant cities as Lübeck and Cologne were about this big.

The description of Yoruba cities makes it clear that they are actually less urban than Timbuctoo, unless population size and density are all there is to urbanism. We learn that "nearly all Yoruba engage in farming" and that "the farmers are city dwellers and the city is not really 'a non-farm area,'" but the center of a ring of farmland extending out as much as fifteen miles. Still, these centers had their urban side even in the precolonial period. The communities were socially stratified; there were specialized crafts organized along guild lines; trade and commerce were predominantly local but important; market transactions were impersonal in nature. Yet even in the expanded Yoruba cities of today, one-third to two-thirds of the employed population is engaged primarily in agriculture.[10] Although there is a disinclination to designate such communities as "cities,"[11] there is some justification for such usage. We are apt to forget that, in the earliest cities, the

[9] Barth, referring to his 1853 visit to Timbuctoo (1890:325). Our own estimate is that this size was achieved at an earlier date.

[10] Bascom, 1962:703.

[11] N. C. Mitchell suggests that they be designated as "agricultural towns" (1961:281). Sjoberg calls them "quasi-urban" (1960:33).

population grew at least part of its own food. As Max Weber expressed it, "The full urbanite of antiquity was a semi-peasant."[12] Yoruba cities thus represent a very old type of incipient urbanism which might well be called "rurban."

In addition to their greater size and more agrarian nature, Yoruba cities also differ from Timbuctoo in being ethnically homogeneous. Ninety-five per cent or more of the present urban populations are Yoruba. This is certainly one reason why the bonds of kinship remain strong and lineage is still basic to the fabric of life. Although the Yoruba escape the sorts of conflict found in more cosmopolitan cities, *caveat emptor* is still the rule in their markets. In this, the effects of division of labor resemble those of ethnic heterogeneity.

What was learned in Timbuctoo and in the Yoruba cities acquires additional meaning in a broader context provided by Gideon Sjoberg. He defined a generalized "feudal" type of society, as distinguished from the folk and from urban industrial society.[13] The immediately relevant feature of such a feudal society is the fact that it embraces two distinct, yet interdependent, ways of life— that of the "preindustrial city" and that of the rural peasantry. Such a city is the residence of the governing elite, of scholars and priests, of artisans and traders. Yet, despite this degree of socio-economic differentiation, the social order is sacred, personal, and traditional.[14] Timbuctoo closely resembled this model in formal structure, but seemed to show greater evidence of disorganization.[15] It was ultimately found, however, that fraud, prostitution, petty crime, and adulteration of goods are characteristic features of all preindustrial cities.[16]

Summarizing a broad sweep of ethnological and historical evidence, we find that population concentrations

---

[12] Weber, 1962:78.
[13] Sjoberg, 1952.
[14] Sjoberg, 1955.
[15] *Ibid.*, 444.
[16] Sjoberg, 1960:211–212, 249.

of urban proportions have come about to serve myriad specialized functions, from defense to worship. A strand of commonality runs through this diversity, however. The first appearance of cities in every part of the world has been associated with the development of economic and politico-religious differentiation in the society at large. Cities and civilizations have developed together and the heterogeneity with which cities are most clearly identified is that resulting from specialization. Because the extent of such differentiation is difficult to measure, the presence of certain inventions associated with social complexity is used to distinguish preindustrial civilizations and cities from their somewhat less complex precursors. The use of money is one such distinguishing mark. Sjoberg uses the criterion of a system of writing.

Despite the size of the Yoruba cities and the fact that they were involved in a money economy, the associated social order was not sufficiently complex to require writing. The rural elements of the society were still ecologically part of the urban centers which developed along with local trade and the emergence of governing and priestly groups. The way of life of these groups, however, was still only little differentiated from that of the farmers. No "high culture" set the non-literate elites apart from the masses, who have been described as being only "incipient peasants."[17] Compared to life in Timbuctoo, that in incipient cities seems better ordered and more sacred and personal in character. The Yoruba case tells us that the distinctive features of urban life are not so much a product of sheer numbers as they are the result of the degree of social differentiation usually required to achieve such density.

The societal developments in which Timbuctoo had its origin involved the emergence of successive empires across the breadth of the western Sudan. These wider systems of interdependence paralleled the sharper class distinctions and greater cultural diversity evident in the structure of

[17] Fallers, 1961.

the city. The specialized economy of Timbuctoo depended upon a hinterland extending even beyond the boundaries of any of the empires which embraced the city. Its elites sprang from conquering strangers. Its literate intelligentsia grew from the seeds of conversion to a foreign creed sown six centuries ago. The urbanism of Timbuctoo stems from both division of labor and culture contacts.

Despite such far-flung ties through time and space, Timbuctoo is as indigenous a city as Athens or Thebes. It is possible for preindustrial cities to develop through the elaboration of a single cultural tradition, but powerful cities seek to extend their areas of influence and distant peoples seek such cities. Thus, while ethnic heterogeneity is not definitive of the city, it is a natural outcome of urban growth.

While all this helps us place Timbuctoo in a developmental context, we did not go there to probe the origins of cities. We went to see what could be learned about the nature of urban life by studying a city which had developed "without drawing upon the Euro-American tradition of the Industrial Revolution." Life in such a community was found to be a surprising mixture of traditional folkways with secular and impersonal behavior of an urban sort. Subsequent comparison has now shown that communities like Timbuctoo represent a distinctive type of city in which most of the round of life is sacred and folk-like. The economy, however, shows a non-folk level of specialization and is marked by conflict, dishonesty, and theft. Preindustrial cities are the natural habitat of "city-folk."

The Ecology of Communication
with Timbuctoo

Timbuctoo prospered as a commercial center because it was accessible to both land and water traffic. All locations on the banks of the Niger do not provide these conditions because of the seasonal rise and ebb of the river over its broad flood plain. Village locations which are near the edge of the river during low water are either inundated by the high water or are isolated as islands in the sea of flood waters. The latter condition is characteristic of Djenné which lies two hundred and fifty miles up the Niger, to the south of Timbuctoo. Seasonally the river valley between these two points becomes a huge morass over fifty miles wide. Shortly before the Niger reaches Timbuctoo, it turns sharply to the east and, from that point on, the high water morass is confined to a more definite channel bounded by banks of dunes. The factors which favored the growth of a commercial center at Timbuctoo were: a) its position at the point where the Niger penetrates the desert most deeply, favoring the junction of river and desert-borne traffic; b) its location just beyond the area of wide inundations making possible a port settlement open to land traffic the year round; c) the early political and commercial dominance of the area to the west and southwest of Timbuctoo. This factor is largely responsible for the location at the western end of the Niger bend rather than farther east.

Djenné and Timbuctoo always maintained a close commercial connection, most of the commercial goods of Djenné passing on to Timbuctoo or coming from there. Djenné itself was physically isolated, by flood waters, from the caravan trade just as Oualata was isolated by its desert location from the river traffic. Timbuctoo was accessible to both.

Although Timbuctoo functions as a river port, it is located five miles north of the normal course of the river at high tide and twice that distance from its main channel. The city managed to act as a port by means of the satellite village of Kabara, located on the high water channel itself. Kabara apparently vied in importance with Timbuctoo for some time. The location of noncommercial functions, particularly religious and governmental, at Timbuctoo established the dominance of this community which was always readily accessible by land.

When the river experiences very high waters, the main flow passes beside Kabara and the waters fill a slough which extends up to Timbuctoo and partially isolates Kabara. At such times canoes can reach Timbuctoo directly. In years when the water is not so high, boats unload at Kabara and the produce is taken on donkeys to Timbuctoo. At lower tides, Kabara is accessible by water through a canal built centuries ago to join it with a side channel of the Niger.

Dubois (1897:201) attributes the construction of this canal to Askia the Great. Barrows (1927:143) erroneously attributes it to El Hadj Omar. Caillié visited the city before Omar's time and recognized the canal (1830:II, 44). Later Barth thought the channel might be natural (1890: 285). Es-Sadi (1900:114–115) mentions that Sonni Ali started a canal from Ras-el-Ma (near Goundam) to Biru (Oualata). This is a different canal and, in fact, its intended course appears to have been misstated. It is more likely that Ali intended to construct a canal to run from Goundam to Ras-el-Ma, which would facilitate year-round movement of troops toward Oualata, which lies 160 miles across barren desert from Ras-el-Ma. By deepening the high water channel between Goundam and Ras-el-Ma, an additional sixty-mile overland trek could have been eliminated. The Kabara canal appears to be a work of this sort.

Some North and West African Comparisons with *Kambu* and *Gulli*

In spite of the fact that Arabs do not believe in the power of Gabibi sorcerers and *tyinibibi koy*, there are numerous connections between the Gabibi fetishes and charms and Moroccan practices. *Tyinibibi koy* make string charms of knotted or braided black, red, and yellow cords. Other varicolored cords used to suspend Koranic charms are known as *fasu keytan*. The Kettani are a Moslem order of Fez. Knotted red thread charms are recorded for Fez (Westermarck, 1926:1, 572). The colors black, white, yellow, and red all have supernatural significance in Morocco (*ibid.*, II, 15–22). The *kambu* is associated with specific metalcrafts probably introduced by the Arabs, although metalwork is known to be Negro as well. The making of the *kambu* contains a mixture of Arab and Negro elements. The basic element of the *kambu* is a pair of metal tongs, the manufacture of which is not part of the *kambu*-creating ritual. This suggests that this is not basically a metalsmith's ritual. The colored strips occur again in the *kambu*. The written Arabic charm, the Moslem prayer, and the cloth from a shrine are Arabic. The spirit-fetish, the blood sacrifice, the cowries, and the kola nut spitting are African in origin.

It is significant that the cord charms occur in Timbuctoo entirely divorced from Koranic talismans and that *kambu* are also made by Gabibi non-smiths. The Negro Moslems of Gnawa, in Morocco, are believed to be particularly powerful in controlling genii and exorcising them. Animal sacrifice is used in the ceremonies. The victim of the genii is carried on the shoulders, as the victim of a witch is carried in Timbuctoo (*ibid.*, I, 347–351). Westermarck (*ibid.*, I, 379) and J. B. Andrews, 1903, consider the African influence on Moroccan genii beliefs to be strong. While the *torkoy* and *tyinibibi koy* have taken over many Arab traits, their base would still appear to be Sudanese, as their names and the terms *kambu* and *gulli* indicate. The local recognition of their distinctive character plus the fact that they are associated with the most Negroid and Songhoi elements of the population lends credence to this belief.

The similarity of *kambu* and *gulli,* as described in Chapter 6, to Ashanti *suman* is striking. One of the best known Ashanti fetishes, *Nkabere suman,* consists of three sticks bound together with a piece of cord. Preparatory to creating this fetish, a fowl is sacrificed. After this, the "medicine man" sprays pepper and Guinea corn from his mouth onto the sticks and then wraps the cord around them. Later, from time to time, fowls are sacrificed to the fetish (Rattray, 1923:310–311). The Ashanti *Yentumi suman* is a knotted cord charm worn about the neck (Rattray, 1927:14). The *Kunkuma suman* protects the wearer, among other things, from harm which might befall him before bathing after intercourse. It consists of old broom fibers "which have come in contact with every kind of filth" and six small pieces of iron from a flintlock (*ibid.*, 12–13). The *Ahunum suman* contains cloth in which a dead body was carried, as well as strips of leopard, lion, and hyena skin. Cowrie shells are also a part of the complex (*ibid.*, 15). Eggs are sacrificed on some fetishes (*ibid.*, 21). In Timbuctoo eggs and cowries are identified in witchcraft lore.

Some of the Dahomean *gbǒ*, particularly the *sǎ* and *kâ,* show similarities illustrating the indigenous character of *kambu* and *gulli* as well as the similarity of the Sudanese Songhoi to Guinea Coast cultures (Herskovits, 1938:II, 263–288. Note particularly *gbǒ* types 4–6).

Glossary

Abaradyu. The area of huts, occupied by Arabs and Arab slaves, on the northern outskirts of Timbuctoo.

Alfa. A learned, religious man or the social group of such men and their families.

Alkhali Sidali. A tribe of Tuareg slaves who speak Arabic and Temajegh. They reside in Abaradyu.

Arma. The descendants of the Moroccan army which conquered Timbuctoo in 1591. As a group they constitute the upperclass of the Songhoi, whose culture they have adopted in large part.

azalai. A caravan going from Timbuctoo to Taodeni, in the central Sahara, and bringing back rock salt.

Badyinde. The name of the northwest quarter of Timbuctoo.

baraka. A supernatural power which lies in holy men and sacred words, acts, or objects.

Bela. The term applied by the Songhoi to the sedentary, Negroid slaves of the Kel Inerkunder Tuareg.

Bela Farandi. The area of huts, occupied by the Bela, on the eastern outskirts of Timbuctoo.

Berabich. The name of the nomadic Arabs around Timbuctoo, sometimes called "Moors."

cadi. A Moslem judge.

cowries. Small marine shells (gastropods), widely used as decoration and earlier as currency in Africa.

Daga. The term applied by the Songhoi to Tuareg serfs, known as *imghad* in Temajegh.

Djerma. The eastern dialect of Songhoi or the people speaking that dialect.

Dyingerey Ber. The "Great Mosque" or the name of the southwest quarter of Timbuctoo in which the mosque is located.

emir. The title of the native political chief of Timbuctoo.

It earlier referred to the local comptroller who represented the Sultan of Morocco.

fātiḥah. The opening sura of the Koran, often used as a prayer.

Gabibi. The term in Songhoi means "Black Body." It is used to designate those Songhoi in Timbuctoo who are not descendants of the Moroccan conquerors and who stood in a serf relationship to the latter.

imam. The prayer-leader of a mosque.

kola. The nut of an African tree (*Cola acuminata*). Such nuts contain caffein and are chewed by the natives.

koterey. The Songhoi term for an age-set, the members of which are called *kondey.*

koyraboro. Literally, "Townsman" in Songhoi. Used to distinguish the Songhoi from other residents of Timbuctoo.

Madersa. The French school for natives which specializes in teaching Arabic literature.

muezzin. The crier who announces the hours of prayer.

pasha. The title of Arab military leaders and political administrators in certain areas, such as in Morocco and Timbuctoo.

Sankore. The name of a mosque and of the northeast quarter of Timbuctoo in which the mosque is located.

Sara Keyna. The name of the southeast quarter of Timbuctoo.

shea butter. The solid, yellowish fat obtained from the seeds of the shea tree (*Butyrospermum parkii*).

shereef. A patrilineal descendant of a son of Mohammed's daughter, Fatimah.

Sidi Yahya. The name of the mosque in the city quarter of Sara Keyna.

Temajegh. The language of the Tuareg.

Tijani. The name of one Moslem religious order or fraternity.

tira. A written charm based on the Koran.

References

Andrews, James B. 1903. *Les fontaines des génies (Seba Aioun) croyances soudanaises d'Alger.* Algiers.

Barrows, David P. 1927. *Berbers and Blacks; Impressions of Morocco, Timbuktu and the Western Sudan.* New York and London, The Century Co.

Barth, Henry. 1890. *Travels and Discoveries in North and Central Africa. Including Accounts of Timbúktu, Sókoto, and the Basins of the Niger and Bénuwé.* Vol. II. London, New York, and Melbourne, Ward, Lock, and Co.

Bascom, William R. 1944. *The Sociological Role of the Yoruba Cult-Group,* Memoir 63, American Anthropological Association. Menasha, Wisconsin.

————. 1955. "Urbanization among the Yoruba," *American Journal of Sociology,* LX, 446–454.

————. 1962. "Some Aspects of Yoruba Urbanism," *American Anthropologist,* LXIV, 699–709.

Beals, Ralph. 1951. "Urbanism, Urbanization and Acculturation," *American Anthropologist,* LIII, 1–10.

Becker, Howard. 1950. "Sacred and Secular Societies Considered with Reference to Folk-State and Similar Classifications," *Social Forces,* XXVIII, 361–376.

Blackman, Winifred S. 1927. *The Fellāhīn of Upper Egypt; Their Religious, Social and Industrial Life Today with Special Reference to Survivals from Ancient Times.* London, Bombay, Sydney, George G. Harrap & Co., Ltd.

Bogardus, Emory S. 1929. "The City: Spatial Nearness and Social Distance," *Sociology and Social Research,* XIII, 572–577.

Bohannan, Paul. 1960. *African Homicide and Suicide.* Princeton University Press.

Burgess, Ernest W. (Ed.) 1925. *The Urban Community; Selected Papers from the Proceedings of the American Sociological Society.* Chicago, University of Chicago Press.

Caillié, Réné. 1830. *Travels through Central Africa to Timbuctoo; and across the Great Desert, to Morocco; Performed in the Years 1824–1828.* 2 vols. London, Henry Colburn and Richard Bentley.

Cavan, Ruth S. 1928. *Suicide.* Chicago, University of Chicago Press.

Coon, Carleton S. 1931. *Tribes of the Rif.* Peabody Museum of Harvard University, Harvard African Studies, Vol. IX. Cambridge.

DeVos, George, and Miner, Horace. 1960. *Oasis and Casbah: Algerian Culture and Personality in Change.* University of Michigan Museum of Anthropology, Anthropological Papers No. 15.

Dubois, Felix. 1897. *Timbuctoo the Mysterious . . .* trans. from the French by Diana White. London, William Heinemann.

du Picq, Ardant. 1933. *La Langue Songhoi, Dialect Dyerma.* Paris, Larose.

Dupuis, Auguste (Yakouba). 1913. "Notes sur les principales circonstances de la vie tombouctienne," *Revue d'Ethnographie et de Sociologie,* IV, 104.

————. 1914. "Notes sur Tombouctou," *Revue d'Ethnographie et de Sociologie,* V, 248–263.

————. 1917. *Essai de méthode pratique pour l'étude de la langue Songhoi.* Paris, Leroux.

Durkheim, Emile. 1897. *Le Suicide.* Paris.

————. 1915. *The Elementary Forms of Religious Life,* trans. by Joseph W. Swain. New York, Macmillan.

————. 1933. *On the Division of Labor in Society,* trans. by George Simpson. New York, Macmillan.

Es-Sadi, Abderrahman Ben Abdallah Ben Imran Ben Amir. 1900. *Tarikh es-Soudan,* French trans. by O. Houdas. Publications de l'Ecole des Langues Orientales Vivantes. Series IV, Vol. XIII.

Fallers, L. A. 1961. "Are African Cultivators To Be Called 'Peasants'?," *Current Anthropology*, II, 108–110.

Faris, Robert E. L. 1931. *An Ecological Study of Insanity in the City*. A part of a dissertation submitted to the Faculty of the Division of the Social Sciences in Candidacy for the Degree of Doctor of Philosophy, Department of Sociology. Private Edition, Distributed by the University of Chicago Libraries.

de Gironcourt, M. G. 1914. "L'art chez les Tuareg," *Revue d'Ethnographie et de Sociologie*, v, 43.

Goldziher, Ignácz. 1890. *Muhammedanische Studien*. Vol. II. Halle a. S., Niemeyer.

Greenberg, Joseph. 1946. *The Influence of Islam on a Sudanese Religion*, Monograph 10, American Ethnological Society. New York.

———. 1947. "Arabic Loan-Words in Hausa," *Word*, III, 85–97.

———. 1963. "The Languages of Africa," *International Journal of American Linguistics*, XXIX, no. 1, Part II.

Hall, Leland. 1927. *Timbuctoo*. New York, Harper & Bros.

Hansen, Asael. 1954. *Review of "The Primitive City of Timbuctoo."* American Journal of Sociology, LIX, 501–502.

Hell, Joseph. 1925. *The Arab Civilization*, trans. from the German by S. Khuda Bukhsh. Cambridge, W. Heffer & Sons, Ltd.

Herskovits, Melville J. 1937. *Life in a Haitian Valley*. New York, Knopf.

———. 1938. *Dahomey, An Ancient West African Kingdom*. 2 vols. New York, Augustin.

Ibn-Battuta. 1893. *Voyages*. Trans. from the Arabic by Defrimery and Sanguinetti. 4 vols. Paris, Société Asiatique.

Joffre, Joseph J. C. 1915. *My March on Timbuctoo*. London, Chatto & Windus.

Junek, Oscar W. 1946. "What Is the Total Pattern of Our Western Civilization? Preliminary Observations," *American Anthropologist*, XLVIII, 397–406.

Kati, Mahmoud (ben El Hâdj El Motaouakkel Kâti). 1913. *Tarikh el-Fettach*. French trans. by O. Houdas and M. Delafosse. Publications de l'Ecole des Langues Orientales Vivantes, Series v, Vol. x.

Lenz, Oskar. 1884. *Timbuktu. Reise durch Marokko, die Sahara und den Sudan, ausgeführt im Auftrage der Afrikanischen Gesellschaft in Deutschland in den Jahren 1879 und 1880*. Vol. ii. Leipzig, Brockhaus.

Leo Africanus. 1896. *The History and Description of Africa, done into English by John Pory*. 3 vols. London, Hakluyt Society.

Marie, E. 1914. *Vocabulaire français-djerma et djerma-français*. Paris, Leroux.

Marty, Paul. 1920. *Etudes sur l'Islam et les Tribus du Soudan*. Vol. ii, *La Région de Tombouctou (Islam Songaï); Dienné, le Macine et Dépendances (Islam Peul)*. Paris, Leroux.

Migeod, Frederick W. H. 1911. *The Languages of West Africa*. 2 vols. London, Kegan Paul, Trench, Trubner & Co.

Miner, Horace. 1942. "Songhoi Circumcision," *American Anthropologist*, xliv, 625–631.

————. 1952. "The Folk-Urban Continuum," *American Sociological Review*, xvii, 529–537.

————, and DeVos, George. 1960. *Oasis and Casbah: Algerian Culture and Personality in Change*. University of Michigan Museum of Anthropology, Anthropological Papers No. 15.

Mitchel, N. C. 1961. "Yoruba Towns," in K. M. Barbour and R. M. Prothero (eds.), *Essays on African Population*. London, Routledge & Kegan Paul. Pp. 279–301.

Molouk es-Soudan, Akhbar. 1901. *Tedzkireten-Nisian*. French trans. by O. Houdas. Publications de l'Ecole des Langues Orientales Vivantes, Series iv, Vol. xx.

Monod, Théodore. 1937. *Méharées*. Paris, Editions "Je Sers."

Monteil, Charles. 1923. *Les Bambara du Ségou et du Kaarta. Etude historique, ethnographique et littéraire d'une peuplade de Soudan Français*. Paris, Emile La-rose.

———. 1932. *Djénné, Métropole du Delta central du Niger, une cité soudanaise*. Institut International des Langues et Civilizations Africaines; Sociéte d'Editions Géographiques, Maritimes et Coloniales, Paris.

Montet, Edouard. 1902. *Les confréries religieuses de l'Islam Morocain*. Paris.

Mowrer, Ernest R. 1927. *Family Disorganization*. Chicago, University of Chicago Press.

Murdock, George P. 1949. *Social Structure*. New York, The Macmillan Co.

Nicolaisen, Johannes. 1963. *Ecology and Culture of the Pastoral Tuareg*. The National Museum of Copenhagen, Nationalmuseets Skrifter, Etnografisk Raekke IX.

Ortoli, Jean. 1939. "Coutume Bozo," *Coutumiers juridiques de L'Afrique Occidentale Française*. Publications du Comité d'Etudes historiques et scientifiques de l'Afrique Occidentale Française, Series A, No. 9, 172–173.

Park, Mungo. 1815. *The Journal of a Mission to the Interior of Africa in the Year 1805*. Philadelphia, Edward Earle.

Park, Robert E. 1925. "Culture and Cultural Trends," *Publications of the American Sociological Society*, XIX, 24–36.

———. 1928. "Human Migration and the Marginal Man," *American Journal of Sociology*, XXXIII, 881–893.

———, Burgess, E. W., and McKenzie, R. D. 1925. *The City*. Chicago, University of Chicago Press.

Pefontan, Lt. 1922. "Histoire de Tombouctou de sa fondation à l'occupation française (xii siècle–1893)," *Bulletin du Comité d'études historiques et scientifiques de l'Afrique Occidentale Française*, 81–113.

Perret, Robert. 1935. "Le climat du Sahara," *Annales de Géographie*, XLIV, 162–186.

Radcliffe-Brown, A. R. 1913. The Social Organization of the Kariera of Australia in "Three Tribes of Western Australia," *Journal of the Royal Anthropological Institute*, XLIII, 143–194.

Rattray, R. S. 1923. *Ashanti*. Oxford, Clarendon Press.

————. 1927. *Religion and Art in Ashanti*. Oxford, Clarendon Press.

————. 1929. *Ashanti Law and Constitution*. Oxford, Clarendon Press.

Reckless, W. C. 1941. *Vice in Chicago*. Chicago, University of Chicago Press.

Redfield, Robert. 1939. "Primitive Merchants of Guatemala," *Quarterly Journal of Inter-American Relations*, I, No. 4, 42–56.

————. 1941. *The Folk Culture of Yucatan*. Chicago, University of Chicago Press.

————. 1947. "The Folk Society," *American Journal of Sociology*, LII, 293–308.

Rinn, Louis. 1884. *Marabouts et Khouan, Etude sur l'Islam en Algérie*. Algiers, Adolphe Jourdan.

Rodd, Francis. 1926. *People of the Veil; Being an Account of the Habits, Organisation and History of the Wandering Tuareg Tribes which Inhabit the Mountains of Air or Asben in the Central Sahara*. London, Macmillan and Co., Ltd.

Rouch, Jean. 1945. "Culte des génies chez les Sonray," *Journal de la Société des Africanistes*, xv.

————. 1954. *Les Songhay*. Paris, Presses Universitaires de France.

————. 1960. *La Religion et la Magie Songhay*. Paris, Presses Universitaires de France.

Schwab, George. 1947. *Tribes of the Liberian Hinterland*. Papers of the Peabody Museum of Archaeology and Ethnology, Harvard University, Vol. xxxi. Cambridge.

Seabrook, William. 1934. *The White Monk of Timbuctoo*. New York, Harcourt, Brace and Co.

Seligman, C. G. 1930. *Races of Africa*. (The Home University Library of Modern Knowledge) London, Thornton Butterworth, Ltd.

———— with B. Z. Seligman. 1918. "The Kabâbish, A Sudan Arab Tribe," *Harvard African Studies*, II, 105–184. Cambridge, Cosmos Press.

Shabeeny, El Hage Abd Salam. 1820. *An Account of Timbuctoo and Housa*, edited by J. G. Jackson. London.

Shaw, C. R. and McKay, Henry D. 1942. *Juvenile Delinquency and Urban Areas, A Study of Rates of Delinquents in Relation to Differential Characteristics of Local Communities in American Cities.* Chicago, University of Chicago Press.

Sjoberg, Gideon. 1952. "Folk and 'Feudal' Societies," *American Journal of Sociology*, LVIII, 231–239.

———. 1955. "The Preindustrial City," *American Journal of Sociology*, LX, 438–445.

———. 1960. *The Preindustrial City, Past and Present.* Glencoe, Illinois, The Free Press.

Sumner, W. G. 1907. *Folkways.* Boston, Ginn & Co.

Tauxier, Louis. 1942. *Histoire des Bambara.* Paris, Librairie orientaliste Paul Geuthner.

Tax, Sol. 1937. "The Municipios of the Midwestern Highlands of Guatemala," *American Anthropologist*, XXXIX, 423–444.

———. 1939. "Culture and Civilization in Guatemalan Societies," *The Scientific Monthly*, 463–467.

———. 1941. "World View and Social Relations in Guatemala," *American Anthropologist*, XLIII, 27–42.

Thrasher, Frederic M. 1927. *The Gang; A Study of 1,313 Gangs in Chicago.* Chicago, University of Chicago Press.

Tönnies, Ferdinand. 1940. *Fundamental Concepts of Sociology*, trans. by Charles P. Loomis. New York, American Book Co.

Trimingham, J. Spencer. 1961. *Islam in West Africa.* London, Oxford University Press.

———. 1962. *A History of Islam in West Africa.* London, Oxford University Press.

Weber, Max. 1962. *The City*, trans. and edited by Don Martindale and Gertrud Neuwirth. New York, Collier Books.

Welch, Galbraith. 1939. *The Unveiling of Timbuctoo; the Astounding Adventures of Caillié.* New York, William Morrow & Co.

————. 1949. *North African Prelude, the First Seven Thousand Years*. New York, William Morrow & Co.

Westermarck, Edward. 1914. *Marriage Ceremonies in Morocco*. London, Macmillan and Co., Ltd.

————. 1926. *Ritual and Belief in Morocco*. 2 vols. London, Macmillan and Co., Ltd.

Wirth, Louis. 1938. "Urbanism as a Way of Life," *American Journal of Sociology*, XLIV, 1–24.

Wisse, Jakob. 1933. *Selbstmord und Todesfurcht bei den Naturvölkern*. Zutphen, W. J. Thieme & Cie.

Index

Abaradyu, 38–41, 63, 103, 211, 270, 311; ethnic concentration in, 39, 43, 44, 270

Abomey, 53 n

Abortion, 15, 124, 191, 203

Acculturation, xi, 41, 51, 99 n, 282, 295

Administration, French. *See under* France and the French

Adoption, 140–42, 149, 164–65, 297

Afterlife. *See* Death and afterlife

Age-sets, 44, 131–32, 135, 137, 175–86, 290, 291, 292, 295, 298–99; circumcision and, 168–83; dance parties (*hina hina*), 181–83; formation of, 178–81; participation at birth, 175, 227–29, 231–34; participation at death, 175, 246; participation at marriage, 175, 206; solidarity of, 135

Agriculture, xiii, 18 n, 62–63, 65–67, 93, 270, 302–4. *See also* Farmers and farming

Ahmadou, 260

Air district, 18 n, 22, 249 n, 250

Alfa, 19, 77–78, 87–88, 103, 105, 120, 131, 272 (*see also* Marabouts); described, 4 n, 311; hair patterns of, 26 n; marriage of, 192, 206, 207, 283; occupations of, 54, 61, 68

Alfa Moy, 120–21, 138

Algeria, 12, 72, 214 n, 222 n

Algiers, 298

Ali Yaya, 173

Alkhali Sidali, 41–42, 270–71, 291, 311

Alkura (rain hockey), 256–58, 291, 294–95

Allah, 5, 86, 96, 136, 173, 195, 197, 203, 243, 249, 255, 266 (*see also* Islam; Moslems); belief in as unifying force, 78; and saints, 89, 124

Almsgiving, 104, 124, 133, 136, 138; common belief in, 79, 85–87, 97, 148

Almudu, 126, 130, 133–34

Andrews, J. B., 310

Apprenticeship, trade, 54, 57–60, 104

Arabic language, use of, ix, 3 n, 4 n, 10, 16, 17–22, 41, 168 n, 282, 289; chronicles, vii, 1; cures, charms, magic, 92, 93, 95–96, 104, 106, 181, 309; kinship terms, 149–55; learned by marabouts, 5, 77, 87–88, 131; names for months, 126; prayers, 83, 181, 249

Arabs, 3, 17–23, 41, 63, 83, 84, 87–88, 92, 95–96, 146,

ANCHOR BOOKS

SOCIOLOGY

ALLPORT, GORDON W. The Nature of Prejudice, A149

BARTH, KARL Community, State and Church, A221

BELL, DANIEL The Radical Right, A376

BENDIX, REINHARD Max Weber: An Intellectual Portrait, A281

BERGER, PETER L. Invitation to Sociology: A Humanistic Perspective, A346

BROWN, ROBERT MCAFEE, & WEIGEL, GUSTAVE, S.J. An American Dialogue, A257

CABLE, GEORGE W. The Negro Question, A144

CHEVALIER, MICHAEL Society, Manners and Politics in the United States, A259

DOLLARD, JOHN Caste and Class in a Southern Town, A95

FORTUNE, EDITORS OF The Exploding Metropolis, A146

GOFFMAN, ERVING Asylums: Essays on the Social Situation of Mental Patients and Other Inmates, A277

——— The Presentation of Self in Everyday Life, A174

GRANICK, DAVID The Red Executive: A Study of the Organization Man in Russian Industry, A246

HANDLIN, OSCAR The Newcomers, A283

——— Race and Nationality in American Life, A110

HERBERG, WILL Protestant-Catholic-Jew, A195

HOOVER, EDGAR M., & VERNON, RAYMOND Anatomy of a Metropolis, A298

HUNTER, FLOYD Community Power Structure, A379

JONES, ERNEST The Life and Work of Sigmund Freud, ed. & abr. in 1 vol. Trilling & Marcus, A340

LENSKI, GERHARD The Religious Factor, A337

LIPSET, SEYMOUR MARTIN Political Man: The Social Bases of Politics, A330

MARTINEAU, HARRIET Society in America, ed. Lipset, A302

MILL, JOHN STUART John Stuart Mill: Essays on Politics and Culture, ed. Himmelfarb, A373

NEGLEY, GLENN, & PATRICK, J. MAX, eds. The Quest for Utopia, A326

PETERSEN, WILLIAM American Social Patterns, A86

RAAB, EARL, ed. American Race Relations Today, A318

RIEFF, PHILIP Freud: The Mind of the Moralist, A278

RIESMAN, DAVID Constraint and Variety in American Education, A135

——— Selected Essays from Individualism Reconsidered, A58

SCOTT, GEOFFREY The Architecture of Humanism, A33

SIGAL, CLANCY Weekend in Dinlock, A269

SMITH, LILLIAN Killers of the Dream, A339

SOMERS, HERMAN & ANNE Doctors, Patients and Health Insurance, A309

SOMERVILLE, JOHN, & SANTONI, RONALD, eds. Social and Political Philosophy: Readings from Plato to Gandhi, A370

TAYLOR, WILLIAM R. Cavalier and Yankee: The Old South and American National Character, A351

VERNON, RAYMOND Metropolis 1985, A341

VICO, GIAMBATTISTA The New Science of Giambattista Vico, trans. Bergin & Fisch, A254

VIDICH, ARTHUR J., & BENSMAN, JOSEPH Small Town in Mass Society: Class, Power and Religion in a Rural Community, A216

WASKOW, ARTHUR The Worried Man's Guide to World Peace, A377

WHYTE, WILLIAM H., JR. The Organization Man, A117

WIENER, NORBERT The Human Use of Human Beings, A34

WILLIAMS, RAYMOND Culture and Society, 1780–1950, A220

ANCHOR BOOKS

MYTHOLOGY AND LEGEND

BEDIER, JOSEPH   The Romance of Tristan and Iseult, A2
COULANGES, FUSTEL DE   The Ancient City, A76
FRAZER, J. G.   The New Golden Bough, ed. Gaster, A270
KRAMER, SAMUEL NOAH, ed.   Mythologies of the Ancient World, A229
MALINOWSKI, BRONISLAW   Magic, Science and Religion, A23
MURRAY, GILBERT   Five Stages of Greek Religion, A51
MURRAY, MARGARET   The God of the Witches, A212
VIRGIL   The Aeneid of Virgil, trans. Lewis, A20
WESTON, JESSIE L.   From Ritual to Romance, A125

ANTHROPOLOGY AND ARCHAEOLOGY

ALBRIGHT, WILLIAM FOXWELL   From the Stone Age to Christianity, A100
BENDIX, REINHARD   Max Weber: An Intellectual Portrait, A281
COULANGES, FUSTEL DE   The Ancient City, A76
CROSS, FRANK MOORE, JR.   The Ancient Library of Qumran, A272
FRANKFORT, HENRI   The Birth of Civilization in the Near East, A89
FRAZER, J. G.   The New Golden Bough, ed. Gaster, A270
GASTER, THEODOR H.   The Dead Sea Scriptures, A92
HOWELLS, WILLIAM   Back of History, N34
KRAMER, SAMUEL NOAH   History Begins at Sumer, A175
——, ed.   Mythologies of the Ancient World, A229
MALINOWSKI, BRONISLAW   Magic, Science and Religion, A23
MURRAY, MARGARET   The God of the Witches, A212
TURNBULL, COLIN   The Lonely African, A374
WESTHEIM, PAUL   The Sculpture of Ancient Mexico/La Escultura Del
  Mexico Antiguo (Bilingual edition, trans. Bernard), A335
WESTON, JESSIE L.   From Ritual to Romance, A125
WRIGHT, G. ERNEST, & FREEDMAN, DAVID NOEL   The Biblical Archaeologist
  Reader, A250

8

BRIGHTON BEAU

Rachelle Edwards

FAWCETT CREST • NEW YORK

A Fawcett Crest Book
Published by Ballantine Books
Copyright © 1994 by Rachelle Edwards

Library of Congress Catalog Card Number: 93-90874

ISBN 0-449-22281-0

Manufactured in the United States of America

First Edition: May 1994

10 9 8 7 6 5 4 3 2 1

ONE

It was early in the afternoon. Miss Emmeline Stanbury was feeling somewhat listless, and, having decided she could no longer entertain herself usefully in the house, returned to her bedchamber to fetch a chip-straw bonnet and a Norwich silk shawl with the intention of going out. Because she had nothing better to occupy her time, a botanizing expedition was called for, although she could not summon up much enthusiasm for it. However, it was certainly better than waiting impatiently in the house.

As she hesitated on the landing, one sandaled foot poised to go down the stairs, Miss Stanbury glanced out of the oriel window in the direction of the park gates and was surprised and delighted to espy a curricle bowling down the drive, having just passed the gateman's cottage.

Her demeanor immediately brightened. Her wide brown eyes shone with pleasure, and her bronze curls began to bounce with excitement. Just past her seventeenth birthday, Miss Stanbury was an exceptionally pretty girl, having inherited her fair share of the famed Stanbury looks. In her youth Lady Stanbury had caused quite a sensation in the beau monde, and Sir Stephen had set many a female heart aflutter.

The girl watched the curricle's approach with unconcealed pleasure. There, in the depths of the Sussex countryside, such a fine equipage was rarely to be seen. It was painted such a dark green, it sometimes appeared to be black, the elegant lines picked out with gold paint. Drawing the curricle, a team of four matched chestnuts moved in perfect harmony under the direction of the gentleman on the box.

He, too, presented a stylish figure, clad in a drab greatcoat adorned with no fewer than fifteen capes and a high-crowned straw hat atop a mass of carefully disarranged bronze curls.

When the curricle came ever nearer, Emmeline abandoned her point of observation and ran down the curving staircase. When she reached the bottom of the stairs, she almost cannoned into her mother, who had just entered the hall carrying a trug full of cut flowers.

"Emmy, why the unseemly rush?" Lady Stanbury inquired, straightening her lace cap, from which any number of bronze-colored curls escaped.

"Oh, Mama, don't scold me now! Gavin is arriving."

"So soon?" her mother gasped. "I hadn't expected sight of him much before dinner."

"You must know he is such an expert whip, he travels everywhere in record time!"

Lady Stanbury emitted a sigh as she placed the trug on a hall table. "Yes, I recall that run he made from London to Fossley Hall—and all for the sake of a wager."

"He won, Mama."

2

"I know, but how I wish he wouldn't be so reckless. It's so easy to overturn a carriage. I know of several disastrous instances."

The sound of the carriage rattling to a halt outside brought the conversation to an end and caused the two ladies to hurry toward the door just as the footman flung it open.

A young man of about twenty-eight years was climbing down from the curricle. He handed the ribbons to his tiger and then turned to run up the wide flight of stone steps to the front door, taking them two at a time. Lady Stanbury's air of concern and censure had disappeared, and she beamed with unreserved pleasure as her son came bounding up the stairs toward her.

"Mother, how fine you look," he told her as he bestowed a kiss upon her proffered cheek.

"How fine *you* look" was her smiling reply.

Emmeline dimpled when he turned to her. "Well, Emmy, what a picture you make. You grow more fetching every time I see you."

"Coming from such a connoisseur of females, Gav, that is indeed a compliment, and I thank you for it!"

They embraced, and then Mr. Stanbury turned to his mother once again to observe, "When Emmy makes her debut next Season, she will take the ton by storm. I trust you're prepared for the onslaught."

The girl chuckled. "I cannot wait. I intend to break so many hearts, I shall lose count—just like Lady Allerton!"

Her mother looked wry as Mr. Stanbury replied, "I fear for every eligible young gentleman, for only the one can claim your heart."

"Need I remind you that *you* are considered to be among the most eligible?"

"That, I think, is doing it too brown! I am surely long past the time I could set myself up as a debutante's catch."

"That is the crux of the problem," his mother observed, frowning slightly.

"How is Father?" Mr. Stanbury asked then in an obvious attempt to change the subject from one that had become painfully familiar on his visits home.

"In fine health, I thank you. He is out on the estate but in a great fidge to see you. How long do you stay, dearest?"

The young man looked abashed. "Only until tomorrow, Mother. I'm tooling down to Brighton in the morning."

"Oh, Gav," his sister lamented, "that is a great pity. I had hoped for a drive in your splendid new curricle. It's far superior to the old one."

He glanced over his shoulder to where his tiger was unloading a cloak bag from the basket of the elegant equipage. "The horses are tired after the journey down from London, but I daresay we could tool around the park for a while."

Emmeline began to jump up and down with excitement as she put on her chip-straw bonnet at last. "How I wish you were staying longer," she told him as they went down the steps. "You could relate to me all the latest on-dits from town."

"The Season's over. The biggest scandal at present is Byron's association with Caro Lamb."

"So it still continues?"

"On her part, at least."

"How I long to make *his* acquaintance."

"He is a singularly charmless fellow, Emmy. You'll be sorely disappointed, I promise you."

"Leave me some illusions, I beg of you! Seriously, Gav, I do wish you were staying a little longer. We scarce see you nowadays."

"Brighton isn't far away. You and Mother can come down to stay if you wish."

"I would certainly find that diverting, but Papa is anxious for us to spend some time with Uncle Freddie in Yorkshire."

"Ah, to catch the end of the racing season, no doubt."

"No doubt," she echoed with a grin. "I daresay you'll not be averse to attending Lewes and Brighton courses yourself." Then she cast him a sly look. "In any event, I fancy you'll be too busy with those you'll find in Brighton to concern yourself for us."

The young man merely smiled, but before he could hand his sister onto the box, Sir Stephen came striding round the corner, his muddy boots crunching on the gravel.

"By all that's blue!" he cried when he caught sight of his son.

The two gentlemen greeted each other heartily. "It's good to see you, Father."

"And I you, you may be sure."

Mr. Stanbury's eyes narrowed slightly. "You look rather flustered, sir. Is anything wrong?"

Sir Stephen waved his hand dismissively in the air. "It's nothing untoward. Just the trials of being a good landlord. A fox got into Clackett's henhouse last night and killed several hens. The others, naturally, stopped laying. If that isn't enough, last week's storm damaged no less than five roofs, and it's always a race to have them repaired; *and* in addition to those catastrophes Harrington's bull took a fancy to one of Maydock's heifers and trampled down the hedge in his ardor." As his two offspring laughed at the tale of woe, Sir Stephen continued, "I tell you, Gav, all this will be yours when I slip the wind, so you may as well enjoy yourself while you may!"

"I sincerely hope I may continue to do so for many years to come."

"You've arrived earlier than any of us expected."

"It took me only two and a half hours from Chester Square, sir. I made excellent time, despite a farm cart overturned on the road at Croydon."

"Impressive, most impressive, but don't, I implore you, tell your mother." Sir Stephen glanced past his son, saying, "You're not leaving already, are you?"

Emmeline dimpled. "Gav is taking me for a drive in his new curricle, Papa."

"That's a matter of great import," Sir Stephen said with a laugh, "so I'll not detain you. Just don't let Emmy race the curricle. She quite fancies herself a whip, you know."

"The horses are tired, so I'll be certain to restrain her rasher instincts."

"Oh, pooh" was the young lady's response.

As Sir Stephen began to walk away, he added, "I've a new consignment of claret in the cellar, and I'm looking forward to your opinion of it."

"What a splendid set of blood and bone," Emmeline told her brother when they set off at last.

"Glad you approve," he answered with a grin.

"They look expensive."

"They are."

"They're real goers."

"Glad you think so."

She cast him an exasperated look. "How do all those toplofty ladies endure your sarcasm?"

"They love it. They're so glad of any word from me."

Miss Stanbury chuckled. After they'd been riding for some few minutes, he handed the ribbons to her, and she took them eagerly.

"I can't wait to drive my own carriage in Park Lane, and even in Hyde Park at the fashionable hour," she told him as she set the horses at a gentle trot.

"I have a pretty little gig in mind for you."

"La! I'd liefer drive a high-perch phaeton, like Lady Jersey."

Her declaration made him laugh. "Whatever your carriage, you will cause a sensation when you come out. There's no doubt about that."

"I intend to. The gentlemen will, no doubt, flock to my door, but I shall, of course, be most popular among the debutantes because I am the sister of the handsome Gavin Stanbury. Every one of them will seek to ingratiate themselves with me in the hope of finding favor with you."

"Stuff and nonsense! It will be for your own sake, sis."

"That, too," she answered with a grin. "Oh, Gav, it will be so exciting meeting people I have heard of only by repute. Gentlemen like Mr. Brummel."

"You'll find him horridly condescending even in the unlikely event he actually acknowledges you."

She suddenly cast him a curious look. "I am also in a great fidge to clap eyes upon Lady Allerton. I hear she is an accredited beauty."

"She is certainly that," he answered wryly.

"No doubt she will be residing in Brighton for the next few weeks."

"No doubt" was his maddeningly noncommittal answer.

Emmy looked all at once concerned. "Are you *very* fond of her, Gav?"

He hesitated before answering. He brought out his gold snuffbox and took a pinch before answering as he put it away again. "We certainly divert each other."

Emmeline continued to stare at her brother to the exclusion of all else. It was only his quick action in grabbing the ribbons that prevented the curricle from veering off the path and down a deep slope.

When he brought the curricle perfectly to halt outside the house, Mr. Stanbury climbed down and went to give his sister his hand. As he did so, she said, wrinkling her nose, "Oh, I forgot to mention—Mama has invited the Burges to join us for dinner tonight."

The young man groaned. "How subtle of her." Emmeline gave him her hand and stepped down from the curricle. "It will be to no avail. *You* know that, don't you?"

The girl chuckled. "I know, but Mama is quite determined you shall marry."

"Not Miss Burge, surely?"

"Mama is growing desperate."

"So is Miss Burge."

"She's quite a good sort of person."

Her brother had begun to look bored. To those other than his adored sister, the sign was a clear signal to desist or else attract one of his cutting remarks, dreaded by all those who sought his favor.

"It wasn't her fault she didn't succeed in finding a husband in her first Season in London."

"Ah, yes, that is patently true, but what about the second and third Seasons?"

Both burst out laughing and then hurried up the steps and into the house just as Mr. Stanbury's tiger drove the curricle toward the stable block.

TWO

It was midmorning on the following day when the splendid dark green curricle swept into the yard of The Dog and Gun, an inn on the Brighton Road, much used by the Quality.

Mr. Stanbury brought his team to a halt just behind an elegant traveling carriage that was also standing in the yard. As he passed it, he traced his fingers along the coat of arms painted on the door and acknowledged the bow of the lackey on duty by the carriage.

The landlord greeted him with a low bow and then escorted him to a private parlor at the rear of the property. Sitting on a window seat, gazing out at the fields beyond, was Lady Allerton, often described as the loveliest woman in England. The gossips of the ton were, for once, united in praise of her.

Her red velvet pelisse and matching bonnet with its lining of fine pleated silk only enhanced the pale splendor of her flawless complexion, the almost black luminescence of her eyes, and her invitingly pouted cherry red lips.

When Mr. Stanbury entered the parlor, she turned her dazzling smile upon him. A maidservant who had been sitting in the corner of the room got to her feet on his arrival, bobbed a brief curtsy, and went past him out of the room.

"I hope I haven't kept you waiting, Kitty."

"Anticipating your arrival only adds to my pleasure."

He went to take her hand and raised it to his lips. "You look incredibly beautiful this morning, my dearest Kitty."

"Then I fancy we are well suited, sir."

"Oh, yes, I'm persuaded that is so."

When he relinquished her hand, she said invitingly, "Join me for some breakfast."

"I thank you, dearest heart, but I enjoyed a hearty meal before I left Rydal Park."

Her lips curved into a wry smile. "How are Sir Stephen and Lady Stanbury? In good health, I trust?"

"Oh, indeed."

She continued to smile as she asked, "Are they still concerned for your bachelor status?"

"Certainly," he answered with a slightly uncomfortable laugh. "How did you know?"

"Lady Stanbury is often heard to declare it."

He covered her hand with his own. "Dear Mother. She can't understand that the only female in the entire country I would marry is not available to me."

"That is truly flattering, Gavin, and I am indebted to you for saying so, but Lady Stanbury is quite correct. You ought to be thinking of settling down with some respectable female."

His eyes opened wide. "Kitty! Not you, too! That is outside of enough!"

She laughed, and it was a delightful gurgling sound that entranced all who were fortunate to hear it. "You may be sure I have no intention of pursuing the matter if you do not. All I wish to do is enjoy the next few weeks in Brighton and your company whenever it is available to me."

"As often as I can contrive, you may be sure," he promised, his good spirits restored.

Her eyes met his and he said briskly, "If you are rested enough, I believe it's time to leave. Send your carriage on, Kitty, and drive into Brighton with me."

"I can think of nothing more delightful. Let us delay no longer."

As the curricle bowled along the Brighton Road at a fine pace, the couple gossiped and laughed about all they knew.

"How droll you are, Gavin," Lady Allerton told him. "No one diverts me as well as you do."

He stole a glance at her before returning his attention to the road. "As long as I continue to do that, I am certain to remain in your favor."

"You will always be that, whatever else the future holds. I don't expect our wonderful association to last forever. A lady in my position would be foolish to do so. . . ."

"Kitty, don't speak as if our affection is a temporary thing."

"It is, my dear," she answered, sounding sad, "and you would do well to acknowledge the fact."

He turned to cast her an imploring look. It was then that a rider shot across the front of the curricle, having galloped headlong onto the road from a thicket that had obscured her approach, missing the carriage by a hairsbreadth and causing the team to shy.

"Oh, do look out!" Lady Allerton cried in the second or two it took for the rider to flash past them.

There could have been a catastrophe had Mr. Stanbury possessed a lesser skill in handling his team, but he quickly brought it to a standstill with no harm done to any human or animal, or to the coach work of the curricle. The tiger, a lad by the name of Benton, jumped down and went to hold the heads of the team while the horsewoman brought her mount under control without being unseated herself.

"Are you all right?" Mr. Stanbury asked of his passenger, who nodded before she adjusted her bonnet.

Then she turned to look at the horsewoman. "But what of her?"

Gavin shot her a brief glance before he said, "Excuse me for one moment, my dear," and climbed down from the curricle.

Lady Allerton adjusted her pelisse as she watched him stride over to the person who had almost caused them all injury. She was in the process of calming down her horse, patting its neck and murmuring soothingly in its ear.

"Madam," he said in his most severe tone, "you almost caused an accident with your foolhardy behavior."

The lady raised her head to look at him through a pair of large blue eyes filled with unshed tears, and it came as a shock to him to discover she was scarcely more than a child.

"I do beg your pardon most heartily, sir. Bethany just ran away with me. I believe it was the sound of your team that startled her."

"You might do well to keep away from the public

13

highway until you've learned better horsemanship, ma'am," he told her in a less severe tone just as the sound of hooves heralded the arrival of another rider.

Although Mr. Stanbury had expected the belated arrival of a groom, it was a second female who galloped up to the scene, and the moment she arrived she jumped down from the horse and ran up to the young lady.

"Lynette, are you all right? Oh, my dear . . ."

"Yes, I'm fine, dearest. Don't fuss. It's all nothing."

On being so assured, she swung round on Mr. Stanbury, who found himself looking into a pair of very similar blue eyes, these filled with fury rather than tears.

"It is no thanks to you, sir, that my sister is unharmed."

The young man was somewhat taken aback by the unexpected attack and exclaimed, "I do beg your pardon, ma'am!"

He noted then that she was taller than normal for a lady and easily able to look him in the eye, which she did without flinching.

"And so you should. I am out of all patience with so-called Corinthians who tear up and down the roads every summer, bringing chaos to respectable travelers! It is not to be borne!"

Throughout the tirade the young man's demeanor slowly changed from surprise to outrage, and he began to protest at last. "Hold hard there, ma'am—"

"No, I will not. Last summer I lost a valuable horse through the carelessness of some young buck who raced his curricle along the Downs, fancying

14

himself, no doubt, a real bang-up blade when he was no more than a ninnyhammer, bringing terror to all those who were unfortunate enough to cross his path!"

Mr. Stanbury regarded her coldly, something not welcomed by anyone acquainted with him. "Do you equate *me* with such recklessness, ma'am?"

"Yes, I most certainly do!"

"Then I am bound to advise you I take it amiss."

"Flavia," the other young lady wailed, "it was *my* fault, not this gentleman's. Bethany bolted, and I couldn't stop her from dashing across the road. If this gentleman hadn't driven to an inch, I would have been in dire trouble."

For a long moment the elder of the two ladies looked disbelieving, glancing first at Lady Allerton, who said, "It's quite true, my dear," and then back at Mr. Stanbury.

Much of the passion in her manner died away, but she did not flinch from facing him again. "I must heartily beg your pardon, sir, for my assumption, but you cannot blame it on me. Much of what I said still stands. There are many reckless drivers in and around Brighton at this time of the year. I am delighted to discover you are not one of them. Good day to you both."

So saying, she climbed back into the saddle, using the stump of a tree as a mounting block, and rode away at a fast gallop, accompanied by the other young lady, who managed to convey to him an apologetic look before she was gone. Gavin Stanbury watched them go, and then, adjusting his high-crowned beaver into its usual jaunty angle, he walked back to the carriage.

"What a hornet for one so young," he said, still looking amazed.

"She was no toadeater, I'll grant you that," Lady Allerton responded with a chuckle.

As he climbed back onto the box, he indicated to Benton that he should return to his perch before they set off.

"Some young sprigs do race chariots to a reckless degree," Lady Allerton told him.

"I have also seen it, Kitty, but it doesn't give that ... branding iron leave to berate me in that unspeakable fashion."

"No harm was done, so 'tis best forgotten," the countess told him, and when he glanced at her, she mused, "I wonder who they can be?"

"I have no wish to know, Kitty."

"Sisters, I fancy. The elder was quite handsome in a patrician way. The younger was very fetching indeed. Did you notice?"

He gave his full attention to the road as they came into the town itself. "I was too busy admiring the pair of rum prancers they were riding."

Lady Allerton laughed in disbelief. "It is quite a tragedy, Gavin, when the most attractive of gentlemen invariably notice a horse rather than a fetching female."

"Only sometimes, Kitty," he vowed, glancing at her in a meaningful manner. "Only sometimes."

THREE

The house Gavin Stanbury had rented for the summer season was a large one on Marine Parade, complete with stable block, and overlooking the sea. Most Fashionables owned or rented houses on the Steine in proximity to the Prince Regent's Marine Pavilion. However, none of those properties enjoyed a sea view, and Mr. Stanbury was of the opinion that a stay in Brighton should include views of the very thing bringing them all to the coast.

Moreover, by means of his telescope, he was able to enjoy views of passing boats, including the *Dieppe Packet*, which decanted its passengers into small sailing boats to bring them to shore, depositing them—often dripping wet—onto the beach.

On his arrival Mr. Stanbury first escorted Lady Allerton to her own house on the Steine before proceeding to Marine Parade, where he found his servants already in residence, the house spotless, his clothes pressed and put away, and the kitchen a hive of activity.

"I shall be out for dinner tonight," he informed the house steward as he envisaged an enjoyable evening spent in the company of his inamorata, preceded by the obligatory walk on the Steine, where they would see everyone of importance who was staying in Brighton, and, just as importantly, be seen by them.

They'd exchange pleasantries with acquaintances and perhaps listen to various airs being played by the Gloucester Militia, or the Prince Regent's Italian musicians, who performed on the pavilion lawns every afternoon. Afterward they would be entirely alone together for as long as they wished.

The house steward held out a silver salver to his master. "These were awaiting your arrival, sir. Would you care to peruse them now?"

Mr. Stanbury cast them a disinterested glance, knowing that the various invitations to card parties, assemblies, and such would be duplicated in Kitty's house, and he preferred to leave it to her to decide which of them to accept.

"Later, Dowsett, later," he told the house steward, dismissing him with a wave of his hand.

"There is the one communication the messenger stressed was urgent, sir," the house steward persisted, "and I was asked to impress that upon you."

The young man drew an almost imperceptible sigh. "Oh, very well."

He stared at the unfamiliar hand for a moment or two and then turned it over, startled when he recognized the Prince Regent's own seal. He frowned, for although he had, naturally, expected an invitation or two to soirees at the Marine Pavilion, to receive so urgent a summons was puzzling.

After he had read it, he dropped the missive back on the salver, saying, "I am obliged to go out for a while, Dowsett."

As he strolled along Marine Parade through the crowds, he reflected that Brighton in summer was most pleasant and Lady Allerton's presence could only make it more so. Since the prince had bought the Marine Pavilion for his summer residence, the town had grown to an astounding degree with its attendant popularity, and at this time of the year it appeared that most of the beau monde had removed from London to the coast.

He passed several people of his acquaintance, but he didn't stop to speak to any of them. The note he had received indicated a matter of some urgency, and he was obliged to respect that.

When he rounded the corner onto the Steine, he was amazed anew to see how many houses had sprung up in so few years. Originally the prince had rented a humble farmhouse, but over the years, after purchasing the property, he had bought up others nearby to enlarge the area and expand the building, which was now beginning to resemble an Eastern mosque while inside all was of the Chinese fashion. Those who considered themselves acquaintances of the prince followed him to the seaside, often pretending it was purely for the sake of their health. As a consequence, all around houses sprang up in proximity to the Pavilion, but none with so exotic an appearance.

As Mr. Stanbury stepped into the octagonal entrance hall, Sir John Lade was coming toward him, and he raised a hand in greeting.

"Ah, Lade, perhaps you can enlighten me as to—"

"Sorry, I can't delay, Stanbury. I have an appointment, and Prinny has asked me to be back later in the afternoon. I daresay I'll have the opportunity of conversing with you then."

"I daresay," the young man replied smilingly. He

watched Sir John leave and then presented his card to the lackey on duty.

A short while later Gavin Stanbury was escorted into the Chinese Gallery, with its couches and chairs of figured ivory. Everywhere were red-and-black lacquered panels, huge lanterns, and garish chinoiserie. The young man's nose quivered slightly in distaste as always when he entered the prince's domain. How anyone could live among objects of such overpowering bad taste he could not imagine.

The Prince Regent was seated on one of the sofas, surrounded by a number of courtiers, to whom the visitor nodded affably. All were well known to him; Lord Alvanley, the Duke of Devonshire, the Marquess of Conyngham, and Colonel Hugh Fitzsimmons, the prince's personal private secretary, who had written the note he'd received. Gavin assumed that the reason the prince reclined upon a sofa was that a chair would not accommodate his enormous bulk.

He bowed before the prince. "Your Royal Highness."

"Ah, Stanbury, good of you to come so speedily." He glanced around him briefly and then, with some difficulty, hauled himself to his feet. In Gavin's opinion the prince had grown considerably fatter since he'd last seen him. "Walk with me to the stables. I would have words with you in private, sir."

Gavin noticed that the prince walked with great difficulty owing to his increasing girth. "I don't ride much nowadays," he informed his companion, "but I still like to inspect the cattle. I'm holding some excellent diversions this summer. I hope you'll be free to attend some of them."

"It will be an honor to do so, sir."

"It's devilish difficult having no official hostess, but the ladies arrive after dinner, and we have a very gay time."

They walked slowly, leaving the Pavilion itself and moving toward the luxurious stables, built as a circular construction with a glass dome. It was the construction of this particular building, causing some to remark that the prince's horses lived in greater splendor than he, that led to the spate of building and overbuilding of the Pavilion itself.

So far nothing in the prince's conversation had solved the puzzle of so urgent a summons, and Gavin found himself venturing, "The note I received, sir, indicated you had business with me of an urgent nature."

"Stanbury, were you at the Lewes races last Thursday?"

"No, sir, I was not. Unfortunately, business kept me in London."

"That is a great pity. It was a splendid meeting. Quite splendid. One of the best I've attended in years. The Ladies' Plate was won by a horse called Brighton Beau."

"I'm afraid I've never heard of it, sir," Mr. Stanbury replied, feeling even more mystified than ever. "Did it race at Ascot?"

"No, not as yet. In fact, I'm given to understand it has raced on very few occasions, but when it does, it wins."

"I wish I *had* seen it, sir."

"You have that pleasure to come. The colt is quite exceptional, and, to be brief, I have set my heart upon owning him. What could be more fitting than owning a horse called Brighton Beau?"

Mr. Stanbury smiled. "It is most fitting. Is it a miler or middle distance?"

"A miler, and the best you will ever see. I am convinced of it."

As they entered the great circular building with its drinking fountain in the middle, Gavin asked, "Do you have it in your stables yet?"

"No, dammit!" The prince slapped the riding whip he was carrying against his huge thigh. "The doxy won't sell!"

The young man frowned. "I do beg your pardon, sir, but I'm not quite sure I understand."

"Quite! How could you?"

A gray stallion was being led out to the fountain, and the prince paused to pat his flank. "What a horse, eh, Stanbury?"

"He is quite splendid, sir," the young man replied.

"What was I saying?" the prince asked as they moved on.

"Brighton Beau, sir."

"Ah, yes. I can see you are mystified, and I don't blame it on you. Just thinking about it brings out my choler."

Grooms and stable lads were leading out various of the prince's very impressive collection of horses to drink at the fountain.

"Do you recall the name Frank Allenbrooke?"

Mr. Stanbury considered for a moment before answering, "No, I don't believe I do, sir."

"He fancied himself a racing man, and, to be generous, he raised some reasonable cattle, but his ambition, like so many others', was to breed a champion racehorse. In pursuing that dream, he almost brought himself to buckle and thong."

22

"That isn't uncommon, sir."

"No, indeed. Look there, Stanbury." He pointed the whip in the direction of a handsome mare being led out of her stall. "Rosie. A favorite of mine. She's one of the best, but nothing I possess can compare with Brighton Beau."

"Pardon me for asking, sir, but what has this to do with Frank Allenbrooke?"

"Ah, yes. Well, Allenbrooke stuck his spoon in the wall last year. He keeled over at the last race meeting of the season. Slipped the wind without ever knowing he had bred a champion at last."

"Ah ..." Mr. Stanbury murmured, understanding more at last.

"I'll wager, Stanbury, this colt can beat anything set up against it."

"What you have told me, sir, has considerably whetted my appetite, and I shall certainly look forward to seeing the horse in action before too long."

"You will, Stanbury, and in my colors, too, if I have anything to say in the matter! That is why I need your assistance." Gavin looked at him curiously, the prince's once-handsome countenance now hidden behind copious folds of flesh.

"If it is possible, sir."

"Allenbrooke left no male heir, just a spinster daughter who inherited everything, including the colt. It is she who has refused to sell, and you can well imagine how mortifying that is to me."

"Mortifying, indeed, but can you blame her, sir, if the colt is only half as good as he seems?"

"The woman has windmills in her head. The estate is in dire need of funds, and what can some old tabby want with a racehorse? It's my belief the besom only dithers in the hope of forcing up the price."

"The colt must have attracted the attention of others, sir," Gavin ventured.

"Oh, indeed it has. I am certainly not the only one interested, by any means, but I have offered a generous price. You know me, Stanbury."

"Yes, sir," Gavin answered with a heavy heart, knowing how extravagant the prince could be.

"First I sent Johnny Lade, and the thornback sent him away with a flea in his ear, if you please. Then Fitzsimmons made it clear to her it was I who was seeking to buy and it was her loyal duty to sell." Gavin couldn't help but smile. "The jade still refused."

"She is evidently a formidable female, but tell me—how can I be of assistance in this matter?"

"I want you, Stanbury, to go and persuade her to sell."

"Me, sir?" Gavin asked in great astonishment. "I cannot see where I can succeed where your own personal emissaries have failed."

"Come, come, Stanbury, you are unusually diffident today." He began to walk out of the building, the unwilling young man following behind. "You know a great deal about horseflesh and, I'm persuaded, even more about female sensibilities."

Gavin couldn't help but laugh, feeling somewhat embarrassed. "Sir, I am flattered—"

"You needn't be. Your current situation vis à vis a certain countess has many gentlemen envious of you. Truth to tell, I am a little smoky myself."

Once again the young man laughed uncomfortably, and the prince went on. "The most sought-after demireps and accredited beauties, as well as

24

bread-and-butter misses, fall prey to your charm. Don't be bashful about it."

"I warn you, sir, that my charm, such as it is, is unpracticed on squeezecrabs."

"She'll be unused to the wicked wiles of a rake like you. She'll have no defense against your charm. Will you give it a try?"

"If Your Royal Highness wishes it, but I can guarantee nothing."

"I have great faith in you, sir. Tell her to name her price. Fitz will give you directions to where she lives, not far from Brighton itself. Join me here for dinner tomorrow evening, and you can report to me, hopefully, your success."

He waddled off as fast as his legs could carry him, leaving Gavin to stare after him in astonishment. Then, realizing he had nothing to lose by making one last attempt to persuade this female to part with her prized colt, he shrugged philosophically before going to find the prince's personal private secretary.

FOUR

On the following morning Gavin Stanbury's elegant curricle could be seen driving toward the house of the late Frederick Allenbrooke. So detailed were Colonel Fitzsimmons's directions, the young man didn't take one wrong turn.

The prince's faith in his ability amused Gavin. However, as he approached the modest house high up on the Downs, he hoped he would be successful. He wished, naturally, to please the prince, but on any account he disliked failure. Privately he had always believed he could persuade any female to do his bidding. It was always surprisingly easy to bring them about. It appeared obvious to him that the real failure was in their initial approach. For some reason both Fitzsimmons and Johnny Lade had put up the woman's bristles.

Recounting his conversation with the prince to Lady Allerton later that evening, Gavin could only make her laugh. "That is a preposterous burden to put upon you," she protested.

"But rather a flattering one, don't you think?"

"If Prinny had asked me for my opinion, I would have had to agree with him on the strength of your persuasive powers, but then I am no ape-leader."

He caught his breath. "No, you are certainly not that, my love."

"I only wish I could accompany you to Marston to witness your attempts to wheedle this female."

"That won't fadge, Kitty. Nothing is more certain to put her on her high ropes than the sight of a dazzling beauty like you showing up her shortcomings."

"All the same, Gavin, one does wonder whether Prinny is afflicted by the same madness as the king."

Now he approached the property without haste, preferring to assess the situation at his own leisure. He had not sent word of his arrival, preferring surprise in this instance. Miss Allenbrooke could not then arrange to avoid him.

He left the curricle on the gravel drive outside the modest stone house, with its uninterrupted views across the Downs as far as the sea. He was bound to admit to himself as he turned his back on the house to survey the scene, it was a pleasant vista that met his eyes.

An elderly maidservant answered the rattle of the door knocker, and he handed her his card. "Be so kind as to ask Miss Allenbrooke to spare me a few minutes of her time," he said as he removed his hat and gloves and handed them to the startled woman.

She continued to gaze at the elegantly dressed gentleman, the likes of whom she had rarely seen, for a moment or two before he urged, curbing his irritation, "Be so good as to inform your mistress that I am here."

Belatedly the woman bobbed a curtsy before showing him into the tiny parlor off the hall.

When she had gone, he did not sit down on any of the shabby chairs but wandered around gazing at the many sporting prints that adorned the walls. He was studying a print of the Godolphin Arabian, from which all thoroughbreds were descended, when the door opened, causing him to swing round on his heel to find himself being observed by a squab of a woman who was fingering his card. She was well into middle age, dwarfed by his own height, and stout. In his brief appraisal Mr. Stanbury was pleased to discover that the woman's expression appeared rather benign and was not what he had expected at all. This woman could not possibly be as difficult as she had been described.

"Mr. Stanbury . . . ?" she asked hesitantly.

"Indeed I am. I do hope I haven't called at an inconvenient time."

He bestowed upon her one of his devastating smiles, and she became rather flustered, which was a good indication, he thought.

"Not especially, but—"

"Good. I'm sure you're very busy, and I wouldn't wish to delay your going about your business."

"You are not, I assure you, sir."

"Miss Allenbrooke, I assure you I have no wish to take up more of your time than is absolutely necessary. . . ."

Just then the woman's face broke into a foolish smile. "Oh, I am not Miss Allenbrooke. I am Bella Bowman, Miss Allenbrooke's aunt."

"I do beg your pardon most heartily, ma'am," Mr. Stanbury replied, feeling chagrined at his error.

"My niece always rides out with the horses every morning, but she will be back very shortly."

"May I wait?" he asked, bestowing upon the flustered woman another of his famous smiles.

"By all means, sir. May I bring you some refreshment while you wait?"

"There is no need to trouble, ma'am. My business with your niece will not take too long, I fancy."

She smiled again, knowingly this time. "I'm persuaded it won't, sir. I was about to take a breath of air myself, and you have about you the look of a man who prefers the outdoors. Would you care to walk with me?"

"What a delightful suggestion, ma'am. I am all anxiety to see the famous Allenbrooke cattle."

"Only the one horse as yet, Mr. Stanbury," Mrs. Bowman told him as they came out of the house. "The others are not out of the ordinary at all, and I'm persuaded they won't interest you in the least."

"The purpose of my visit is somewhat transparent, I feel."

She chuckled. "We have had very few visitors over the years, sir, especially those from the highest strata of Society. Of late there have been a good many. Why, sir, do you know we have received emissaries from one of the highest-placed gentlemen in the country?"

"The colt must be very special to have attracted so much attention."

"Oh, he is, but I feel it only fair to warn you my niece is not inclined to sell. She has set her face against it, despite the remarkable amount of persuasion put to her of late."

"We shall see," he murmured, inhaling a lungful

of the good Sussex air as they neared the surprisingly large stable block.

It seemed evident that the late Frederick Allenbrooke had impoverished himself and his family to pander to his desire to breed and race horses. If only his daughter proved less dedicated, but he had feared from the outset this could prove to be a fool's errand, and nothing he had heard or seen since had persuaded him otherwise.

"Does Miss Allenbrooke train the horses herself?" he asked.

"Munnings, our head groom, takes on the task." Mr. Stanbury's eyebrows rose slightly, and Mrs. Bowman went on, "Tommy, one of the stable boys, is our jockey. He has a remarkable rapport with the animals. We couldn't wish for better."

"How long have you lived here with Miss Allenbrooke?" he asked in a conversational tone as he mentally digested the information she had supplied so readily.

"Ever since her dear mama died, which was several years ago. I was by then a widow, and my brother asked if I would come to Marston to look after his girls, which I was more than happy to do. It served all our needs."

"Girls, ma'am?"

"Oh, yes, I have the two nieces, sir; the younger is but a child. We do hope to launch her into Society next Season, but I'm afraid that will depend entirely upon the future success of Brighton Beau."

"You have evidently already received several offers to buy the colt, ma'am."

"It would be useless to deny it."

The conversation was abruptly brought to an end by the arrival of two horses ridden into the stable yard by grooms. One glance told Gavin that neither of these was the celebrated racehorse, and he was beginning to feel more anxious to see Brighton Beau and get the measure of his owner for himself.

When a few moments later a glorious chestnut colt was ridden into the yard, the young man knew he was looking at Brighton Beau, and the excitement generated by his appearance on the racecourse had not been in the least exaggerated.

The stable boy who had been riding him dismounted, and Mr. Stanbury glanced at Mrs. Bowman to ask, "May I . . . ?"

"By all means, sir. You are not like to see anything as splendid in England today."

"No, indeed," he replied as he ran an admiring hand over the horse's steaming flank. "He is certainly a most splendid specimen of blood and bone."

"I am not certain I am doing you a service," Mrs. Bowman told him, looking rather uneasy. "I have it in mind all this will do is make you more determined to have him."

He raised his head to tell her, "I have great faith in my persuasive powers."

As the stable boy led the horse away, three more galloped into the yard, two of them ridden by females, the third by yet another of the stable hands.

Gavin Stanbury's eyes narrowed as he gazed across the yard, watching the two ladies dismount. He wasn't certain if they'd noticed him, which gave him a welcome opportunity to appraise them. Both were wearing rather shabby riding habits, something that didn't surprise him in the least from what he had already observed. Miss Allenbrooke would require several winning races before she could find herself financially comfortable, he suspected. If he was to be honest with himself, he did admire her stance so far. The temptation to sell and solve all her financial difficulties must be great.

One of the ladies was laughing at something the other had said as they dismounted, and when they both turned to walk in Mr. Stanbury's direction, he experienced a sharp stab of dismay as his memory was jolted into a painful reminder. The incident on the road the previous day had been entirely forgotten in his pleasure to be in Kitty's company. Now, however, he was going to be forced to recall it, for these were the two young ladies involved in the lamentable affair, and that did not bode well for the purpose of his visit.

"My dears," Mrs. Bowman greeted them, "this is Mr. Stanbury. He has been kind enough to call upon us."

Lynette Allenbrooke laughed delightedly, and he was reminded of her youth and considerable beauty. "You're the gentleman in the curricle yesterday, are you not?"

He smiled wryly and was glad to note that she at least did not hold the incident against him. "I regret to say that I am, ma'am."

"Why regret, sir?" she asked pertly, and instantly he knew that if this was the lady with whom he must deal, he would have no problem whatsoever. Unfortunately she was not. "Had Bethany encountered a gentleman with lesser driving skills, the outcome might have been disastrous for us all."

"I had no notion you were acquainted," Mrs. Bowman murmured, looking perplexed.

"Aunt Bella, it was a very brief encounter, I assure you! Mr. Stanbury is the gentleman in the curricle on Marston Down yesterday."

While this brief exchange had been taking place, Flavia Allenbrooke had taken the opportunity to observe him, a circumstance Mr. Stanbury found unusually uncomfortable.

When he found himself with no alternative, he forced himself to turn his attention to the elder sister. "Miss Allenbrooke, I wonder if I could take up a few minutes of your time?"

She raised the veil of her riding hat at last. There was no warmth in her manner. Her blue eyes regarded him like two pieces of ice. He had not expected anyone quite so young from the descriptions of her. He thought she could not be more than five and twenty, and he considered her more handsome than he had expected, although certainly not, by any means, as fetching as her sister.

"Why don't you go along to the house with Aunt Bella?" she suggested to her sister when she spoke at last. "Mr. ..."

"Stanbury," he supplied, forcing himself to continue in a pleasant manner when he wanted nothing so much as to deliver her a choice put-down.

"Mr. Stanbury and I will follow. I'm persuaded he will be able to reveal to me his business in that short time."

"I do so hope we will see each other again, Mr. Stanbury," Lynette told him wistfully.

"I'm sure we shall," he answered, injecting as much pleasantry into his manner as he could contrive.

"Good day to you, sir," Mrs. Bowman added as she hurried her young niece away.

He swept off his hat as he watched them go, and

33

then he returned his attention to Flavia Allenbrooke, his manner becoming a fraction less amiable.

"Brighton Beau is a most splendid horse, ma'am. He does you much credit, and you must be expecting a great deal of interest in him."

"I have made it quite clear I will not sell him, however high someone might bid."

His smile was rather sheepish. "Then it appears you have me at a stand."

Flavia Allenbrooke toyed with her gloves as she added, "There is an alternative I can offer. I have a yearling out of the same sire and dam, Royal Prince and Lady Mary. The yearling is for sale if you wish to purchase it."

"I doubt that the gentleman I represent would want a horse that is so far untried. Bloodlines are a good guide, but by no means infallible, as you must know very well."

"As you please," she answered coolly. "I have already received numerous offers for him."

Gavin was becoming impatient. "Miss Allenbrooke, I shan't mince words with you. I represent a very important gentleman who is so anxious to own the colt—Brighton Beau and no other—you may name your own price."

"Some things are beyond price," she answered, and he was more irritated than ever.

"Not in my experience, ma'am."

She gave a little gasp of exasperation. "Can you not see it would be foolish of me to sell just now? He is worth a fortune in prize money and eventual stud fees, much more than any outright amount you or anyone could offer me now."

"If you receive a lump sum, imagine to what use you can put it."

"I already have—many times," she told him candidly. "In any event, is it not true the gentleman you represent is in no position to offer any amount, however small?"

Mr. Stanbury laughed uncomfortably at his quest being so transparent to her. "I have no notion as to that, ma'am. Suffice to say I am empowered to offer anything you want."

Her face suddenly became animated. "All I have ever wanted was a winner—a champion. I have one now. Your principal will surely understand that."

"So you can offer no hope of an eventual change of mind?"

"None at all, and you would oblige me, Mr. Stanbury, if you would spread abroad among interested parties that very fact."

"I shall not be heeded."

Her head came up defiantly, and her eyes were full of the most disquieting passion. "If I were not a woman, I would not be pressed to sell."

All at once Gavin was anxious to be gone. "I won't keep you any longer, ma'am. Be certain I shall convey your refusal to the gentleman concerned."

"And anyone else who will listen to you."

He took her hand in his and raised it briefly to his lips. Her eyes met his over her hand for a brief moment.

As he relinquished his hold on her hand, she stepped back a pace and looked at him curiously. "Do you have racing stables of your own, sir?" She glanced at the team of chestnuts straining at the ribbons and added, "You have a good eye for horse-flesh, I fancy."

"Thank you, ma'am. I don't own racing horses as yet, although I have promised myself the indulgence one day. Perhaps when I settle down to matrimony."

"Would it be impertinent of me to ask if that is like in the near future?"

He smiled faintly as he backed away from her. "It is not in the least like, ma'am."

"Well, I bid you good day, sir. I am sorry I cannot give you the answer you require."

"Not good-bye, Miss Allenbrooke. Surely not good-bye." She looked at him quizzically and he added softly, "We are bound to meet again before long."

By the time he had climbed onto the box of the curricle, she had gone into the house, but he fancied he saw a curtain twitch on the upper story. Guessing it would be the apparently irrepressible Lynette, he raised his hat in her direction and turned the curricle, pointing it toward the lane.

He was almost out into the lane when a very opulent high-perch phaeton turned into the drive. Gavin recognized it instantly as that belonging to Sir Percy Cavander, an exquisite who fancied himself a pink of the ton and certainly a tulip of fashion. Gavin considered him more a man-milliner. He had pretensions to the racing world, as did many gentlemen of the ton, but his expert eye told Gavin that the team pulling the phaeton was ill-matched, and one horse was definitely touched in the wind. Gavin supposed that ownership of Brighton Beau would elevate him somewhat in the eyes of the more knowledgeable racing pinks.

When the curricle drew abreast of the phaeton, Gavin greeted Sir Percy cordially. "No prizes for guessing why you are here."

A peevish glint came into the gentleman's eye. "You may well be mistaken, sir. This is the home of Miss Flavia Allenbrooke."

"I know it. I have just had the pleasure of conversing with her."

"Then you are bound to agree she is the most delightful female, a diamond of the first water."

"Oh, indeed," the other man replied, unable to hide his sarcasm.

"I hope I might persuade her to drive with me on the Downs and discuss our mutual love of the turf. I can think of nothing more congenial."

Gavin smiled wryly. "I would not for anything accuse you of wanting anything more."

"It is clear to me why *you* are here," Sir Percy said accusingly, his tone growing considerably cooler. "May I inquire of Miss Allenbrooke's response to your . . . inquiry?"

"I am merely an intermediary, and therefore you will forgive me if I cannot reveal the substance of our conversation."

Sir Percy grinned knowingly. "No need, Stanbury, for I can hazard a guess. Poor Miss Allenbrooke is plagued by those who care for nothing except her horse. No wonder she takes it amiss. May the best man win!"

So saying, he flicked his whip over the back of his team and drove on in the direction of Marston House. A moment later Gavin Stanbury drove on, too, in the opposite direction, formulating in his mind how to break the unwelcome news to the prince that he had failed in his quest.

Flavia Allenbrooke had not been swayed by his charm, which was obviously not as great as everyone had credited. When Mr. Stanbury returned to Brighton, he was more than a little vexed at the outcome of the morning's visit.

FIVE

When Bella Bowman entered the parlor, it was to find her younger niece engaged in embroidery at the tambour frame, the elder standing at the window, gazing out at Sir Percy Cavander's departing high-perch phaeton.

"I thought I heard Sir Percy leaving," Mrs. Bowman murmured as she came into the room carrying a basket filled with linen, which she put down on a table.

"He has finally departed," Flavia replied, "but not forever, I fancy."

She turned to smile at her aunt, who had begun to sort through the linen in the basket. Both young ladies had changed out of their riding habits. Lynette wore a gown of jonquil jaconet muslin decorated with a modicum of honiton lace while her sister wore blue-and-white-striped poplin with a paisley shawl across her shoulders.

"What a court card he is," Lynette murmured.

"Oh, for shame!" Mrs. Bowman scolded as she began to mend a torn hem on the petticoat she had brought out of the basket. "Sir Percy is a very elegant as well as wealthy gentleman. We should be flattered he condescends to call upon us."

Flavia chuckled as she came away from the window at last. "I daresay Brighton Beau should be flattered, if only he knew what attention he was attracting! For myself I fear my nose is too short, my brow too narrow, and I have only the two legs!"

Lynette and her aunt both laughed before Mrs. Bowman said, "We mustn't be too hard upon ourselves, ladies. It is not inconceivable that Sir Percy rides over to pay court to you, Flavia, even though his initial interest may well have been Beau."

"Stuff and nonsense, Aunt. If Sir Percy is in search of a wife, he can do far better than a spinster of four and twenty with no fortune."

"You do have a fortune," her sister pointed out. "Brighton Beau."

"Ah, yes," Flavia answered thoughtfully, "so I do, and that is the reason for my popularity of late. It is not in the least flattering but most interesting to contemplate, *if* I were desperate to enter the parson's pound."

"I don't believe that is in Sir Percy's mind!" her aunt protested. "It is evident to me he is most taken by you, Flavia."

"If Flavia is to marry on those terms, I would far rather she choose a more elegant beau," Lynette pronounced.

"Oh, yes? Which of all my suitors, assuming I wish to be leg-shackled to some town spark, would you have me choose? I don't recall there being that many of them, in all truth, even with Beau as a lure!"

Looking somewhat uncomfortable, Lynette applied herself to the embroidery once again. "I thought . . . Mr. Stanbury was rather handsome."

For a moment her sister looked astonished, and then she laughed again. "Mr. Stanbury indeed!

What a crack-brained notion. The gentleman has only a care for a horse. Why, he never even looked at me properly."

"I disagree, dearest. I observed him examining you very closely indeed."

Two spots of color flamed in the young lady's cheeks. "I believe you are talking nonsense, my dear."

"If you say so, Flavia," Lynette answered demurely, "but I still think him very handsome, and his tailoring was quite out of the ordinary. There was nothing of the chawbacon or man-milliner about him."

"What a nonsensical conversation this is becoming," Flavia declared. "Let us be done with all the funning, my dears. I did not seek a husband before we had Beau and I shall not now."

"You could have married very well indeed," Mrs. Bowman mused as she observed her stitchery. "I recall Mr. Delavie—"

"He had buck teeth and thin hair," Lynette reminded her. "I did not like him at all."

"He was very well placed. Then there was the Reverend Fanwell, cousin to the Earl of Hope, not to mention Mr. Dudley, who bought that pretty little filly from us. . . . You treated them all most coldly, Flavia."

"Only because she wasn't in love with any of them," Lynette pointed out.

"La! What is that to anything?"

"Oh, Aunt Bella, it is everything."

"Dear, foolish child. You will learn better, I trust. In any event, your sister refused to put herself about socially, that was the trouble. All her waking hours were spent in the stables among the horses.

Far too much to my mind, but your father, dear to me as he was, refused to heed my warnings."

"Do you know if we have any more cerulean blue silk in the sewing box?" Lynette asked her sister as she regarded her sampler.

"I really cannot recall, dearest," Flavia answered vaguely, not having listened to the conversation for the last minute or two.

She was not in the least interested to hear an account of her failed romances, not one of which she regretted. She couldn't even recall the gentlemen to whom her aunt had alluded. By comparison she recalled Mr. Stanbury all too well, although she knew his type. Cold, heartless, vain, and selfish. A Corinthian. A nonesuch. A man to be wary of, if not actually avoided.

"If you have no notion, it is evident I shall be obliged to go and see for myself," Lynette decided, and Flavia looked at her blankly, so lost was she in her own thoughts.

When the girl had gone, Mrs. Bowman frowned in Flavia's direction. "You look somewhat troubled, dear. What is it? Will you tell me?"

"Oh, it is nothing untoward. I'm just a trifle unsettled. Having a horse the caliber of Beau means constant pressure from gentlemen of the ton. Owning him is such a triumph, and yet I am under pressure from people who know only to flash a wad of notes and think they can buy anything. Well, they'll be obliged to learn that they can't. Beau means more to me than anything or anyone, save you and Lynette."

"I know that, dear, but what concerns me more is that one day you may be left here alone, and that isn't in the least natural."

"I shall be content enough to see my sister well settled, and we are fully agreed that will not be a difficult task to achieve. If I am obliged to spend the rest of my days here at Marston, I shall consider myself fortunate indeed."

"That is not a natural ambition for a handsome woman in her very prime."

"I wasn't prepared to consider gentlemen who were interested in me for my own sake. Now that there is a reason for them to pay court to me, I want none of it."

"Foolish pride," her aunt muttered. "Few girls of your standing have a dowry of such value."

"Let Beau provide Lynette with a portion, and I will be well satisfied."

"You haven't begun to think what would result if Beau did not come up to your hopes for his future." When Flavia cast her a curious look, she went on. "What if he were to pull a muscle before an important race, or, heaven forbid, damage a tendon? We have seen that before, have we not? He will be of no value whatsoever, and we will be under the hatches!"

"I cannot allow myself the luxury of such extravagant fears, Aunt. Injury is a risk faced by all horses whether they race or just pull a plough."

"You'd do well to ponder on the possibility before you dismiss out of hand all those offers you're receiving, and while you're doing so reconsider this crack-brained notion of launching your sister into Society next Season."

"It isn't a crack-brained notion," Flavia protested. "You know full well I promised Papa—"

"Yes, yes, I know. . . . Will you be kind enough to thread this needle for me? My eyes are not what

43

they were." As Flavia went to do her aunt's bidding, Mrs. Bowman observed, "Your Papa was the dearest man, my only brother, but like some others with whom I have been acquainted, he concerned himself with little apart from the content of his stables. Money—or the lack of it—never concerned him in the least. Only when he backed a winner at the races did we contrive to have new gowns. There were times when we were all terribly shabby."

"No doubt that was why Mr. Stanbury looked down that long nose of his with so much disdain this morning while attempting to be conciliatory to us."

Mrs. Bowman laughed. "He did no such thing." All at once she became serious again. "Promise or no promise, I cannot see how we can *afford* to launch Lynette—not that with her looks she wouldn't cause an absolute sensation because we both know she will, and I am not in the least averse to spending a Season in London. Thank you, my dear," she murmured as Flavia handed her back the needle and thread.

"If Beau wins the Brighton Premier Plate, we will have more than sufficient funds to launch Lynette and provide her with a portion. Moreover, we will have no difficulty selling any foals we produce at Marston on the strength of his success. Our problems will be over, Aunt!"

"*If.*"

"You cannot doubt his ability, even with your limited knowledge of horses."

"There is a world of difference between a race at Lewes at the outset of the Season and the richest race at Brighton."

"I don't see that, Aunt."

Mrs. Bowman sighed and put down her sewing as Flavia sat down facing her. "The Brighton Premier Plate is a considerable prize, so it's logical the finest racehorses in the south of England will be entered."

"I'm aware of that, but he has no peers. He will win every race in which he is entered."

"That is very likely true, but—"

"So you see, Aunt," Flavia said with a smile, "you are being unnecessarily Friday-faced. Don't worry your head on such matters."

As she started to get up again, Mrs. Bowman said, "I am bound to worry. For all your knowledge of bloodlines and the like I feel you are shockingly naive about other matters."

"What other matters?"

"All those other owners, rich and influential, are not going to allow you to come in and win the greatest prize of the summer Season."

Flavia sank down into the chair again, her brow set into a deep frown. "Aunt Bella, what exactly are you trying to tell me?"

"One way or another you will not be allowed to win every prize in the racing calendar. There are too many deep gamesters with a great deal to lose."

"I don't wish to win *every* prize, even though I'm persuaded Beau can with no real effort, just the largest."

"It is all the same, dear. Mayhap you'd be best having pride in knowing a horse you have bred is in the royal stables."

A look of stubborn intensity came over her niece's face. "We have already discussed that matter at length, Aunt, and I have made my position clear.

As for the other, I believe you are being unnecessarily alarmist."

"I hope so." Mrs. Bowman sighed.

Flavia patted her comfortingly on the shoulder, but just as she was about to leave the room, her aunt ventured, "I know we roasted you before regarding matters matrimonial. . . ." Flavia turned to look at her again, an expression of resignation on her face. "All those gentlemen of fashion and fortune could be of use to Lynette."

"I don't see how. It is their wives and mothers we need to cultivate so that she has entry into the most exclusive circles of the ton."

"She might not need to go so far as London to achieve that. There are some very high-placed people here in Brighton this summer."

Flavia smiled. "I scarce think gentlemen like Sir Percy Cavander would interest themselves in Lynette, or she in them."

"There are others apart from Sir Percy. Mr. Stanbury, for instance." When Flavia drew in a sharp breath, her aunt demanded to know, "Well, why not? He is young, handsome, and it is evident to me he has made some kind of impression upon your sister."

Flavia shook her head. "It's impossible. He's too sophisticated for a green girl like Lynette."

"As far as I have observed, he has all the requisite qualities you are seeking in a husband for her. Moreover, I don't believe he is married—"

"He isn't," Flavia answered unthinkingly.

Her aunt cast her a surprised look before she went on. "I know the family by repute. They are respectable, and Mr. Stanbury is heir to a title and a substantial fortune."

"I am bound to confess I was not in the least impressed by Mr. Stanbury, Aunt, and even though I'm determined Lynette has a Season in London, her happiness is of greater import to me than even position and fortune."

"To me also, I assure you, but there is no harm in putting her in his way, for it is certain we have not seen the last of him at Marston."

Flavia cast her aunt a sharp look and was still considerably thoughtful a few minutes later when Lynette returned carrying several skeins of blue silk.

"Flavia, there is a rather splendid landau coming up the drive. Do you think it's another prospective buyer?"

Her sister groaned as she drew her shawl about her and went to the window. "The return of Sir Bonham Creevey, if I am not mistaken."

"I'm not acquainted with that particular gentleman, but you must ask him to stay for tea," Mrs. Bowman told her as she quickly folded up her sewing.

"You would oblige me by saying I'm out," her niece replied.

"Oh, surely not," her aunt protested, glancing meaningfully at Lynette.

Flavia smiled knowingly now. "Aunt Bella, Sir Bonham is all of five and sixty and"—she glanced out of the window again as the landau drew up outside the house—"gouty as well as married. In fact, Lady Creevey is with him. If you please, Aunt!" she added laughingly as she hurried out of the room.

"I seem to have missed the joke," Lynette complained, looking bewildered.

Mrs. Bowman gathered up the sewing basket. "It isn't in the least funny, my dear. I'm bound to confess it is a matter of the utmost seriousness!"

SIX

A number of elegant carriages were making their way toward the Marine Pavilion that evening when Mr. Stanbury arrived to take up his invitation for dinner. Although a stay in Brighton invariably meant several invitations from the prince, he couldn't help but wish he were about to spend this evening with Kitty. He hoped he would be able to slip away and enjoy a cozy supper with her later in the evening.

When he entered the lobby of the Marine Pavilion, he found another gentleman just arrived, and Mr. Stanbury couldn't help but admire his evening coat.

"Why, Stanbury," the other man greeted him, and the young man was flattered by the acknowledgment.

"I had heard you were in Brighton, Brummel."

"Ah, yes, where I go everyone knows." He glanced around at the ridiculous opulence of the decor. "There are more lamps in this place than in Harper's shop. Does Prinny not know when enough is sufficient?"

"Apparently not."

The Beau wrinkled his long nose in an eloquent gesture. "One could suppose King Midas has run amok through the pavilion rather than a demented prince. Not quite up to the knocker, eh, Stanbury?"

"What does it matter if some of his subjects don't approve, as long as it keeps His Royal Highness happy?"

"Nothing is of greater import than that," the Beau sniffed. "Don't you think Prinny is growing a little *too* fat? I'm concerned his legs might one day buckle beneath him."

Mr. Stanbury was obliged to stifle his laughter. "Concerned or not, I would counsel you to keep that piece of comment to yourself, sir—if you value the prince's friendship, that is."

"Pooh! I do him the greatest favor by being here. It is fashionable only where I am, sir!"

Although acquainted with the Beau from old, Mr. Stanbury was nonetheless confounded for a moment by that monumental piece of overweening vanity. By the time he had recovered himself, an equerry had arrived to escort him to the prince's inner sanctum for a private cose before dinner.

Beau Brummel looked curious and no doubt wondered what business he had with the prince to warrant a private interview. The Prince Regent was waiting in the library, which adjoined his private apartments. Thankfully it had escaped most of the decorative excesses of the remainder of the pavilion. When Gavin entered the library and the equerry bowed himself out, the prince waved the young man forward. He was sitting in a silvered chair, upholstered with scarlet silk, bearing the print of a dragon, a feature seen in much of the pavilion. He was dressed for dinner, incomprehensibly, in the uniform of a colonel in chief of the Tenth Hussars, a regiment barracked close to Brighton and also known as the Prince Regent's Own Royal Hussars. Maneuvers on the Downs orchestrated by their colonel in chief were held at regular intervals and said to be colorful to witness.

"Will you join me in a glass of Madeira, Stanbury?" the prince asked as Gavin bowed low before him.

"It will be a pleasure, sir."

"Then be so good as to pour a glass for us both while you are about it."

When he had done so, the prince indicated he should sit in a chair that was the twin of his own. "Brighton is becoming busy. I have a full table tonight. Lord and Lady Conyngham are coming. Deuced fetching female, Lady Conyngham."

Gavin smiled wryly into his glass of wine, for it had been rumored of late that Lady Conyngham was about to oust the redoubtable Lady Jersey as the prince's current favorite. Ladies of opulent dimensions and over a certain age did not attract Gavin, but he contrived to reply, "Her ladyship is most condescending, sir." As he settled into the chair, he added, "I encountered Brummel as I arrived."

"Damned popinjay!" the prince growled. "Did you know he's been slandering me?"

"No, sir, I didn't," Gavin answered diplomatically as he sipped at his wine.

"The fellow thinks he made me. I tell you, Stanbury, I can unmake *him* if I so choose. I made this town, too. Twenty years ago it was a village by the name of Brighthelmstone with nothing but the sea to recommend it. My presence has turned it into the town it has since become."

"Undoubtedly, sir."

All at once the prince's manner softened. "Enough of Brummel and Brighton. What luck did you have with Miss ... er ... Allenbrooke?"

The young man saw no advantage in prevaricating, so he answered heavily, "None at all."

Although the prince displayed no surprise at the news, he shook his head and clucked his tongue. "You disappoint me, Stanbury. Truly you do."

"With respect, sir, I think you must have known at the outset my chances were small."

The prince downed his Madeira and held out the goblet. "With respect, sir, I expected success from you."

As Gavin went to refill the goblet, he ventured to say, "I see no point in persevering. She is no goosecap and won't be persuaded to part with the colt, which she sees as her greatest asset."

The prince slammed his fists down on the silvered arms of the chair. "Dammit, man! I'm not accustomed to refusals. How dare she gainsay the first gentleman of Europe!"

Gavin remained silent as the prince went on. "My stars! Why could you not persuade her? I have seen you with females, Stanbury, and admired your style. I'm talking about fetching females of the ton, used to bucks pouring the butter boat over them. Tell me why she, of all females, is able to resist you?"

"I was attempting to purchase her colt, not make love to her," the young man replied smilingly.

"Balderdash! The principle is the same. Persuasion is the secret. I have seen the most sensible females become mooncalves without realizing it had even happened."

"I'm afraid you appoint me with qualities I do not possess, sir."

"Stuff and nonsense! This is no time to be bashful, man."

"Miss Allenbrooke has time only for her horses. The attentions of any gentleman, however charming, would be to no avail. She would know why she was being courted."

"Find me any female who is impervious to a gentleman's charm, especially when it's persistent." The prince sat forward in the chair, as much as his bulk allowed. "I mean to have that colt, and any other that catches my eye."

Gavin let out an almost indiscernible sigh before he ventured to say, "You haven't raced seriously for years, sir. Why is this horse so important to you now?"

"Possessing the finest racehorse in England will serve as a facer to those fools in the Jockey Club. With Brighton Beau in my stables I'll give them all the apoplexy." He chuckled at the thought before turning angry. "Do you know what they did to me, Stanbury?"

"I had heard a little of the matter, sir. A shameful episode—on their part," he added quickly.

The prince thumped the arm of his chair with a pudgy fist. "The monstrousness of it! To accuse me, the Prince of Wales, and my jockey of pulling a horse. I have rarely been more mortified in a life full of aggravation."

"You were quite right to cut up stiff, sir."

"Chufney would never have pulled a horse. What a facer it would be for my horse—Brighton Beau!—to win on every racecourse save Newmarket. Now that would set up the bristles of that pokerish establishment." He turned to look at Gavin again. "Did you truly do your very best to try and persuade her?"

"Truly I did, sir, but she is adamant, and even entreated me to broadcast her refusal to sell to all who would listen."

"I offer a great deal of blunt, and I am in almost all senses the king. It should be her privilege to please me."

"I'm persuaded she means no disrespect to your person, sir."

The prince stared morosely into his goblet. "It seems a very long time since I won the Brighton Cup with Ormerod. I don't suppose you recall that particular triumph."

"No, sir, but I have certainly heard tell of it on many occasions."

"Did you, by any chance, see the colt when you were at Marston?"

"I did have that privilege, sir, and he is, of course, everything you say of him. His legs are those of a real champion. However, the colt is not done proper justice in the Allenbrooke stables, which are run in the most ramshackle manner imaginable."

"How is that possible?"

"Heaven only knows, sir. The trainer is the head groom, and the jockey one of the stable boys. As far as I could observe, there is no logical regime for training. The breeding of this colt was nothing more than pure good fortune on Miss Allenbrooke's part."

"I have never been so fortunate, and I possess the finest facilities in the land."

"It is quite ironic, sir," Gavin agreed.

"There must be a way of persuading this woman," the prince insisted.

"I did wonder if there were debts—a mortgage perhaps that could be used as a lever."

"My inquiries have revealed that there is a mortgage, and Miss Allenbrooke is always short of funds, but there are no huge debts. She contrives to pay her way with some difficulty, so that won't fadge, I'm afraid."

"Then it's going to be difficult to know how to proceed."

For a long moment the prince regarded his guest with a gaze that disturbed the young man greatly, and then at last he spoke again. "You must make her fall in love with you. Make her so much in love, she will no longer care a jot for her horses, only her passion for *you*."

"Sir!" Gavin protested.

"Now, don't pretend you're put to the blush, 'cause I won't have it. The ladies don't call you 'Honey' Stanbury for nothing, sir."

Although he had been aware of the ridiculous appellation given to him by some ladies of the beau monde, he had never acknowledged it, nor had he minded it—until now, when he cursed it roundly to himself.

"It won't fadge, sir. Miss Allenbrooke is no mooncalf."

"She can't be to have produced the colt, but where the heart is concerned, all females tend to be a trifle cork-brained. Just make her throw all caution to the wind in your own inimitable way. I have great confidence in your abilities. You've already captured the heart of one of the loveliest creatures in the country, so don't go all niff-naffy on me,

Stanbury. Just make the chit throw her cap over the windmill long enough for me to slip in and relieve her of the colt while she looks upon you sweetly. Give her something other than horses to occupy her thoughts, and she will be grateful to you for it, I promise!"

"But, sir ..." Gavin continued to protest.

"No buts, Stanbury. Any female, especially one given the go-by, would far rather act the spoon than concern herself with cattle."

Recalling his two encounters with the elder Miss Allenbrooke, Mr. Stanbury somehow doubted it, but, knowing full well that once Prinny got a notion into his head there would be no discounting it, he drew a sigh before replying, "Very well, sir, I will give it a try if you wish it of me."

"What a nail you are, to be sure! Stout fellow. Fill up the glasses, and we'll drink a toast to the success of our little venture."

As he went to do so, Gavin pictured Flavia Allenbrooke's face as she had spoken to him that very morning and on the day prior to it. He recalled her contempt and high-handed attitude, and as he filled the goblets once again he smiled to himself. Perhaps bringing her to heel wouldn't be such a foolish idea after all. She was evidently spoiled and willful, the motherless product of an indulgent father. Perhaps at the end of the escapade Miss Flavia Allenbrooke wouldn't be quite so haughty as before.

He handed the prince his glass. "To Brighton Beau," the prince toasted. "May your success be as great as his!"

"As long as your plan doesn't oblige me to marry the woman, sir."

"Certainly not, provided you don't compromise her, and you are far too clever to do that. No female is like to inveigle you into the parson's pound, and I admire it in you. Marriage is a poor bargain, and no one is more aware of that than I. Once I have the colt in my ownership, you may give Miss Allenbrooke turnips. Good luck!"

"No doubt I shall need it," Gavin whispered as he downed the wine and contemplated silently how he might go about his unwelcome task.

SEVEN

Race day at the Lewes racecourse was a very colorful affair. Members of the beau monde, enjoying
their summer residency in Brighton, had flocked to
the course, anxious for yet another opportunity to
see and be seen.

The ladies were in their summer finery. A myriad
range of colors adorned fashionable bonnets, and
parasols twirled as various carriages took up a vantage point at the edge of the course. Those not fortunate enough to own a barouche, tilbury, curricle,
or high-perch phaeton crowded into the stand for a
better view of the proceedings. Those who hadn't
the means to pay for a place in the stand attempted
to find a good view not obscured by an aristocratic
carriage.

Lady Allerton, resplendent in a royal blue crepe
de chine high-waisted gown with matching pelisse
and a gypsy straw hat decorated by silk flowers,
eagerly strained her neck to see some of the others
present as Mr. Stanbury maneuvered the curricle
into a tight space between an elderly landau and a
stylish tilbury, the driver of which smiled admiringly at the beautiful countess as he tipped his hat.

Apparently oblivious to the admiring glances she
was receiving, Kitty Allerton raised her telescope

to her eye to quiz the crowds. "Oh, there is Emily Cowper. She looks shockingly old, I fear." Mr. Stanbury cast her an indulgent smile as he finished the maneuver and the curricle was in place. "Alvanley and Brummel are here, naturally. I daresay the Beau will wager more than he can afford as usual and expect his cronies to fish him out of the river tick."

"Do you see Prinny?"

"Ah, yes, I do see him now. He's in his barouche, quite close to Sir Percy Cavander's high-perch phaeton. It must be a relief to Prinny to be able to appear in public and not be booed."

"That is why he is so fond of Brighton." Gavin toyed idly with the ribbons. "There was no doubt he would be here to see Brighton Beau race today."

Lady Allerton handed him her telescope, and he peered through it in the direction of the prince. "Isn't that why most of us are here?"

Gavin lowered the telescope and frowned. "I hope the colt loses. In fact, I'd liefer it came last. Then Prinny might lose interest."

Once again Kitty Allerton laid a hand on his arm. "You've been blue-deviled ever since your dinner with Prinny the other evening."

The young man laughed harshly. "Do you blame it in me, Kitty? I came to Brighton to enjoy a diversion with the woman I adore, not to assist the prince in his grand plan to acquire everything that takes his fancy."

"I'm afraid it is incumbent upon all of us to indulge him."

"I had not seen my role in life in exactly those terms."

Gavin tossed a coin at one of the peddlers moving

through the crowds calling out their wares. A moment later he presented the countess with a red rose. As she took it from him, her cheeks flushed with pleasure.

"Kitty, Miss Allenbrooke, the young female who owns Brighton Beau, appears anxious to launch her sister into Society next Season. . . ."

Lady Allerton's exquisite features wrinkled into a frown as she held the rose up to her nose to inhale its fragrance. "That is not an uncommon wish."

"No . . . but I do wonder if you could be of some assistance to her."

Lady Allerton laughed. "Launching some chit of a girl is not my style."

"I did not exactly mean you to launch her, just to assist in making her Season a success."

The countess raised her shoulders into a slight shrug. "I daresay I could invite them to my soirees and salons and ensure that they are introduced to the most elevated people of my acquaintance, but how would that assist you?"

He smiled without mirth. "I agreed to do Prinny's bidding simply because he wouldn't be gainsaid, but paying court to this female is distasteful to me. At the time it seemed like a lark, and she does warrant a set-down of some sort, but in all truth, Kitty, I wish only to address myself to you."

"Dear Gav—"

"In any event, I have it in mind that if Miss Allenbrooke hasn't to concern herself about financing her sister's future, mayhap she will be much less anxious to hold onto the colt, and so release me from this fix."

"From all you have told me, this female seems to

be made of sterner stuff. Although I am loath to say this, I believe you're wasting your time and effort on her. You can't be the first to try this ploy, and there are some females, I regret to tell you, who cannot be cajoled, however charming the gentleman."

Her companion smiled wryly. "Prinny thinks I have an excess of charm; you don't believe I have enough. I've a mind to take a pet."

She laughed at his teasing. "You have address sufficient for a dozen others. Now I must apply myself to the race card. I shall certainly have a substantial wager upon Brighton Beau, but what others, I wonder?"

As she perused the list of runners, he told her, "A wager on Brighton Beau will be useless today, Kitty. Everyone will be putting their money on the colt after his last showing. The odds will be impossible."

"Nevertheless, it will be a great thrill to win for once." She reached into her silk reticule and brought out a purse. "I have made up my mind, and you shan't dissuade me."

"As if I could," he teased.

"Equal amounts on Brighton Beau, Gray Lightning, and Quiet Girl, and be good enough to place the wagers on my behalf before I decide otherwise."

He shook his head as he took the purse from her. "You are anxious to be parted from your money, my dear."

"What does it matter?" she asked, her eyes shining. "It is such a beautiful day. How foolish Allerton is to spend his time shooting grouse on some Yorkshire moor with his cronies when he could be here!"

"It is undoubtedly to my benefit that he is not."

He left her in the curricle, quizzing the crowd for sight of her acquaintances once again. Placing the wagers took very little time. Mr. Stanbury knew he was being foolish to go against the trend and not place a wager on Brighton Beau, but he did sincerely hope the colt wouldn't win today.

When that task was accomplished, he began to wander around, enjoying the atmosphere and acknowledging those with whom he was acquainted. On several occasions he stopped to exchange a few pleasantries with those who were particularly knowledgeable about racing matters, and it was obvious from those encounters all hopes were on Brighton Beau. Interest was even greater because the colt didn't come from one of the more familiar stables.

When Gavin found himself close to the Prince Regent's barouche, pulled by six black ponies, he knew he couldn't very well pass by. Indeed, his perambulation around the course had, in some measure, been in the hope of encountering Flavia Allenbrooke so he could at least try to become on warmer terms with her. Even though it was true he had never encountered any difficulty in making himself amiable to ladies, now that it was for a particular purpose other than his own inclination, he was feeling as awkward as a callow youth.

"Fine day, is it not?" the prince greeted him as Gavin bowed low.

"Yes, indeed, sir. Lady Jersey. Your servant, ma'am."

"Just wait until you see the colt run, Stanbury," the prince could hardly wait to say. "You'll covet him for yourself, but don't you dare!" He leaned forward and asked, "Have you contrived as yet to advance yourself with the chit?"

Gavin laughed uncomfortably. "The opportunity has not yet arisen, sir. I deemed it unwise to call again so soon after my last visit lest she take it amiss."

"Ah, yes, you are a master in the art of seduction, Stanbury. I have every trust in you."

Contriving to hide his discomfort well, Gavin ventured, "I have given the matter some thought since the other evening, sir, and I wondered if the situation might be improved if, say, you were to meet the young lady yourself."

"Protocol forbids me to deal in such matters," the prince protested.

"I was not suggesting that Your Royal Highness should negotiate the purchase. There are those of us who are willing, even honored, to do so in your stead. However, it might make my ... er ... task easier if I were to encounter her at one of Your Royal Highness's musical soirees at the pavilion, where she will be subjected to a little of your own celebrated charm."

For a moment the prince thought on the matter, and then he became more animated. "Capital notion, Stanbury!"

As the prince chuckled, Gavin bowed, withdrawing quickly before the prince could think of anything of a greater challenge. He wandered across to the saddling enclosure, and there was no doubt that Brighton Beau stood out as an animal quite superior to most of the others put up against him.

Just as he was turning away to return to Kitty for the commencement of the first race, he stopped, catching sight, as one of the other horses was led away, of Munnings, Flavia's head groom, in earnest, almost furtive conversation with Sir Percy Cavander. He wasn't sure why he considered their conversation furtive. It merely seemed so to him, and he found himself somewhat disturbed by it.

When a moment later Sir Percy caught sight of him, he took his leave of the groom and smilingly hailed Gavin. "Couldn't resist a closer look," he explained somewhat unnecessarily as he led Gavin away from the enclosure. "Munnings assures me the colt is in fine fettle and there are none others in contention."

"Do you believe he will win this race today?"

"I am certain of it, but Miss Allenbrooke will have her sights firmly fixed upon the Brighton Premier Plate. That is the big one for any owner."

"The competition will be greater," Gavin pointed out.

"I'm persuaded there will be no competition. Well, Stanbury, much as I enjoy discussing racing matters with you—you're a goer when it comes to cattle—I must return to the ladybird I left in my carriage. I do so hope the day proves profitable for you."

"I'm sure it will," he answered with a smile as he watched Sir Percy disappear into the crowd.

After a moment or two, when he glanced around him, he caught sight at last of the Allenbrooke party, and his smile grew wider. "Yes, indeed," he murmured. "I am sure it will."

EIGHT

While Gavin Stanbury made his way back to Lady
Allerton, the Allenbrooke party was seated in its
old-fashioned landau in another part of the course.

Flavia could scarcely contain her agitation as she
waited for the meeting to begin, and after a while
her aunt begged, "I wish you would not fiddle so,
Flavia. It is most distracting."

"I do beg your pardon, Aunt, but I am all of a
quake. Perhaps I should go along and make certain
all is well with Beau. You know that waiting for
him to race always oversets my nerves."

Lynette, a picture in her chip-straw bonnet and
homemade gown of white sprigged muslin, giggled.
"It's so exciting. I cannot conceive of anything more
exciting. Just look at all these people, *and* the soldiers. They look so handsome in their uniforms."

As her sister cast her a reproving look, Mrs.
Bowman pointed out, "Beau is in excellent hands,
so you need not be in such a taking, dear."

"I shall just be glad when Beau's race is over and
I am able to sit back and enjoy the remainder of
the day."

"After the race money is in our hands," Lynette
added pertly.

"How avaricious you have become, dearest," her

65

sister responded with a laugh, "but I own it will be very welcome."

"I imagine at this very moment His Royal Highness wishes more than ever he owned Beau," Lynette commented.

"Oh, do not, I beg of you, remind me of the Prince Regent." Flavia sighed, looking troubled again.

"He cannot make you sell against your will," her aunt pointed out, "so you need not trouble your head about it."

"I believe I'd like to wander in the crowd a little before Beau races," Lynette announced, glancing around.

As she got up, Flavia put one hand out to restrain her. "Have a care. There are so many people here today and no small number of riffraff."

"I will be careful. I just have it in mind to make a purchase or two from the peddlers. They sell such interesting gewgaws, I simply cannot resist!"

Flavia watched her disappear into the crowd, and then she turned to her aunt in a confiding manner. "Aunt Bella, do you recall the other day suggesting we might do well to put . . ."—here she encountered some difficulty in formulating her words—"to put Lynette in the way of Mr. Stanbury?"

Mrs. Bowman affected an air of surprise. "Why, yes, I do recall saying something of that order, but you were most dismissive."

"Nevertheless, I have been thinking on it, and it does seem to me an idea of some merit, although, in truth, I confess I dislike Mr. Stanbury quite heartily."

"I cannot conceive how that might have come

about. You have encountered the gentleman only once, and then briefly."

"Twice," Flavia said darkly.

"So you did, but, Flavia dear, I found him most pleasant, *and* he is an excellent catch, believe me."

Her aunt's statement seemed to decide her. "It's more important that Lynette seems to look sweet upon him. She has made mention of his name on several occasions since his call, and I have almost decided to try and act the matchmaker—but only if she is receptive to him."

"Your sister is not in the least like you, not in nature, in any event."

"Or looks," Flavia answered with a smile. "She is a beauty."

"So are you in your own way, but you must forgive me when I say your sister is far more biddable than you ever were. It won't be difficult to encourage her to look upon Mr. Stanbury with favor, and I am quite persuaded he cannot fail to be entranced by her. From all I have heard of him, he has quite an eye for a fetching female."

"Then it is agreed between us, is it not? *I* do not have to like him in the least. It will be sufficient for me to know that Lynette is well settled and will never want for anything."

"Flavia dear," Mrs. Bowman said kindly, seeing the light of fervor in her niece's eye. "Why do you not emulate your sister and go for a little stroll before Beau races? You will feel much better for doing so."

She appeared about to protest but then thought better of it. "I shall endeavor to discover where Mr. Stanbury's carriage is situated and perhaps guide Lynette toward him, which will be a start."

"That is an excellent notion," her aunt agreed.

When, however, she entered the hurly-burly of the exuberant race-day crowd, she began to realize that trying to find any particular person was perhaps a matter of overoptimism on her part. Avoiding the pleas of various peddlers and keeping well away from the drinking booths where more merrymakers than enough were enjoying copious amounts of heavy-wet, she bobbed in and out of the crowd, but she could see no sign of Mr. Stanbury's curricle or of Lynette. It had been a stupid plan, in any event, she told herself as she started back toward the landau, deciding at last that Lynette had in all probability made her own way there by now.

As she turned on her heel, a drunkard barred her way. "If you please," she said in a manner that was usually interpreted by those who did not know her as imperious. "I wish to pass."

The drunkard swept off his hat in a mock salute. "Why not knock me off me feet and walk all over me in the way of the Quality, Your Highnessship?"

"Don't be a ninnyhammer," she snapped. "Be pleased to allow me to pass."

Aware that the fellow was considerably the worse for drink, Flavia sounded less frightened than she actually was. Whenever she attempted to sidestep the fellow, he was there in her way. While several of his drinking companions were laughing and urging him on, Flavia was becoming more and more alarmed.

"She wants to pass, Seamus. She'll chop off your head if you don't let her."

"I'll let her pass only if she dances with me first," he replied, in response to a gentleman who'd begun to play a fiddle nearby.

To Flavia's horror he lurched forward, arms out-stretched. She turned away, beginning to panic now, and immediately bumped into one of the crowd. Before she had a chance to realize he didn't smell of ale, she cried out and began to struggle.

"Off with you wretches," an authoritative voice ordered as a pair of hands drew her away from the scene. "You're quite safe now," he told her.

Amazingly the drunkards did go without so much as another word, and she looked up at her rescuer to find herself gazing into Gavin Stanbury's limpid brown eyes. He was holding her close to him, and Flavia was suddenly very much aware of his sup-pressed strength, the feel of rock-hard muscles be-neath the elegant buff coat.

"Why, a damsel in distress," he said with a slow smile, and she stepped out of his grasp rather quickly, averting her eyes from his and feeling both foolish and self-conscious.

"Mr. St-stanbury," she stammered. "Thank you. I—"

He held up one hand to forestall her gratitude. "It's nothing, I assure you. They meant no harm, but I appreciate your anxiety. You shouldn't ven-ture far from your own party unaccompanied."

Her head came up proudly and her eyes flashed blue fire. "I am perfectly used to venturing out on my own, sir."

"I don't doubt it for a moment."

His eyes were brimming with laughter, and that caused her to avert her gaze again. Then, recalling her resolution to curry his favor on her sister's be-half, she smiled and said in a conciliatory manner, "I truly am grateful, sir."

He glanced around at the profusion of refreshment booths and asked, "May I buy you a glass of lemonade to help restore your spirits?"

She was about to refuse, but then she inclined her head and replied, "I am most obliged to you."

As they walked toward the booth together, she ventured, "After our last two meetings you must consider me a most unobliging person, Mr. Stanbury."

He considered her carefully as he ordered two glasses of lemonade. "You can have no notion how I consider you, ma'am."

Two bright spots of color appeared in her cheeks, even though she did not avert her eyes from his on this occasion. Once the drinks were purchased, he observed her outmoded gown of flowered chintz and realized she possessed an unexpectedly fine figure. Fleetingly he wondered how she would look dressed in the first stare of fashion like the many ladies of the ton with whom he was acquainted, with her hair styled *à la Russe* or *à la victoire*.

"You must be anxious for your colt's race," he ventured.

Flavia couldn't help but laugh. "That was one reason for my taking a stroll. I am all of a twitter, as you have no doubt observed."

"It's very becoming to you, I assure you."

He was once again rewarded by the appearance of the two spots of color in her cheeks and the hasty way she applied herself to her drink.

"I had expected you to call again at Marston," she admitted. "You are not a gentleman to give up a task so easily."

Gavin felt unaccountably uncomfortable and once again reflected that she was not in the usual way of females, who invariably adopted missish airs. Her directness could be most discomposing.

"While it always pleases me to see you and the other members of your family, Miss Allenbrooke, I felt I no longer had a reason to call."

"I see," she answered thoughtfully. "Am I to understand, then, your task is ended?"

"I cannot in all truthfulness be sure about that," he told her in a guarded manner. "His Royal Highness has his whims, but I'm persuaded he recognizes your stand, although I'm sure he's still anxious to purchase the colt." Feeling it might be best to change the subject away from her horse, he went on. "I believe your aunt made mention of your intention to launch your sister next Season."

"If it is financially viable. It is certainly my ambition to do so."

"There is a lady I would like you to meet. She is bound to be of assistance to you in London."

"I should hate you to go to any trouble on our behalf, especially as I have been so unobliging to you and your associates."

Gavin subjected her to a long, considering look and was surprised that she did not flinch away from it. "It's no trouble at all," he answered abruptly a moment later.

After he had returned their empty glasses to the booth, he guided her skillfully through the crowd to where Lady Allerton was still sitting in the curricle, only now she was surrounded by acquaintances anxious to claim her attention for their own. A few minutes after Gavin and Flavia had arrived, the others began to drift away, whereupon Lady Allerton gave her undivided attention to the newcomer at last.

"Miss Allenbrooke, how glad I am to make your acquaintance. I have heard much mention of your name since our arrival in Brighton."

Flavia bobbed a brief curtsy and observed the famous beauty from beneath the brim of her own unfashionable bonnet. "My lady, I am honored by your interest."

"Gav told me a little about you, and I confess I didn't expect one so young or so lovely."

The use of the diminutive form of his name told Flavia a good deal about the countess's relationship with him. She was neither shocked nor surprised, for she was bound to acknowledge they made a handsome pair. The realization that Lady Allerton and Mr. Stanbury enjoyed a close relationship did not daunt her ambition in the least. Lady Allerton was unattainable, whereas Lynette was perfectly eligible. The countess was both beautiful and sophisticated, but Lynette was lovely, too, and would make an ideal Lady Stanbury.

"You have no doubt heard that I am something of a virago," Flavia replied, something that made Kitty Allerton laugh delightedly.

"I certainly see that you are not. You must bring your sister to see me, Miss Allenbrooke. To tea one afternoon, perhaps."

"We'd be most honored, ma'am," Flavia replied, struggling to keep herself from appearing too pleased at this undoubted piece of good fortune.

"Why don't you join us to watch the race from this vantage point? I promise you it is very good."

Flavia looked genuinely regretful. "I would like to very much indeed, ma'am, only I needs must return to my aunt and sister, who are bound to wonder where I have gone."

Lady Allerton glanced across to the course. "If I am not mistaken, the race is about to begin."

"Oh, my goodness!" Flavia gasped, watching the horses and jockeys lining up for the start.

"By all means, join me," the countess invited, and after an initial hesitation Flavia allowed herself to be handed up onto the box.

As soon as she was seated, the gun was fired to start the race. Gavin was watching it with great interest, but equally he observed Flavia, who, under her breath, issued instructions like "Hold him steady," "Bring him through," and finally, as the finishing post came into view, "Give him his head!" This last one was shouted as Brighton Beau made a great spurt for the winning post.

When he passed it by a head, Flavia was momentarily stunned into silence, and then Gavin exclaimed, "My stars! He won!"

At that point Flavia's smile lit up her whole countenance, and Gavin turned to say, "Congratulations, Miss Allenbrooke. That was a most deserved win."

"Most exciting!" Lady Allerton agreed.

Flavia began to get up, saying in her excitement, "I must go to our landau and collect Aunt Bella and Lynette before we accept the prize. I'm so happy," she added shakily, and Mr. Stanbury could only feel glad, too.

The countess held out her mittened hand and touched Flavia's briefly. "You may be sure I look forward to renewing our acquaintanceship in the very near future."

"Allow me to escort you back to your carriage," Mr. Stanbury told her as he exchanged a knowing look with the countess.

"There is no need to do so, I assure you," she protested.

"Perhaps not, but I wish to."

Recognizing that it might be a good idea to allow him to return to the carriage with her, as Lynette would undoubtedly be waiting with Aunt Bella, she inclined her head in submission.

After bobbing a curtsy to Lady Allerton, she fell into step beside her escort and after a moment ventured, "Her ladyship is as lovely as she is gracious."

As he walked with a long-legged stride, swinging his ebony cane, he replied, "She is indeed."

"Have you been acquainted with her for long?"

"Yes."

She cast him a quick, apologetic look before admitting, "You must think me impertinent for asking, sir."

"You are direct, and that is a quality to be admired."

She laughed. "I have yet to meet a gentleman who admires it in a lady."

She wondered if he would find Lynette's docile nature attractive and felt sure he would consider her biddable ways most admirable in a wife.

While Flavia had been anxiously seeking sight of her sister, Lynette had been seated in the booth of one of the gypsy fortune-tellers, having her palm read. Ten minutes afterward she emerged with her heart beating wildly and her head in a spin. The gypsy had said much that Lynette found difficult to take in at once, but there was the one thing that did echo around her head: great fortune and a happy future were to be hers, and that was connected to a handsome man who would steal her heart.

In her excitement and her desire to put up her parasol against the injurious effects of the sun, she dropped the bag of barley sugars she had purchased to share with her aunt and sister during the races.

Before she could stoop to retrieve the bag, someone else had snatched it up, saying, "Do allow me to assist you, ma'am."

Lynette found herself looking into a pair of sparkling eyes as blue as her own. "Why, I thank you, sir," she answered breathlessly, hiding her confusion as best she could as she took the now crumpled bag from him.

"It is my pleasure entirely."

Recovering a little now, she noticed that the young man was dressed in the uniform of the Prince Regent's Own Royal Hussars—the Tenth—and she couldn't help but observe he looked very handsome in his yellow boots, red pantaloons, and the regimental jacket encrusted with lace, reputedly designed by the prince himself. The Byronic curls escaping from his shako were romantically fair.

"Do allow me to introduce myself, ma'am. Lieutenant Timothy Spendlow of the Tenth Hussars—as you've no doubt noticed." Then he gave her a considering look. "If it is not impertinent of me to ask, whom do I have the pleasure of addressing?"

"What a chucklehead you must think me," she responded, smiling wryly. "Lynette Allenbrooke."

"I am more than delighted to make your acquaintance, Miss Allenbrooke."

A flower seller was passing by, and when she

called out her wares, saying, "Buy the lady a flower, sir, such pretty flowers for a lady," it was with some difficulty that he drew his gaze away from Lynette to the array of cornflowers in the woman's tray.

He selected a bunch, which he then presented to the astonished girl. "They match your eyes almost exactly, save that your eyes are more beautiful."

She gasped. "I scarce know what to say," she murmured as she clutched them to her breast.

"Just tell me if you live hereabouts, or are you down from London for the summer?"

"I live at Marston with my aunt and sister."

"Splendid! I'm so glad."

All at once the girl looked uncertain, and her smile faded a little. "I must return to our carriage. My family will be concerned for me."

"Allow me the privilege of accompanying you."

"No." She smiled then in a conciliatory manner. "It is but a short way from here, and you've already been most kind. . . ."

As she began to move away, he followed. "Don't be so hasty. I must see you again, Miss Allenbrooke."

Lynette's feelings veered between delight and fear, but she answered shyly, "I visit Donaldson's Library, usually on a Monday morning."

A smile of sublime pleasure lit up his face. "Monday. Monday morning!"

He watched until she had been swallowed up by the crowd, and then with a light step he went to find his companions to tell them of his delightful encounter.

When Flavia and her escort approached the landau, Lynette was sitting next to her aunt, smiling demurely and still clutching the bunch of cornflowers to her bosom. No man could fail to be moved by her, Flavia thought as Lynette turned to smile a greeting to them. Unfortunately the man who had been so entranced by Lynette's beauty was not the one chosen by Flavia as her ideal match.

NINE

Gavin Stanbury walked slowly along Marine Parade, reflecting that he had no heart for the shabby task the Prince Regent had set him. Despite his increasing distaste, however, he knew he could not withdraw now, not until the prince's desire to own the colt was satisfied in one manner or another. Gavin felt that the least he could do was try to ensure at the end of the affair Flavia Allenbrooke would not be left too badly bruised.

He was very much afraid, however adamant she might be, she would in the end be persuaded, in some manner, to part with Brighton Beau. Each win the horse had would make the likelihood more certain, and as he paused to watch the red-and-blue bathing machines being pulled out to sea, he realized he hoped quite ardently she would be able to resist all the lures put out to her.

When he set off again, he walked a little farther until arrested by the unexpected sight of the object of his thoughts. She was gazing out to sea, and although she carried a parasol and her straw bonnet partially obscured her face, he could see that she was enjoying the view. Suddenly a flock of sea gulls rose up from the shore, screaming a cacophony as their wings beat madly. Flavia turned her face upward as they flew overhead, her features formed into an expression of delight. The look on her face arrested him, for he was more used to the bored affectations of the ladies of the ton, who would prefer to suffer all manner of discomfort and maladies rather than admit they actually enjoyed something as rustic as a pleasant view, or the sight of a flock of sea gulls.

Flavia didn't become aware of him until he was almost upon her, and when she turned, her face took on a fleeting look of surprise—or even fear—before she bestowed upon him a genuine smile.

"Mr. Stanbury, what a pleasant surprise."

"After our initial encounters I am delighted to hear you greet me in such a pleasant manner, ma'am."

She regarded him from beneath her long lashes. "I had hoped that unfortunate episode long forgotten. I feel totally ashamed whenever I recall it."

He stared at her in amazement, for it appeared she was actually flirting with *him*. He could scarcely believe his good fortune. Distasteful as the matter may be to him, he was never averse to a little flirtation, and Flavia Allenbrooke was taking the initiative. He couldn't possibly resist.

"I would not for anything wish to cause you any discomfort, ma'am. As you wish it to be forgotten, I couldn't be more pleased to accommodate you."

"Good. Now we can begin in a more civilized manner."

" 'Civilized' to the ladies of my acquaintances usually means being missish. It would be difficult to regard you in such terms."

A light flashed in her eyes. "Then I shall be obliged to act . . . uncivilized."

He laughed as he said, "I trust that Mrs. Bowman and your sister are in good health."

"Yes, I thank you." She glanced across to where the bathing machines were halfway down the beach. "Aunt Bella believes sea bathing is beneficial, and so I am kicking my heels in this pleasant manner while she is being dipped."

"And Miss Lynette . . . ?"

Flavia noted his interest—or did she detect anxiety in his manner?—and felt gratified. "My sister chooses to spend her time in Donaldson's Library, although I hasten to assure you she is no bluestocking. Her taste is somewhat mundane and veers toward the romantic, but she enjoys browsing and watching those who play loo."

"You evidently do not share her interest in matters of literature."

"With little time to spare I choose to spend it enjoying the sight of the sea, something of which I never tire. When we come into town, I am often to be found at the seashore while my sister and aunt go about their business."

"I was on my way to Mahomed's Baths when I saw you standing here."

Again she subjected him to the flirtatious look. "I wouldn't wish to detain you, sir."

"I have all day in which to enjoy a vapor bath. An encounter with a fetching female is not to be rushed. Tell me, has Brighton Beau recovered from the excitement at Lewes the other day?"

"He has, but we have not." Flavia turned her back on the sea and looked at him for a long moment before saying, "You could, if you have a mind to, ride him when he goes out on the Downs."

"That is an incredibly generous offer, ma'am."

"You are, by all accounts, an expert horseman who is bound to appreciate the experience. Beau rides out every morning—if you are about early enough."

"I ride early every morning myself, but that will be a special treat for which I thank you most heartily. I cannot think why you should be so indulgent of me above all others."

She looked thoughtful for a moment or two before admitting, "Truth to tell, I still feel a trifle guilty about our first meeting and my hasty condemnation of you. I had no notion then you were Mr. Stanbury of the renowned Whip's Club. This will be my way of making reparation to you for any slight rendered on that occasion."

He looked wry. "I assure you I shall be more than happy to assist you in so doing, ma'am."

As he escorted her across the road toward the library, she turned to him to say, "The most remarkable thing has happened. We are invited to the Marine Pavilion tomorrow evening! Imagine! An invitation from the Prince Regent himself. I thought at first someone was shamming us, but the invitation is indeed genuine. Aunt Bella and Lynette are crying roast meat to all who will listen."

Gavin's eyes twinkled with amusement. "Am I to take it, Miss Allenbrooke, that you are not?"

"I am delighted on the one hand for an opportunity to see inside the fantastic pavilion, which teases us every time we pass. It wouldn't be natural to be anything other than delighted. However, I am not such a peagoose as to believe it has nothing to do with my ownership of Brighton Beau."

"You are far too needle-witted to be hoodwinked

by the prince, if indeed that was his intention—and I am sure it was not."

Flavia's chin came up proudly. "If he believes he can come the artful with me, he is bound to be sorely disappointed, but," she added, smiling again, "I confess it will be exciting to see all his toplofty associates togged out in the finest style."

"I trust you don't include me in those you regard as toplofty, ma'am."

"Oh, no!" she protested, her gloved hand flying to her lips. "You are not in the least stiff-rumped, sir."

"You didn't always think so, I fancy."

"Why, no—"

"I'm afraid I'm guilty of roasting you. I do hope you'll forgive it in me."

Her face relaxed into a smile again, and she averted her gaze as shyly as any green girl. "Lynette," she said with some difficulty a moment later, "has been an unconscionable time in the library. I cannot conceive what is occupying her for so long. She would hate to know she has missed seeing you."

"She might be indulging in a game of loo, rather than observing, for the once."

"I do hope not. Lynette is a mere baby when it comes to gaming, and she will lose her pin money for certain."

"I'm persuaded Miss Allenbrooke possesses far too much sense to do any such thing."

Flavia eyed him slyly. "You evidently hold her in very high esteem, sir."

"Oh, indeed," he answered just as she glanced past him, along the street.

When he turned in that direction, it was to see

Mrs. Bowman, her bonnet slightly askew, hurrying toward them.

Flavia welcomed her with a smile. "Aunt Bella, you look quite overset. Is something amiss?"

"You may well ask. Those wretched coal barges are outside of enough! Something should be done about them with no further delay. The cargoes were discharged *just* as I was being dipped, would you believe? Mrs. Carlinghowe was obliged to dip me all over again to remove the coal dust this time!"

Her breast was heaving with indignation, but then she turned to bestow a belated smile upon Gavin. "Why, Mr. Stanbury," she said breathlessly as he bowed over her hand, "how nice it is to see you again."

"And you, ma'am, but I regret you have had such a trying time of what should be a healthful experience."

"Indeed. Your sympathy is most welcome. Only last week some young buck was arrested by the constable for disrobing on the beach, which I regard as a petty affair. Those coal barges are far more in want of prosecution in my mind. Tell me, sir, did you witness Beau's win at Lewes the other day?"

As he relinquished her hand, he replied, "I most certainly did, and it was a great pleasure to me."

"I suppose that is why the Prince Regent has invited us to the Pavilion tomorrow evening. I was never more astonished when the invitation arrived. Whatever next, I ask myself!" Suddenly she looked abashed. "Here I am going on like a rattle when you are, no doubt, in a fidge to be going about your business."

"Not in the least, ma'am. I cannot think of anything more pleasant than conversing with two most taking ladies on a fine day like this."

"What a fine way with words you have, sir," she told him while her niece smiled wryly. "My only reservation about our engagement at the Marine Pavilion is that our carriage will look so shabby among all the others there."

"What does it matter, Aunt?" Flavia asked dismissively.

"You mustn't concern yourself on that score," Gavin assured her. "It will be my pleasure to call for you in my carriage and escort you there."

"We wouldn't dream of imposing upon you," Flavia answered quickly.

"Indeed not," her aunt concurred. "I did not mean to put you to inconvenience on our behalf."

"No, I insist. You will do me the greatest honor, I assure you. It will give me great pleasure to escort three lovely ladies to the soiree. Few others will be able to boast of such an achievement."

"That is most generous of you, sir," Flavia told him.

She sounded slightly breathless, and her cheeks had taken on a pinkish hue. There was also a strange gleam in her eyes that he had perceived before at the racecourse, and it puzzled him greatly. He didn't like to be puzzled by any lady's behavior, but before he had any chance to ponder further on the matter, Sir Percy Cavander came strolling round the corner from the direction of the Steine, and Gavin found himself unusually irritated by the intrusion.

Sir Percy stopped in his tracks when he espied the trio conversing outside the library, and then he proceeded toward them, his face bearing a smile that didn't quite reach his eyes.

"Ladies. Stanbury," he greeted them, raising his hat. "What a pretty picture you present, excepting Stanbury, of course, but I mean no disrespect by that, you must know!"

"No one has yet seen fit to call me pretty," Gavin responded, only half-amused at the fellow's attempt at wit.

"Certainly no one has said it and lived to tell the tale," Sir Percy added, laughing at his own witticism. "Miss Allenbrooke, I am bound to confess I am well pleased with the yearling you sold me. I feel that he will shape up to perhaps eclipse his brother in due time."

"I hope so, sir," Flavia responded, looking pleased. "At Marston we take pride in the quality of our cattle."

"Quite so. You will see me there again, you may be sure. Some are shortsighted in wanting only to-day's winner. I possess sufficient foresight to envisage the future." Gavin made some small noise and Sir Percy went on, looking well pleased with himself. "I must protest, ladies. Why am I honored by the sight of only two lovely creatures this morning? I am sorely disappointed that the third is not here to gladden my eye."

Flavia glanced briefly at Gavin before she explained, "My sister is in Donaldson's Library, sir. She will join us presently."

"She cannot be taking all this time to choose a book," Mrs. Bowman murmured, and then smiling at Sir Percy she asked, "Have you heard our good news, sir?"

"Not as far as I'm aware, ma'am, but do, I beg of you, acquaint me with it."

"We are invited to one of His Royal Highness's musical soirees at the Marine Pavilion tomorrow evening!"

For a moment Sir Percy looked somewhat taken aback before he recovered himself sufficiently to reply, "You do not in the least surprise me, ma'am. I told His Royal Highness myself only the other day that there were three delightful residents of Brighton who would grace his soirees most admirably. I am only gratified he has lost no time in taking my advice."

"So it is you we have to thank for the invitation," Flavia responded, looking surprised.

"It is entirely possible, although I cannot, you understand, officially take any credit. Suffice to say I enjoy the prince's confidence. I look forward to seeing you there on the morrow. Good day to you, ladies. Stanbury."

Flavia continued to look surprised as she watched him continue up the street, tipping his hat frequently to all and sundry. "What a whisker that is," she declared when he was out of earshot. "Does he regard me as such a peagoose, I'd believe that high-flyer? Anyone who knows I am the owner of Brighton Beau will certainly know why we are invited to the prince's musical evening."

Gavin remained silent but looked ironic, for he knew full well it was his suggestion that had resulted in the issue of the invitation. Naturally he had no intention of admitting the fact to Flavia Allenbrooke or anyone else.

"At last!" Flavia declared a moment later when

her sister came out of the library. "What a sluga-bed you are."

Once again Gavin was struck by the girl's pretti-ness, the pert way her fair curls bounced beneath her straw bonnet, its shabbiness masked by a dec-oration of fresh flowers, cornflowers that matched her eyes so well.

Lynette appeared to be experiencing some diffi-culty in managing her books, her parasol, and the cord of her reticule, but an officer of the Hussars who had followed her out of the library proved adept at assisting her, and she thanked him laugh-ingly as she approached the little group assembled outside the building.

"We were wondering where on earth you had got-ten to," Flavia told her.

The girl's eyes were bright, her cheeks were flushed, and she was not in the least dismayed. "I do beg your pardon, dearest, but I got into conver-sation with Lieutenant Spendlow and entirely for-got the time. I do hope you will forgive me the omission."

Gavin thought that anyone could forgive Lynette anything when she asked in such a manner, but Flavia was looking askance at her choice of books. "Oh, for shame! You borrowed these only a few weeks ago. Do you not recall?"

The girl bit her lip and looked somewhat abashed before she turned her attention to the officer who was hovering expectantly nearby. "You must con-sider me a complete goosecap. Allow me to intro-duce Lieutenant Spendlow. Lieutenant, my aunt, Mrs. Bowman, and my sister, Flavia. Mr. Stanbury is an acquaintance of ours."

The two ladies regarded him curiously. Gavin

studied the couple as Lynette gazed at her new acquaintance with a look he recognized all too well. He was grateful that for once it was not directed toward him.

"Timothy Spendlow, Mrs. Bowman, Miss Allenbrooke. I am delighted to make your acquaintance. You are both just as Miss Lynette described you. She has told me all about you at length."

Lynette laughed uneasily while Flavia gave him a cool, appraising look. "Lieutenant Spendlow, forgive me, but this is the first time I have heard mention of your name. I had no notion you were acquainted with my sister."

"We met at Lewes races the other day," the girl explained rather breathlessly. "Beau's win put the matter entirely from my mind. By coincidence we bumped into each other again today. Is that not the most amazing thing?"

"Yes, indeed," her sister responded, and to Gavin's amusement her voice was heavy with irony.

When the young officer contrived to draw his adoring gaze away from Lynette, he glanced at Gavin. "Are you, sir, by any chance Mr. *Gavin* Stanbury?"

"I am, but I'm afraid I'm not aware of being acquainted with you, sir."

"It has not yet been my privilege, but your prowess as a whipster precedes you. Actually we did once almost meet, but it was some years ago."

"Really?"

"You did once ride your uncle's filly in the Saint Ledger, did you not?"

Gavin was amazed to hear him say so. "I was but a youth. You couldn't possibly recall."

Flavia was looking astonished, too. "I had no notion of that, Mr. Stanbury. Did you win?"

He cast her a deprecating smile. "I'm afraid not."

"It was a spirited try," the other young man assured her, and then he added with more timidity, "My family lives quite close to your uncle, Lord Flinton, in Yorkshire. That is how I recall you, sir. You were something of a hero to me."

"Good grief!" Gavin exclaimed. "Is it *that* Spendlow family?"

"Yes, sir," the young man replied, looking abashed.

Gavin was all at once aware that the young officer had a degree of anxiety in his manner, and after a moment or two he understood why.

"Is this not the most delightful conversation!" Lynette declared in her artless manner, looking from one to the other.

"It is," Mr. Stanbury replied, giving her his attention, "but I regret I must leave you to continue it without me." He bowed slightly. "Until tomorrow, ladies. Good day, Spendlow. Delighted to make your acquaintance."

"And I yours, sir, I assure you."

Mr. Stanbury hesitated for a moment before he said, "I'm about to take a vapor bath at Mahomed's, Spendlow. Why don't you join me and we can exchange memories of Yorkshire?"

Lieutenant Spendlow's face took on an expression of relief as he replied, "Delighted, sir. Ladies, by your leave."

The ladies murmured their good-byes, and when Mr. Stanbury glanced at Flavia again, he noted that she appeared somewhat miffed at her sister's unexpected attachment to the young officer.

89

On his part he was amused and had a mischievous urge to help matters along a little. Sometime later, when he returned to his house, he lost no time in penning a note to Colonel Fitzsimmons at the Marine Pavilion, respectfully suggesting that Lt. Timothy Spendlow of the Prince Regent's Own Royal Hussars should be issued an invitation to the coming musical soiree.

TEN

In the oddest way Gavin started to look forward to the musical soiree, but his only regret was Kitty's pouting disappointment when he told her he wouldn't be escorting *her* to the pavilion that evening.

"Only fancy, Gav, I am obliged to go with Lord Cambourn and Lizzie Montacute when I would liefer be hanging onto your arm."

He assured her he would far rather be with her, as he would be for much of the evening just as soon as Prinny had seen him make a brief attempt at flirtation with Flavia Allenbrooke. With that resolution in mind he returned to his house after a pleasant afternoon in the countess's company, looking forward to an equally delightful evening at the Marine Pavilion, sparring verbally with the unexpectedly stimulating Flavia Allenbrooke. However, on his arrival, he was astounded to discover Lady Stanbury and her daughter arrived and fully settled in.

"Mother!" he exclaimed, understandably bemused. "I certainly didn't look to see you here in Brighton just now. I didn't receive so much as a Scarborough warning of your arrival."

"I am truly sorry about that, dearest," Lady

Stanbury apologized. "It was, I confess, a sudden whim on my part. I vow it wasn't done with any intention to annoy you."

He smiled sheepishly and kissed her cheek. "Nothing you could ever do would annoy me, but to what do I owe the pleasure of your visit?"

"You did say we might if we wished," Emmeline pointed out, and she was as ebullient as ever.

"Yes, naturally, but—"

Lady Stanbury ran a hand through her graying locks. "Your father is laid low with an attack of the gout, and has turned decidedly testy. I regarded a short sojourn in Brighton a good cure—for us if not for him." Then she began to look reproachful. "You could be a mite more welcoming, even if it is a sham."

"I promise you I am genuinely glad to see you both, only you have taken me somewhat by surprise, which you must own is natural. As a consequence I'm afraid I shan't be able to stay home with you this evening."

"I didn't expect that you would," his mother replied. "In any event we are quite done up by the journey, short as it is. The traffic is atrocious, what with the mail coach believing itself to be the only vehicle of import on the road, the stage driven by some young buck at a reckless speed for a wager, farm wagons and any number of heedless young sparks in their amazing chariots who are totally disobliging." She smiled then in a conciliatory way. "Emmy and I will just rest this evening. Do go on with your own plans, Gavin."

"Thank you, Mother," he answered with heavy sarcasm. Then he began to back toward the door.

"Do excuse me, ladies, I must leave you to change for dinner."

"I suppose you're dining with Lady Allerton this evening," Emmeline said pertly, and her brother paused in the doorway to wag his finger at her.

"There you are wrong, puss."

"Don't press your brother to tell us," Lady Stanbury warned. "He will only become as close as oak on the matter."

"Mother!" he protested with a laugh. "There is absolutely nothing to be secretive about in my dining arrangements. I am dining at Ragget's before going on to escort three ladies to the prince's musical soiree, that is all."

"All!" Emmeline exclaimed, her eyes wide as her mother sat bolt upright in the chair. "Even for you, Gav, *three* ladies is coming it too strong!"

The young man affected an air of bewilderment. "Why does everyone assume my every action is connected to amorous intrigue?"

"Because it usually is," his sister told him in an uncompromising tone. "The trouble is you're a victim of your own reputation."

"I won't argue with you on that score," he answered with great feeling.

"Who are these remarkable females who have been able to take you from Lady Allerton's side?" Lady Stanbury asked. "At least one of them must be remarkable, in any event. You've been attached to Kitty Allerton like a barnacle for the past six months."

Gavin sighed deeply, wishing he had kept his own counsel on the subject. "The three ladies are a Mrs. Bowman and her two nieces, the Misses

93

Allenbrooke. There is nothing in the least remarkable about any of them, I assure you."

His mother remained disbelieving as she repeated, "Two nieces," and her eyes narrowed shrewdly.

"Mother, I can clearly see the way your mind is working, and you can be assured you are beside the bridle on this matter."

"If you say so, dear" was her maddening reply.

When he had gone, Emmeline hurried gleefully to her mother's side. "Mama, what can be afoot?"

Lady Stanbury did not appear too hopeful herself. "In all truth, Emmy, I don't know what to think, but I must own to feeling a trifle optimistic."

"*You* are optimistic when Gavin so much as bids 'Good day' to any female under the age of fifty."

"That is a high-flyer, Emmy, but do you recall Miss Fishburn, that delightful brunette, the niece of Lady Donaldson, with whom he enjoyed a flirtation? And Lady Felicity Holbourn, whom I regarded as the perfect match for your brother?"

"Mama, your judgment, I regret to say, is sadly lacking. Lady Felicity was mackerel-backed, and I'm persuaded Gav soon grew weary of Miss Fishburn's missish airs."

Lady Stanbury appeared not the least put out by her daughter's observations and decided, "In any event I shall investigate these girls for myself before I return to Rydal Park."

On that particular evening Mr. Stanbury was finding his neck cloth difficult to fold. Owing to all the interference in his life, his concentration was not all it should have been, and when he finally succeeded in tying the length of spotless linen to his satisfaction, he anchored it with a diamond pin.

As his valet helped him into his evening coat, he surveyed his reflection dourly in the pier glass. "I have it in mind, Tredeagar, to return to London in the very near future."

The valet looked aghast. "London, sir? No person of any import at all remains in London at this time of the year, sir. Those of any consequence at all are gone to the country or the seashore."

"Precisely, Tredeagar. It would afford me the greatest pleasure to know I am not in the least like to encounter anyone of my acquaintance for the next few weeks. Brighton has become a trifle too congested for my liking."

"I have never heard you utter such a sentiment before, sir."

"No, and I never thought to before now, I assure you," Mr. Stanbury replied as he drew a profound sigh.

"Complete to a shade," Lynette Allenbrooke murmured as she glanced at her reflection in the pier glass.

Flavia also observed her sister with a rare degree of critical attention. The gown of pink tamboured muslin with slashed sleeves and ribbon decoration was not in the first stare of fashion, but with her fair curls clustered around her heart-shaped face and restrained by a filet of plaited silk, recently purchased at Mr. Hannington's Emporium on North Street, Flavia was quite certain Lynette would draw attention for her fine looks alone.

Some inner sense told her Mr. Stanbury was interested in Lynette. Why else would he be so attentive *and* obliging? He was no longer pressing her to sell Brighton Beau, so that couldn't account for his interest. Apart from a very natural interest in the colt's performance on the racecourse, Gavin Stanbury scarcely mentioned him. The object of his interest could now only be Lynette, Flavia was certain. If only her new friendship with Lieutenant Spendlow did not prove too much of a distraction, there was a good deal about which to be hopeful.

Mrs. Bowman came into the room and also cast her niece a critical look before glancing at Flavia, who was dressed in outmoded blue satin, which, nevertheless, flattered her coloring and enhanced her fine figure.

"I fancy we shall all cut a dash at the pavilion this evening," Mrs. Bowman declared as she pulled on her mittens.

"We present ourselves as a shabby trio," Flavia answered wryly. "The ladies of the ton, who'll be present this evening, are bound to be togged out in the most handsome manner imaginable, and we'll just fade to insignificance beside them."

"How can you be so Friday-faced when I'm persuaded tonight will be the most memorable of my life?" Lynette accused.

"Your sister is correct," Mrs. Bowman pointed out. "We must set out to enjoy an experience not like to happen again."

"I have every intention of doing so," Flavia assured them. "I should not have spoken in that manner, even if it is no less than the truth."

"Mr. Stanbury was so very kind to offer to take us in his carriage," Lynette ventured. "No one else will arrive in so fine a style. We'll be the object of envy of every lady present, however shabby our clothes!"

Flavia eyed her sister critically again before replying, "I'm so glad you like him, dear."

"How could I not? He is everything fine in a gentleman. There is not a fault to be found in any aspect of his demeanor."

Satisfied, her sister went to fetch her cloak, and by the time she had returned Mr. Stanbury had arrived in his carriage, driven by four matched grays, over which she cast her expert eye, something that did not go unnoticed by their escort.

When he handed Mrs. Bowman into the carriage, she exclaimed, "What an exquisite carriage this is, sir! I am most impressed."

"I am delighted to put it to such excellent use in transporting you and your nieces to the prince's musical soiree."

"Whenever it is mentioned I am all of a quake," Lynette admitted when the carriage set off toward the town.

"You mustn't be," he assured her. "You will be one of the loveliest young ladies present."

Lynette chuckled delightedly. "Flavia thinks we shall be shockingly shabby in such elevated company."

"Anyone who has the temerity to harbor such uncharitable thoughts can only be regarded as having no sensibility at all."

Gavin's answer made Flavia smile faintly, and she wondered if he would ever be at a loss for the correct word in any situation. She thought not, and that was bound to be a factor in his success. As she settled back into the squabs, she was able to observe him as he conversed easily with her aunt and was forced to admit to herself that he looked very handsome in a black evening coat with gilded buttons directly contrasting with his white shirt and silk breeches.

The large diamond in his pin flashed white fire whenever a shard of light caught it. His clothes, she was sure, even though she rarely perused the fashion plates, which made popular reading for her sister, were of the finest.

"You are strangely quiet, Miss Allenbrooke," he said a few moments later, addressing Flavia at last. "Surely you're not apprehensive, too."

"Would you consider it odd if I said I was?"

"Yes," he answered in a thoughtful manner while continuing to observe her, "I'd say it was a little out of character."

"My niece," Mrs. Bowman confided, "is not always the self-sufficient female she would have us all believe."

"Aunt Bella . . ." Flavia protested, feeling discomforted by Mr. Stanbury's intense scrutiny.

"But it is absolutely true, dear. You have shouldered so much responsibility from such a young age, but there are times when you must admit to doubt or fear. It is quite normal, is it not, Mr. Stanbury?"

He had continued to regard Flavia closely while her aunt was speaking, increasing her feeling of discomfort. "I believe," he replied, after a moment's consideration, "Miss Allenbrooke is equal to any situation."

"I'm obliged to you for thinking so," she answered with a smile. "I should hate anyone to consider me not up to all the rigs."

"Heaven forfend anyone should," he responded, and such was the sarcasm in his tone, Flavia immediately bridled.

Lynette sat further forward in her seat. "Mr. Stanbury, is it true you are actually acquainted with Lieutenant Spendlow's family in Yorkshire?"

He turned his attention to the younger sister. "Very slightly, ma'am, but that is all."

The girl flushed with pleasure. "Such a coincidence, don't you think?"

"It is almost as great a coincidence as your encounter in the library," Flavia retorted, and Mr. Stanbury pressed one finger to his lips to suppress a smile.

There was no disguising, however, the amusement brimming in his eyes. However, Flavia's sarcasm seemed to pass her sister by entirely as she went on. "Would it not be an even greater coincidence if he was also present at the Prince Regent's soiree?"

Flavia looked horrified at the suggestion, but Mr. Stanbury didn't reply. He just settled back against the squabs and smiled faintly as Mrs. Bowman began to remark about the pity of the prince's estrangement from Princess Caroline.

ELEVEN

There was a long line of carriages in the drive of the Marine Pavilion when they arrived. Lynette displayed the greatest impatience in waiting to get down, but Flavia was satisfied that during their short drive her sister had claimed Mr. Stanbury's attention for most of the time, and most indulgent toward her he had been.

"Do you think His Royal Highness will condescend to speak to me?" Lynette asked in a breathless whisper as they waited their turn to alight under the porte cochere.

"The prince is not a fool, Miss Allenbrooke," Gavin replied, "and he most certainly would be if he missed the opportunity of addressing you."

The girl chuckled happily. "Mr. Stanbury, you mustn't fill me with flummery. It is like to turn my head."

"If you are to make your debut in Society, you must grow accustomed to it."

When at last they were able to enter the Marine Pavilion, the three ladies stared about them in total astonishment.

"Good grief!" Mrs. Bowman exclaimed as they entered the octagonal vestibule, with its Chinese lantern suspended from the center of the ceiling, painted to represent the sky, "I cannot believe we are still in England. We are, are we not, Mr. Stanbury?"

"Yes, ma'am. At least I *think* we are."

The three ladies laughed, but they continued to gaze around them in an awestruck manner as they were escorted through the entrance hall, where they were divested of their cloaks, to the Chinese Gallery, with its profusion of glazed panels and huge lanterns, to the music room, richly decked out in lacquered panels of red, black, and gold.

The room was already quite crowded with guests, and on a quick reconnoiter Gavin could see no sign of the prince, who was no doubt still completing a gargantuan meal. Liveried footmen were passing through the crowd offering glasses of iced champagne punch.

"In a room such as this, how can anyone concentrate on the music?" Flavia asked as she accepted a glass. "My head is reeling with the abundance all around me."

"You will discover," Mr. Stanbury told her gravely, although there was a definite twinkle in his eyes, "once the music begins, you will be glad to have your mind diverted away from it, especially if Prinny decides to indulge in a cello duet."

"Now you are roasting me," she accused. "How can His Royal Highness possibly contrive to play the cello? Am I being disrespectful if I say he's a trifle too fat?"

"Disrespectful only in the most delightful manner, ma'am, I assure you. The secret is in the cello; it's tall and thin, which makes all the difference, as you might imagine!"

They were all laughing merrily when Lady

Allerton emerged from the crowd. For once she did not display her famed sunny disposition, and it was immediately evident to Flavia that the countess was not pleased at being denied her handsome escort that evening. She greeted Flavia cordially, and Gavin presented the other two awestruck ladies to her while the Prince Regent's wind orchestra played above the noise of laughter and conversation.

As Lynette gazed in abject admiration of the sophisticated beauty, the countess mused, "How lovely you are, my dear. You are bound to cause a sensation when you come up to London, even though blondes are quite unfashionable nowadays." She smiled then. "You are like to set a fashion of your very own."

The girl blushed becomingly as her sister said, "It is kind of you to say so, ma'am. We are all, you must know, quite overcome by the honor of being here this evening."

"Tush! I promise you my diversions won't be as tedious as this one."

"I am enjoying myself hugely, ma'am," Lynette responded in her ingenuous manner, something that made Lady Allerton laugh without mirth.

Mr. Stanbury had been watching her, an indulgent smile on his lips. "Why, Kitty," he teased, "I do believe you have already grown peevish with Cambourn's company, although the evening has scarce begun."

She flicked out her fan with only the slightest movement of her wrist, something both Flavia and her sister admired. "You are quite mistaken. Lord Cambourn is most diverting, I assure you."

Then she subjected Mrs. Bowman to one of her

more imperious expressions before saying, "Mrs. Bowman, if you and your niece will come with me, I shall endeavor to acquaint you with one or two ladies who might assist you when you come to town. Lady Jersey may provide you, if she is so disposed, with an entree to Almack's."

Lynette clasped her hands together in a gesture of delight. "Almack's! I had never thought to aspire to an invitation to Almack's!"

"You must at all times aspire to the best in life," the countess told her, cupping Lynette's pointed chin in the palm of her hand and considering her carefully.

"That is what I am always telling her, ma'am," Flavia said, smiling at Mr. Stanbury.

"Come then. There are many people here tonight who will be of great assistance to you."

"You are too obliging, ma'am," Mrs. Bowman enthused. "Most condescending, I own."

She glanced at Flavia in a way that indicated she was a little bewildered before she and Lynette followed the countess into the throng.

The moment they had gone, Flavia turned to Mr. Stanbury and said, "I have it in mind *you* were instrumental in asking her ladyship to come to Lynette's assistance."

"Lady Allerton has a kind heart, even for one so beautiful," he responded.

"I am quite persuaded it was you who prevailed upon her." He didn't answer, and she added artlessly, "As long as I am not called upon to return the favor."

When she cast him a speculative look, she fancied she detected a hint of amusement in his brown eyes. "Miss Allenbrooke, I am far too honorable to expect one."

"Whatever your motive, sir, I am bound to reiterate that I am most grateful on my sister's behalf. It indicates to me that you have taken a liking to her."

"It would be impossible not to, ma'am" was his maddeningly inscrutable reply. "Your sister is all delight."

"Yes, I confess she is most engaging," Flavia replied, and couldn't quite hide the satisfaction in her voice. "She hadn't thought to socialize on quite these dizzy heights, even when she goes up to London."

"It will be a very good experience for her, don't you think?"

"Yes, indeed. For us all," she added with a laugh, feeling somewhat guilty at being suddenly at ease with him.

"Tell me, Miss Allenbrooke, why are you so ambitious for your sister but seek so little for yourself?"

She appeared genuinely surprised at the question. "I have my home and my horses, and a small but devoted family. What more could any female want?"

"What indeed," he murmured, gazing at her intently.

"So *you* are the young lady denying His Royal Highness his heart's desire."

It was then that Flavia drew her gaze away from Mr. Stanbury with some difficulty and found herself face-to-face with an elegant gentleman who was scrutinizing her thoroughly.

After a moment he dropped his quizzing glass

104

and added, "Do not on any account give in to his will, and I declare it will make you famous!"

So saying, he moved on and she began to laugh. "How odd."

"Odd indeed," her companion agreed, "but only in that he deemed to speak to you at all." When she looked at him questioningly, he added, "That, my dear, was George Brummel, the Beau himself."

"Oh, I cannot credit that," she gasped. "He was not in the least out of the ordinary, despite his elegance, I suppose, although there are many others here tonight I would regard as equally stylish."

Even as she spoke she flushed slightly, but he did not pursue any possible compliment she might have been paying him, merely informing her, "His attention to you will have been widely observed, and I assure you the slightest word from the Beau cannot help but be beneficial to you if you were a social aspirant."

"What a pity he has wasted his precious attention upon me, for I am not in the least tonnish, and I'm persuaded Mr. Brummel's fleeting interest won't do anything to restore our previously quiet life."

The moment she had uttered the words, Flavia regretted speaking. After all, she didn't wish to discourage him from calling at Marston House or paying court to Lynette if he was inclined to do so. Observing the gentlemen who were responding to Lynette like bashful schoolboys as Lady Allerton introduced her, Flavia was certain a keen judge of female beauty like Mr. Stanbury would not be able to resist her in the end.

Moving slowly through the crowd at Lady Allerton's behest, Lynette's head began to spin at the attention she was receiving from so many elevated personages. The famous Lady Jersey, who was so influential at Almack's and with the Prince Regent himself, was haughty and distant, but in their brief exchange Lynette was convinced she had not disgraced herself and might even have impressed the countess. Lynette was totally in awe of her, for she was no longer young and not in the least elegant, although the girl did admire her diamonds and the feathers in her turban. Her current rival for the affections of the prince, Lady Conyngham, seemed equally alarming to so inexperienced a socialite as the younger Miss Allenbrooke.

At the outset she just concentrated hard on the introductions but then conceded to herself that she couldn't possibly remember the names of all the lords and ladies presented to her. Instead she responded in as pleasing a manner as she could contrive, wishing that Flavia were at her side rather than Aunt Bella, for she always knew how to behave as well as the correct thing to say, however toplofty the people.

One glance at her aunt's flushed cheeks indicated that Mrs. Bowman was equally bemused by their sudden elevation in Society, but her aunt nodded her turbaned head in acknowledgment of Lady Allerton's numerous introductions.

"I believe you are already acquainted with this particular gentleman," the countess told them as they approached a small group of military gentlemen, who presented a colorful sight in scarlet-and-blue coats with gold trimmings.

They were not in the least eclipsed by the gaudy surroundings of the music room. When Lieutenant

106

Spendlow detached himself from the group of officers, Lynette gasped with the pleasure the sight of him afforded her.

"Lieutenant Spendlow! We were only speaking of you as we arrived. I did so hope you would be here this evening, but I didn't in all truth entertain high hopes of it."

"You cannot be more delighted than I," he responded as Lady Allerton drew Mrs. Bowman away from the couple.

"His Royal Highness will soon be making his entrance, Mrs. Bowman. You may not find the musical entertainment as diverting as the conversation."

"I have never before been privileged to be present at such a gathering, ma'am, so I shall find every moment a fascination, even though I daresay you will consider me unsophisticated for saying so."

When a gentleman of the court drew Mr. Stanbury away from Flavia, she wandered off, too, in search of her sister and aunt. As she searched in vain, she encountered instead Sir Percy Cavander.

"Only the thought of seeing you here made me look forward to this crush," he told her.

Flavia's immediate thought was that he was neither as handsome nor as elegant as Mr. Stanbury, which was an odd notion, as so few men were, and she had never been so critical of a gentleman's appearance before.

"At such a dazzling gathering of so many elevated people I can only be flattered."

"Even though you made it immediately clear to me you would not sell Brighton Beau at any price—for which I only admire you—I am nonetheless delighted the colt has brought us together. Our friendship means a good deal more to me than a mere racehorse, Miss Allenbrooke."

"It's a great honor for me to hear you say so, sir" was her polite response, and Flavia was glad she would not be obliged to listen to any more of his blatant insincerities because at that moment the arrival of the Prince Regent himself was announced.

With her eyes wide Flavia watched him pass through the crowd, stopping from time to time to speak a word to an acquaintance. At close quarters he appeared even larger than when seen riding in his carriage through the town. It had recently been reported that his doctors had insisted he stop wearing the corsets he believed restrained his girth, as they were feared to be injurious to his health.

When everyone went to seek out a seat for the recital, Flavia once again looked around for sight of her aunt and sister but found only Mrs. Bowman, who declared, "Lady Allerton presented us to so many important persons, my head is in a whirl!"

Flavia put one hand on her aunt's arm. "Calm yourself, dearest. It couldn't be better."

"Did you see His Royal Highness?"

"It would be difficult not to" was her niece's rueful reply.

"How stout he has become and how flushed his complexion. I recall how handsome he was when he first deigned to visit Brighton with Mrs. Fitzherbert at his side. He is sadly changed."

"Where is Lynette?" Flavia asked when she was at last able to break into her aunt's excited chattering.

"I left her with Lieutenant Spendlow—"

"Lieutenant Spendlow!"

"Such a fine young man, Flavia. When Lynette complained of feeling a trifle hot, he was kind enough to escort her out of the room to partake of some air."

The young lady groaned loudly. "How could you allow it?"

Mrs. Bowman looked perplexed at her niece's agitation. "I couldn't in all faith allow the child to swoon, although you mustn't be alarmed for her health. I believe she has merely imbibed too much champagne, which she is quite unused to."

"That young man is beginning to haunt us, Aunt Bella. I cannot feel it is a coincidence that he is here this evening."

"I doubt very much that it is," Mrs. Bowman responded laughingly. "After all, Lynette is quite lovely, and he is a red-blooded Englishman."

"We must aspire a little higher for Lynette, Aunt."

"She might be satisfied with a little less than you hope for, dear."

Flavia's eyes flashed with blue fire. "I do not give up so easily when I am intent upon a course."

"Nor will Lieutenant Spendlow, I fancy—or indeed the Prince Regent."

"Or Sir Percy Cavander," Flavia supplied. "He has just been giving me Spanish coin. It's enough to cast me into the dismals."

"You are not so fainthearted. Do you think His Royal Highness will condescend to approach you himself this evening?"

"Oh, I am sure he wouldn't think to do so, but I shall be very much surprised if he doesn't send an emissary while we are being impressed by his establishment."

Some of her good humor faded when she espied Lynette return to the room accompanied by the young officer. Her heart sank at the sight of the euphoric expression on Lynette's face and the adoring one on her beau's. They both had the look of a mooncalf about them, which did not please Flavia one jot.

Lieutenant Spendlow greeted Flavia warmly, but her response was a little cool, and he made much of settling them in seats with a clear view of the proceedings before, to Flavia's chagrin, engaging to take Lynette into supper.

"Did you know Lieutenant Spendlow was engaged in the Peninsula for several months?" Lynette asked her sister.

"I had no notion the Tenth did anything other than parade on the Downs for Prinny's pleasure," Flavia replied with uncharacteristic sharpness.

Stung by her sister's lack of interest in the object of her enthusiasm, Lynette turned to her aunt and began to regale the more sympathetic lady with all the lieutenant's patent virtues.

The musical diversion began with renowned soprano Madam Vestris singing a sentimental ballad—the Prince Regent was known to be fond of them—followed by a glee from Signor Dotti, an equally famous tenor. There followed several airs, sung as solos as well as duets, before the prince was invited up to join them in "Glorious Apollo," which those around the Allenbrooke party thought particularly fitting.

When the prince prepared to play a cello duet with Captain Bloomfield, Flavia recalled Mr. Stanbury's earlier remark, and at just that moment she caught his eye. He was standing with some of the other gentlemen around the perimeter of the room, and his look of gentle irony was so marked, she couldn't stop herself from laughing but contrived to control herself as the duet began.

Mr. Stanbury was studying Flavia intently through his quizzing glass when Sir Percy sidled up to him, saying in a low voice, "The Allenbrooke ladies present quite a singular appearance among so much opulence, don't you think?"

"Refreshingly so."

"The yearling purchased from Miss Allenbrooke shows great promise."

"I'm delighted to hear you say so." Mr. Stanbury's tone, however, displayed only boredom.

Sir Percy glanced in Flavia's direction before returning his attention to Mr. Stanbury. "You're making absolutely certain you keep in favor with her."

The young man was forced to choke back his annoyance as he allowed the quizzing glass to drop from his fingers. "Unlike you, Cavander, I find the company of all three ladies congenial, for their own sakes, naturally."

"Currying favor at all levels may prove to be a distraction. No doubt you hope to crawl in through the back door and buy the colt for yourself."

"I have no intention of buying the colt, Cavander," Mr. Stanbury answered with a degree of iciness that was normally certain to dissuade anyone from further comment. "As for crawling, I leave that kind of thing to you."

He moved away, and when Flavia dared to glance in that direction again, she was disappointed to find Sir Percy in his place, smiling and nodding agreeably at her. Later he engaged her in conversation in the banqueting room, where the opulent array of delicious morsels was rivaled only by the decor.

Myriad lights emanated from tulip-shaped lanterns in every alcove and from the magnificent crystal chandelier suspended from another of the fantastic dragons that was featured throughout the pavilion.

"I shall dream of flying dragons," Mrs. Bowman had confided just before supper was announced.

Flavia, irritably aware of Lynette and Lieutenant Spendlow in laughing conversation nearby, was studying the Axminster carpet with its pattern of dragons and serpents as Sir Percy chattered on about his plans for the yearling he had purchased from her, unaware of her annoyance or her preoccupation with other matters. She had observed Mr. Stanbury escorting Lady Allerton into supper, and the sight of them enjoying an easy conversation had served to discompose her even further.

However deep in her thoughts she might have been, she started somewhat when a gentleman approached her and introduced himself as "Colonel Hugh Fitzsimmons, His Royal Highness's personal private secretary. His Royal Highness presents his compliments to you, ma'am, and wishes to speak with you for a few moments."

Initially Flavia looked astonished before asking, as she swallowed a mouthful of lobster in aspic, "Now, sir?"

"If you please, ma'am."

Acknowledging that the interview was probably unavoidable, she thrust the almost-empty plate into the hands of the equally astonished Sir Percy and made to follow Colonel Fitzsimmons. Owing to her extreme nervousness, she didn't notice Mr.

Stanbury as she passed him and Lady Allerton. It was obvious to him where she was going, and, looking unusually grim as he followed her progress from the room, he felt strangely protective of her.

Lady Allerton fluttered her fan and commented, "If this means Prinny is taking the matter into his own hands, that can only be good news for you, Gav. You can be finished with this ghastly obligation at last, and we can begin to enjoy our sojourn. For a while I was beginning to believe events conspired against us."

Colonel Fitzsimmons ushered Flavia into a mirrored anteroom. For a moment she was dazzled by her surroundings. The mirrored panels reflecting the light, in the form of Chinese fishermen with the lanterns as their catch, were confusing.

Then she blinked and saw the prince, who looked awesomely large at close quarters. His diamond Garter Star attached to his coat at his breast winked in the many lights and mirrors around him. When the prince turned to look at her, she immediately dropped into a curtsy and he came to raise her with his hand.

"We meet at last, Miss Allenbrooke."

"It is a great honor for me, sir."

He indicated one of the ivory-framed chairs with which the room was furnished. "Be pleased to be seated."

When she was seated uneasily at the edge of the cushion, he said after a moment's thought, "I know you to be a most sensible female, ma'am, so I shall not mince words with you. I have made up my mind to purchase your colt, and I know you would want to please me and at the same time enrich yourself." When she appeared to be about to say

113

something in reply, he put up one hand to forestall her. "You refused my very generous offers, which I know would be of the greatest assistance to you."

"Yes, sir, there is no doubt about that. You were most generous, I own."

"I take it you haven't had a change of heart, though."

"It's not a matter of money, sir. I just don't want to part with Beau."

When the prince sighed, his bulk appeared to quiver. "We have come to an impasse, it seems. Stanbury indicated you were an uncommon female, and I understand his meaning now."

Flavia flushed at the thought of being discussed by them, and he added, "You are not so full of juice, you can afford to refuse such a generous offer, are you, my dear?"

Her chin came up proudly as she replied, "We live within our means at Marston, sir."

"That is most unusual of you."

Almost unthinkingly he reached for a diamond-encrusted snuffbox sitting on an ivory-and-gilt drum table. Using only a thumb and forefinger, he flicked it open and took a small pinch, seemingly unaware that several specks had settled on the dark blue superfine of his evening coat.

"I understand you intend to launch your sister into Society next Season. That is an expensive business, so any extra money will be of very great use to you."

"Undoubtedly, sir."

He was once again thoughtful for a moment before he asked, swinging round on his heel, "If I were to offer you instead of an outright purchase price a generous annuity for life, would that, perchance, serve to change your mind about selling?"

Flavia gasped as she looked up sharply. "Sir, that is too generous an offer."

Sensing victory now, the prince smiled. " 'Tis impossible to be too generous. Anyone acquainted with me will confirm that, for I am known to be most generous to those I favor."

"Perhaps Your Royal Highness will allow me to explain something. . . ."

He waved a pudgy hand in the air, all amiability now. "By all means, Miss Allenbrooke, I am all attention."

"When Papa died, I inherited Marston House, the stables and the land attached, such as it is." He nodded affably and she went on. "However, I did not inherit Brighton Beau; he was already mine from birth, so you see, sir, whatever inducements you offer, I could not possibly part with him."

The prince's benign expression grew petulant as he replied, "Then there is nothing more to discuss."

"Regretfully not, sir, but I am sorry I cannot oblige you. Any other horse . . ."

"Yes, yes," he murmured irritably, waving his hand in the air again. "You may go now, but I'm persuaded we shall meet again, ma'am."

When Flavia was hesitant to go, he urged, "Go along for now, Miss Allenbrooke, but do not be surprised if we talk upon this matter again at some future time."

Finally she got to her feet and curtsied before leaving the room. Outside she paused to draw a deep sigh, and then as she made her way back toward the banqueting room, she saw her aunt and

Lynette hurrying toward her, anxious to know what had ensued.

"Do tell what he said—every word," they urged in unison.

"He offered me an annuity for life if I was willing to let him have Beau," she told them in a mournful voice, "and I refused!"

"How could you?" her sister gasped.

"You may well consider me fit for bedlam, but I did refuse him!"

Meanwhile the prince, deep in thought, summoned a lackey and immediately told him, "Send Mr. Gavin Stanbury to me."

A few minutes later, when he was ushered into the anteroom, Mr. Stanbury looked at the prince with interest after he'd raised his head from his bow. "You wished to see me, sir?"

"I have just interviewed Miss Allenbrooke."

"Yes, sir, so I am given to understand."

"What you will not understand is her continued refusal to sell the colt to me."

"I'm sorry about that, sir, but I am not in the least surprised to hear you say so."

"What ails the chit? Are there windmills in her head?"

Mr. Stanbury smiled slightly. "Not in my opinion, sir."

"She is intractable. The most disobliging female I have ever had the misfortune to encounter."

"Yes, sir, I agree she can appear to be most disobliging."

"Until this evening I was totally unaware of the futility of the task I set you. I don't believe the chit's ever heard of buying and selling cattle. I didn't realize just how difficult she would be, even though you warned me and Fitz and Johnny were most fulsome in their description of her."

"I can assure you, sir, I am still attempting to bring her about—in my own way."

The prince smiled fleetingly and then waved his hand in the air. "That won't fadge, Stanbury. I am certain of it now." When the young man looked at him inquiringly, the prince went on, "You may cease this farrago now. It will be to no avail, and let no one call me selfish in pursuing it. The female's impervious even to your practiced charm."

Mr. Stanbury was shocked. "Sir, I am within ames ace of success! You cannot cry off now."

The prince shook his head. "If I cannot succeed, it is certain you will not, and it has been selfish of me to involve you in this matter."

"Not in the least, sir. I would always wish to be of service to you in any way I can."

"I'm most obliged to you for saying so. I know you have done your very best, but from now on you are free to enjoy your sojourn in Brighton—my compliments to Lady Allerton! You are no longer under any obligation to me, even though I confess to you now, Stanbury, I shall continue to hope and perchance to devise some other method of persuasion. Mayhap the chit will soon find herself in the basket and be obliged to sell."

After leaving the prince in the anteroom, Mr. Stanbury paused to consider what he had been told. He felt quite stunned by the prince's change of mind, even though he was known to be capricious, for there was no doubt he was just beginning to be diverted by his bracing encounters with Flavia Allenbrooke.

When he returned to Lady Allerton, she asked, "What did Prinny want with you so urgently?"

"Nothing of any import," he replied airily, smiling across the room at Flavia, who had just caught his eye.

Lady Allerton did not miss the smile, or Flavia's bashful response to it. She just sighed with resignation. "I suppose this means you are not, after all, finished with this tiresome business."

He transferred his attention to the countess and responded, "No, Kitty, I don't suppose I am."

TWELVE

The three ladies from Marston continued to discuss the evening at the Pavilion for several days afterward, Flavia with rather less enthusiasm than her aunt and sister, who could look upon it only as an unqualified success.

By comparison Flavia was more qualified in her judgment of the events. The memory of her interview with the Prince Regent continued to trouble her, for she was persuaded he would not easily give up his wish to purchase the horse. Acquiring it might well have become an obsession, and she was aware he might be very angry at having his wishes thwarted, especially by someone he would consider nothing more than a slip of a girl.

The matter of Lynette's relationship with Lieutenant Spendlow troubled her, too. There was every indication that her sister was becoming totally infatuated with the handsome young officer. Whenever they went into town to shop, he contrived to be there, too, outside the linen draper's, in the library, and once at the saddler's. They had even encountered him early one morning while riding out with the horses on the Downs. Lynette thought he possessed an excellent seat and made mention of how splendid he must look, leading his men into battle.

No longer was anyone pretending the meetings were accidental.

Lastly Flavia was concerned about Mr. Stanbury. They hadn't clapped eyes upon him since the night of the musical soiree at the pavilion, and she blamed that roundly on Lynette's preoccupation with Lieutenant Spendlow. Flavia suspected that a gentleman as proud as Mr. Stanbury wouldn't persist when he saw there was a rival, and although she was reluctant to admit it even to herself, she missed his company, too.

However, some few days after the soiree, Flavia returned to the house to discover a barouche drawn up in front of it. Expecting to find a hopeful buyer awaiting a swift dismissal, she was delighted to discover Lady Stanbury and her daughter ensconced in the sitting room, conversing politely with Mrs. Bowman and Lynette. The two young ladies, Emmeline Stanbury and Lynette, were in heated conversation on the sofa, and it was immediately evident to Flavia that they were getting on exceedingly well.

"Lady Stanbury," Mrs. Bowman said with obvious pride when Flavia entered the room, "allow me to present you my elder niece, Flavia."

For some moments Lady Stanbury observed her critically, and then she smiled. "I am very pleased to make your acquaintance, Miss Allenbrooke. You and your sister have been taking up much of my son's time, and that is most uncharacteristic of him!"

Her comment made Flavia laugh delightedly, for his mother's visit indicated that Mr. Stanbury might well be seriously interested in Lynette after all. There could be no other explanation for her condescension in calling upon them.

"I run a fine stable here, ma'am, insuring that a great many gentlemen visit us, so I'm in no doubt why they call. I cannot take any credit whatsoever."

"You are being too modest, I'm sure." Lady Stanbury turned to Mrs. Bowman again and said, "Allow me to congratulate you on your two charming nieces, ma'am."

"You are too kind, my lady." Mrs. Bowman beamed.

"Would you care to partake of some refreshment with us, my lady?" Flavia inquired, moving toward the bellpull.

"Alas, we cannot on this occasion, for we have many calls to make. I just wished to leave my card."

"Do you intend to remain in Brighton for long?" Flavia was so bold to ask as Lady Stanbury collected up her reticule.

"If only I could. Emmy and I find it most diverting, but we needs must return to Rydal Park before my husband is totally beside himself over our absence."

All five ladies laughed, and then Emmeline Stanbury said, "Only fancy, Mama, Miss Allenbrooke is due to come out next Season, too! Isn't that splendid? We shall be able to enjoy all the same diversions."

Lady Stanbury raised her quizzing glass and examined Lynette's fair prettiness critically for a moment or two before she commented as the glass was lowered, "You will make fine companions for each other for various outings, I'm sure. There is so much to do and to see once the Season commences."

Flavia and her aunt exchanged satisfied glances before Lady Stanbury added, "Unless, of course, Miss Allenbrooke is spoken for prior to her Season."

The girl flushed and averted her eyes, and Emmeline murmured, "It might be selfish of me, but I do hope not. I have set my heart upon our being friends."

Lynette continued to blush. "We shall exchange the deepest confidences," Emmeline went on to declare, not in the least discouraged by her mother's statement. "There will be no secrets between us, I fancy."

Flavia saw Lady Stanbury's visit and her remarks as significant. Mr. Stanbury's mother and sister departed only after promises were exchanged to see one another again soon. Flavia, Lynette, and their aunt stood on the top step of Marston House, waving their handkerchiefs until the barouche was out of sight.

"Miss Stanbury is as amiable as her brother," Lynette declared when they went back indoors.

"I'm sure we are all agreed upon that," Mrs. Bowman replied.

Mrs. Bowman went to see Cook about dinner, and as Flavia ushered her sister into the parlor, she couldn't help but feel a warm glow of satisfaction at the morning's developments.

"Now you can look forward to having a friend when you come out," she told her sister, "and as Mr. Stanbury is known to you, he is bound to stand up with you at balls and routs. That will be so good for the success of your Season, dearest. I'm given to understand he is always sought after among young ladies."

Lynette appeared not in the least happy about the prospect as she went to gaze out the window while Flavia sat down at the table and began to study the household accounts with a worried frown. Even though the sale of the yearling to Sir Percy had eased the financial situation, that was only a temporary matter. Running the stables swallowed money in an alarming manner.

"What ... what if Lady Stanbury is correct, Flavia? What if some ... gentleman offers for me in the meantime?"

Flavia looked up from her accounts, still frowning. "Are you referring to Lieutenant Spendlow, or do you have some other gentleman in mind?"

The girl was twisting her handkerchief between her fingers. "Yes, yes, I do mean Lieutenant Spendlow," she answered in an unusually firm manner. "It is evident to me he is in earnest."

"I daresay, but, my dear, you really should be looking higher in your choice of a husband. Your visit to the Marine Pavilion and the way so many bucks toadied to you should have indicated how brilliant a future you face, if only you exhibit the correct degree of ... attention to others."

Lynette swung round and faced her sister at last, stamping her foot on the ground. "Why are you always so horrid about Tim—Lieutenant Spendlow? I find him most amiable. There is no other gentleman to measure up to him, in my opinion."

"You said that about Mr. Stanbury the other evening." Flavia drew a deep sigh and then, adopting a more gentle tone, she added, "I hope I'm not horrid about him, dearest. I find him most pleasant, I assure you, but you have known him for such a short time, and you really mustn't expect every gentleman who pays court to you to be in earnest."

Lynette averted her eyes. "Do you believe, then, he is trifling with my affections?"

"I'm sure he isn't."

"Then why have you set your face against him?"

Flavia toyed with the corner of the household account book as she replied, "I simply don't want you to be hasty in fixing your interest with the first gentleman who pays you court. When you go up to London, you are going to meet so many handsome and attentive gentlemen, I assure you your head will whirl." When her sister remained mutinously silent, Flavia's voice grew harder. "I confess I am ambitious for you, with very good reason. I don't want you to continue through life without a rag, wearing only outmoded and shabby gowns. Be certain, I want only the best for you, and so did Papa, who was anxious for you to have a Season in London."

The girl turned back toward the window, biting her lip, feeling all at once selfish. She hadn't been thinking too clearly on the matter, that much was obvious. Lieutenant Spendlow had dazzled her with his attentions; she had been slow to recognize that.

Naturally a brilliant match would benefit not only her but also the entire family. If she could only marry well, poor Flavia wouldn't be obliged to juggle the household accounts every month and wear a worried frown every time a tradesman's bill arrived. Lynette drew a sigh before she went to watch her aunt make quince jelly in the kitchen. She had made up her mind what she must do.

As the barouche passed through the gates of Marston House, Emmeline Stanbury could scarcely contain her glee. "Miss Allenbrooke—Lynette—is quite delightful, Mama. She and I are to be the greatest of friends from now on."

Lady Stanbury turned to smile at her daughter and then patted her hand with her own. "I am so pleased for you, dear. It will be pleasant for you both to have a bosom friend when you go up to town next Season."

"Do you truly believe, now that you've met her, Gavin . . . has fixed his interest in that direction?"

Lady Stanbury chuckled. "Not quite, Emmy. A green girl just out of the schoolroom isn't in the least in Gavin's style."

"Then why . . . ?"

"It is the elder Miss Allenbrooke who has taken his fancy."

Emmeline looked shocked as well as disbelieving. "Oh, no, Mama, you cannot be correct in this instance. Miss Flavia Allenbrooke is so . . . well, she is no dasher, is she?"

"Not in the least, and I can only give profound thanks for it. Miss Allenbrooke might well present a shabby figure compared to what we are accustomed to seeing hanging onto your brother's arm, but that can easily be rectified and does not signify. She is eminently suited to your brother, who can be—may I say it?—a trifle rackety. A handsome female, no longer young, who exhibits good sense, is just what he requires, even if he doesn't quite realize it himself as yet."

A look of great satisfaction settled on Lady Stanbury's face, and her daughter added, "If you are correct, Mama, and I am by no means certain that you are, it will be most tolerable having Lynette as a relative—not that I am in any way averse to Miss Flavia. I confess I, too, liked her style.

"However," she went on, glancing at her mother, "if all the on-dits we have been hearing contain a grain of truth, Gav might well be interested only in Brighton Beau. . . ."

Lady Stanbury gave a bark of laughter as the barouche trundled its stately way into town. "If that proves to be his only interest in Miss Allenbrooke, I shall be sorely disappointed. Now, my dear, by way of a celebration let us go right now to buy some useless gewgaw from Mr. Hannington's establishment on North Street!"

Lieutenant Spendlow espied Lynette browsing through the books in Donaldson's Library as was her usual practice of a Monday morning. After observing her with pleasure for some few moments, he made his way toward her.

"Miss Allenbrooke—Lynette . . ."

She looked up, her face breaking into a smile, and then she quickly averted her eyes from him. "Lieutenant Spendlow, you startled me."

"My apologies, ma'am. I was perhaps a little eager in my approach, but you cannot blame it in me." She laughed uncomfortably, and he was suddenly aware of her unease. His own smile faltered then. "Miss Allenbrooke, is something amiss?"

"It is nothing, sir. I was merely reflecting upon my coming Season in London and became carried away with the vision."

"London!" he exclaimed, and then moderated his voice, glancing around in some embarrassment. "You mean to go to London?"

Lynette's entire demeanor stiffened. "I cannot conceive why you thought I would not."

"Why, I thought—"

She fingered the book closest to her. "Lady Stanbury says I am bound to become all the crack. Flavia is certain her ladyship means to take me up. I can scarce wait to join her and Miss Stanbury on all their outings, which they have promised I will do. It will be vastly diverting, I fancy."

"Lynette," the young man said in a low, urgent voice, aware that several matrons present were eyeing the handsome couple curiously, "I had thought . . . You and I . . . I was about to beg leave to speak with your aunt and sister."

She looked at him again, this time with alarm. "You mustn't, Lieutenant Spendlow. There is no point in your doing so. I cannot miss this opportunity to go to London. Do you understand? Please say that you do."

He stepped back a pace, staring at her with shocked realization. "Yes, Miss Allenbrooke, I understand."

Again she smiled uncertainly before looking past him. "My aunt has arrived and will expect me to accompany her to Cowley's Bun Shoppe. Do excuse me, sir. I daresay we might meet again on some future occasion. Mayhap in London next Season."

"Lynette . . ." he begged, and his voice was filled with pain, but she merely clutched the book to her chest and went past him to greet her aunt.

Lady Allerton continually shuffled and glanced through a clutch of invitations recently arrived at her house on the Steine, while every now and again she would glance at Mr. Stanbury, who was enjoying a glass of Madeira wine in her pretty little parlor.

"So many invitations." She sighed. "If one was to accept them all, one would be totally overset after a short time."

The young man gave her his attention at last. "It isn't in the least like you to complain of a surfeit of diversions, Kitty. In London you don't, however frantic the pace becomes."

"I must be growing old, I fancy."

He laughed deprecatingly. "What a high-flyer that is! Old indeed. I don't know any other female with as much zest as you."

She suddenly stopped fingering the cards and cast him a meaningful look. "I did come to Brighton to enjoy a rather quieter time than we do in London."

"If that was your fancy you should have tried Eastbourne," he suggested as he raised the glass to his lips.

When, a moment later, he appeared to have drifted back into his own private thought, the countess asked, "Have you made any further progress with Miss Allenbrooke in your ... negotiations?"

He started out of his thoughts and stared at her blankly for a moment or two before hastily replying, "In truth, Kitty, I haven't pursued the matter of late. It's all becoming too much of a trial to me."

"I wonder what Prinny's reaction will be if the colt wins the plate next week?"

At this suggestion Gavin couldn't help but chuckle. "He might become so incensed, he'll explode. I have seen him dangerously close to it on several occasions."

"He'll be more anxious than ever to own the animal."

"I fear you're correct, my dear," he answered, drawing a deep sigh. "When Prinny puts his mind to something, he does not easily give up."

"From all I have observed, most gentlemen are of a similar nature in that respect." She perused the invitations yet again before she ventured, "Gav, perhaps at this particular time I am too much of a distraction to you."

He looked up sharply then, and she went on, speaking softly. "Perhaps you should concentrate on the matter that is so evidently troubling you."

"You know full well I have lost all heart for Prinny's errand."

She got up from her desk and walked across to the empty fireplace, saying in a thoughtful way, "I wasn't exactly meaning Prinny's quest to buy the horse."

He stared at her hard, and when she turned round to face him, she met his gaze firmly. Then he began to splutter in a most uncharacteristic manner. "I don't know what you're implying, Kitty. We came here to enjoy each other's company, and that is precisely what we are doing."

"We certainly have—for several months, in fact, and I confess that those times have been among the most enjoyable of my life. However, if we are to be honest, this sojourn has not lived up to its expectancy for either of us."

Mr. Stanbury gave a gasp of exasperation. "Blame Prinny for that, my dear."

"If you wish, but," she added, turning away from him again, "I believe you should concentrate on more pressing matters. I am not without company here, as you know. Many of our closest acquaintances are in residence. When you are not so pressed, I shall be here if you want me, you may be sure."

He got to his feet and went to take her hands in his. "You are the most remarkable woman I have ever had the privilege of knowing, Kitty."

A little while later, when he walked slowly back to the house, the last person he hoped to see waiting for him was Lieutenant Spendlow.

"Mr. Stanbury, I do hope I'm not intruding at an inopportune time. . . ."

It could hardly have been *more* inopportune, Mr. Stanbury thought. Events had been moving so swiftly, he had hoped to be alone with his thoughts for a while in order to evaluate them the better, but he affected a welcoming smile, seeing the young officer looking so troubled.

"Not in the least, sir. Come into the study and allow me to offer you some wine."

The young man raised his hand. "No, I thank you, sir. I don't propose to take up more of your time than is absolutely necessary, only . . . I didn't know who else to approach."

Mr. Stanbury poured himself a glass of sherry before he ushered his guest to a wing chair and sat down in a similar one facing him. "Now, sir, how may I be of service to you?"

All at once the young officer looked uncertain, and then he blurted out, exhibiting a degree of embarrassment, "It's about Miss Allenbrooke, sir."

Mr. Stanbury smiled slightly as he sipped at the sherry. "Somehow I thought it might be."

The other man became slightly flushed and looked away in embarrassment. "You cannot have mistaken the fact that I am greatly taken with her."

"And she with you."

Lieutenant Spendlow's eyes grew wide. "Do you truly think so, sir?"

"I'm certain of it. Surely you must have realized the truth of her feelings for you."

"I did believe I had reason to hope, and indeed Miss Allenbrooke seemed responsive to me from the very outset, but ... "

"But?"

"I was also aware from the outset, for some incomprehensible reason, Miss Flavia Allenbrooke seemed to take me in dislike."

"Oh, I think that is doing it too brown, Spendlow. Miss Allenbrooke is merely—and quite naturally—concerned for her sister's future. You should be able to understand it in her."

"She couldn't help but be aware that I would do nothing to hurt Lynette. The truth is I adore her."

Again the young man looked away in embarrassment, and Gavin told him in a sympathetic manner, "I don't doubt it, but you must consider her sister's position. For such a young lady she has been obliged to bear a heavy burden. The running of Marston, as well as her sister's future well-being and happiness are all her sole responsibility."

"Lynette's happiness and well-being are safe with me."

"As I said, I don't doubt it for a moment, but you must excuse Miss Allenbrooke for being a little more cautious." After pausing for a moment he went on in carefully measured tones. "Sir, you would go a long way to proving your devotion if you were to be honest with Miss Allenbrooke."

"So you haven't made mention of that particular matter?" he asked anxiously.

"I gained the distinct impression you were holding your cards close to your chest, and it is not, after all, my place to discuss *your* business with anyone. I confess I do understand your motives, but I also believe it is time to be honest with all members of the Allenbrooke family."

The young man drew a profound sigh. "The fact is, I intended to be completely honest with them when I called to make my offer of marriage."

Gavin sat a little further forward in the chair. "Lieutenant Spendlow, forgive me for asking, but why are you soliciting my counsel on this matter? It appears totally straightforward to me."

Once again the young man drew a profound sigh, which seemed to emanate from the very depths of his soul. "I only wish it were." When Gavin settled back in the chair once again, his eyes narrowed, the young officer continued. "Miss Allenbrooke—Lynette—has been responsive to me from the day we met. You might think me foolish for saying so, sir, but I was sure we fell in love at that very moment. Only in the last day or two she has been cool toward me, and it did make me wonder if there was another, or if, perchance, Miss Flavia has contrived to persuade her against me."

"I cannot tell you that, sir. I don't have Miss Flavia's confidence, and I haven't seen any member of the family since we were at the musical soiree."

"I had rather hoped you would agree to speak with both Miss Allenbrookes on my behalf. I truly don't know what else to do."

"You could go yourself and offer for Miss Allenbrooke with no further delay."

"If I do go now, I'm persuaded my offer will be rejected out of hand. Lynette has told me she fully intends to go up to London next Season to make her debut, which does not indicate to me she harbors any hope for *our* future together. You are liked and respected by them, Mr. Stanbury." Gavin smiled into his sherry glass. "They might listen if you were good enough to speak well of me."

Gavin studied him carefully for a moment or two before he put his glass down on a nearby drum table. "I see no harm in putting in a word or two."

"Oh, I knew you were up to the mark, sir! I'm indebted to you, truly I am."

"I don't guarantee anything, you understand," Gavin told him quickly. "No one is more aware than I that one cannot force a lady to return one's affections if she is reluctant to do so."

"I scarce think that can be true of you, sir."

He smiled faintly. "I ask that you be patient, however." Lieutenant Spendlow looked at him curiously as he went on. "I believe there might be a better chance of success if we wait just a little longer before pressing the matter further."

"Gentlemen in love are impatient, sir."

"I understand that all too well. However, you really don't need to rush. I'm persuaded there is no one else in Miss Allenbrooke's life at present, and as she isn't due to go to London for another several months you don't need to act so precipitately."

"But, sir—"

"She's very young, and she might just be experiencing a very natural doubt in her heart. Hanging in the hedge for a while might just be the catalyst you need." The young man continued to look doubtful, and Gavin pressed on. "Just leave the matter to me and I am perfectly sure you will not be disappointed at the outcome."

Lieutenant Spendlow continued to look somewhat mystified but nodded his head in agreement anyway. "I can think of no one else I would rather trust."

As Gavin walked with him to the front door, he ventured, "If you can bear it, Spendlow, play least in sight for a few days. Love was never lost for a short respite."

"That will be easy, sir. My battalion is engaged in maneuvers on the Downs in the next few days. I'm obliged to be absent from Brighton anyway."

"That couldn't be better," Gavin told him as they shook hands, and Lieutenant Spendlow set off along Marine Parade with a jaunty step.

THIRTEEN

It was very early the following morning when Gavin arrived at Marston House ready to take up Flavia's invitation to ride Brighton Beau. With Brighton races less than a week away, he reckoned he could not leave it much longer. When he rode into the stable yard, it already seemed full of horses, some of them mounted by grooms and stable boys, others still in the process of being saddled. Just as he handed the reins of his own horse to one of the stable boys, Flavia came out of one of the stalls accompanied by Munnings.

"An application of liniment will suffice to solve the problem," Flavia was telling him, but then her voice faded away when she caught sight of Gavin.

"Mr. Stanbury, you are indeed an early riser."

"Is your offer to ride Brighton Beau still open to me?"

"You've been so tardy taking up the offer, I thought you didn't intend to trouble."

"It would be impossible to pass up an opportunity to ride what is possibly the finest racehorse in England."

She looked away from him quickly. "Munnings, will you be so kind as to have a gentleman's saddle put on Beau, and bring Bethany out for me?"

"Yes, ma'am" was his sullen reply.

Munnings, who had been staring at Gavin stonily all through this brief exchange, shot him one last malicious look before he went into one of the tack rooms.

"If you intended to ride him, I wouldn't want to displace you, Miss Allenbrooke," he told her when he drew his gaze away from Munnings.

"You are very welcome to on this occasion. I feel you'll be able to put him through his paces far better than I."

"I'm obliged to you for your confidence, ma'am."

"You needn't be so modest, sir. You are, after all, quite experienced in riding racehorses."

He laughed. "I cannot imagine why you should think so."

"You once rode a horse in the Saint Ledger, and that is an important race."

"Unfortunately I rode my uncle's daisy cutter, and I've never been asked again."

Flavia eyed him up and down fleetingly before she told him, "You shouldn't be surprised. At your weight you'd now present a formidable handicap."

Gavin nodded laughingly in agreement. "Your own jockey has a natural skill I envy."

The young stable boy seated on one of the other horses grinned happily at the compliment. When Munnings sullenly led Brighton Beau out of his stall, Gavin was struck anew at how magnificent he was.

"Is your sister not joining us this morning?" he asked as he swung himself into the saddle.

She glanced across at Gavin then and noted for the first time that he wore a forest green riding coat with buff-colored kerseymere pantaloons and

136

looked devastatingly handsome. She tried to envisage him and Lynette as a couple, but the picture refused to gel. She was just happy to see him again after a gap of several days, and it came as something of a shock for her to acknowledge at last it was not for her sister's sake she was so pleased.

"She'll be sorry to have missed you," Flavia murmured before giving the order to move out of the yard.

"I hope that would also be true of you, ma'am."

Something flashed in her eyes in response to what amounted to a challenge. "It would be totally unnatural if I were not, Mr. Stanbury."

He laughed delightedly as she dug in her heels and rode off. "Do I detect a note of sarcasm, ma'am?" he inquired when he caught up with her.

"Impossible" was her reply as she cantered away. "How could any woman fail to be gladdened by your condescension, sir? That would amount to lunacy."

The Downs were shrouded in mist at that time of the morning, but it was merely a portent of an excellent day to come. The horses trotted obediently, responsive to the slightest touch of the reins by their riders. Gavin, astride Brighton Beau, was aware of all the restrained power in his mount, and he looked forward to experiencing it for himself before they returned to Marston. The glorious Sussex countryside in its green raiment was to one side, the misty gray of the English Channel to the other.

"Has His Royal Highness made any mention to you that he still wishes to acquire my horse?" she asked when they were riding along at a moderate pace.

Gavin regarded her momentarily through narrowed eyes. "I told you, I am no longer involved in the matter, but I believe I have already warned you that in my opinion he will not give up easily."

"I didn't think he would, nor have some of the others."

"While Beau continues to win races, that is something you'll be obliged to bear."

"Yes," she said with a sigh, "as well as the attentions of Sir Percy Cavander, who I'm sure sees effusive flattery as the way, not to my heart but to my horse!"

"You do yourself a great injustice, Miss Allenbrooke. Sir Percy couldn't possibly be quite such a cawker."

She cast him a curious glance. "Do you think he's in earnest?"

He laughed. "I regret to say he is not like to be, unless there are facets to his character I do not already know." He glanced at her briefly before asking, "Are you desolate, Miss Allenbrooke?"

"I am only relieved, sir! How do you like riding Beau?"

"I like it exceedingly well. My wager will be on him for the big race next week."

She looked all at once pleased. "That won't be a wager. It will be a certainty."

"I don't believe there's another horse in the area to beat him. Do you intend to go up to London with your sister and aunt? You'd find it vastly diverting."

"I don't doubt that, but I cannot. Someone is obliged to stay here and take care of everything."

"That's a great pity. You would, I'm sure, enjoy the stay."

"No doubt, but we're not precisely chawbacons

138

here in Brighton, sir. We have seen Mrs. Siddons and Mr. Kean perform at the theater on New Street, and as I'm sure you know we enjoy assemblies twice a week alternating at the Old Ship and the Castle Inn, so we have a taste of the giddy whirl that goes on in London."

"Your sister already appears to have scored a great success—with Lieutenant Spendlow," he ventured.

"You mustn't think that Lynette is as entranced by him, sir," Flavia answered quickly, a mite too fast, to Gavin's mind.

"Pardon my presumption, ma'am, but from my own observation of them I had thought he was at first oars with her."

"You're mistaken," she snapped. "Lynette is like many green girls. She's a rainbow chaser."

"I truly believe him to be in earnest," Gavin persisted.

Flavia began to appear annoyed. "I am perfectly certain that many men will vie for my sister's hand, and it will be a fortunate gentleman who wins her heart."

"Oh, indeed, I don't doubt that for a moment, but if you'll pardon me for being so presumptuous, I fancy you are rather ambitious on your sister's behalf."

Flavia bit her lip, hating herself for being so transparent. "I shall not deny it, sir. Despite my family's financial difficulties, of which you are no doubt aware, Lynette has benefited from everything of the finest."

"That much is evident," he agreed, and she appeared satisfied at last.

"The truth is she cannot afford to marry an army

officer, and I am certainly not prepared to see her living a life following the drum."

"I doubt if she'll be obliged to do any such thing."

Flavia's heart skipped a beat, and she wondered what he meant by that enigmatic remark. Before she had any time to formulate a query that might result in some snub, he said, digging in his silver spurs and setting Beau into a gallop, "Let us see what this creature is capable of, Miss Allenbrooke."

For once Flavia wandered around the house in a disconsolate way instead of in her usual purposeful manner. On this occasion she attempted to find chores, but when she did so she discovered she was unable to concentrate on them. In the midst of any activity she kept finding herself thinking about Gavin Stanbury, and when she began to muse on the possibility of his actually fixing his interest with Lynette, she found she couldn't contemplate it at all. Yet he had, in a small way, professed an interest; she couldn't be wrong about that.

Lynette had always declared her liking for him, and more importantly after their conversation a few days ago, prompted by Lady Stanbury's visit, no mention of Lieutenant Spendlow had been made, nor had the young man himself been at all in evidence. Where Lieutenant Spendlow was concerned, all the signs pointed to a short incidence of calf love.

Everything was going quite splendidly, certainly as well as she could hope for at present. If Lynette could contrive a brilliant match without having to make her debut, that would be even better for their slender resources. However, despite the apparent success of her plotting, Flavia found herself somewhat dissatisfied.

When she went to seek out her sister, Lynette was found ensconced in the parlor with Mrs. Bowman, her nose buried in the latest edition of *La Belle Assemblée*.

The moment Flavia came into the room her sister looked up to say, "Oh, do come and see this, dearest."

Mrs. Bowman was busy with her sewing, and Flavia went to look at the journal. "Don't you think this is the most beautiful gown, Flavia?"

She peered over her sister's shoulder at the fashion plate, which showed a gown of pale pink tulle embroidered with seed pearls. "Yes," she agreed, "it is quite lovely and would be most fetching on you." When Lynette sighed, something she was wont to do frequently of late, Flavia quickly added, "If Beau wins the Brighton Premiere Plate next week, you shall have one just like it."

On hearing the promise the girl cast off her languor and jumped to her feet, flinging her arms around her sister's shoulders and hugging her tightly. "You are so good, Flavia! I only hope I may be as good as you."

"What nonsense you speak," Flavia responded in some embarrassment. "You are all goodness."

"I try, I most certainly try," Lynette vowed as she withdrew. She glanced at the fashion plate again and vowed, "I shall have it made up in cornflower blue tamboured muslin, I think."

Flavia glanced at her curiously for a moment or two before she warned, "Any material you wish, dearest, as long as Beau wins next week."

"He will, I know he will."

A moment later, when a much more cheerful Lynette went back to the journal to gaze at the fashion plate and formulate her own plans for it, Flavia mused, "I was contemplating a ride into town. I need to collect the harness we took for repair last week. Why don't you come with me? The air is bound to be beneficial to you. I don't recall that you've been out much of late."

"I promised Aunt Bella to help with the sewing, and I truly have no fancy to visit the saddler, but you could, if you're passing by North Street, purchase some Tincture of Pearls, if you please. I detected a few freckles on my face this morning when I looked in the glass and needs must obliterate them."

"Your complexion is flawless," Flavia told her laughingly.

"How can you say so?" Lynette asked. "You will obtain the tincture for me, won't you, dearest?"

Her sister smiled at her indulgently. "If you wish it. Heaven forfend if anyone detected a freckle on your countenance!"

"Why do *you* need to go for the harness?" Mrs. Bowman asked, looking up from her sewing. "Why don't you send one of the stable boys?"

"I have a fancy to take the air myself, and the stable boys have a great deal of work to do in the yard today. We don't have nearly enough of them for the work involved in caring for the horses."

Just as she started to cross the room, her aunt peered at her over her sewing. "You seem ill at ease, my dear. I fancy you are worried about the meeting."

Flavia smiled with relief at her aunt's reasoning. "I always do, Aunt."

142

Mrs. Bowman clucked her tongue as her needle moved skillfully. "If only you had kept Beau as just your own personal mount."

"It's too late to wish that," Flavia answered with a sigh. "Mr. Stanbury referred to him as possibly the finest racehorse in England."

One of Mrs. Bowman's eyebrows rose a little, and Lynette lifted her head from the journal. "If it hadn't been for Beau, we shouldn't be enjoying all the attention of people like Mr. Stanbury, Sir Percy Cavander, *and* the Prince Regent!"

"You are not cut out for this kind of life, that's the problem," Mrs. Bowman told her elder niece. "No woman is, if truth be told."

Flavia, who had always been quite content with her life-style, hard as it was, didn't reply as she left the room. She dare not examine too closely why her life seemed all at once less than perfect now.

FOURTEEN

"Now I wish I'd gone with Flavia into town," Lynette lamented only minutes after her sister had driven away in the pony and trap.

Mrs. Bowman paused to glance at her niece, whose brief good spirits had faded and who was now gazing disconsolately out of the window. "Far be it from me to mention it, but I'd have thought you would have welcomed a chance to encounter Lieutenant Spendlow—if nothing else. You have done up until recently." When she didn't reply, Mrs. Bowman put down her sewing and subjected her to a particularly searching look. "Is something amiss with you, too?"

Lynette appeared to hesitate for a moment or two and then replied, "I didn't go to town with Flavia precisely because I wished to avoid an encounter with Lieutenant Spendlow."

"You two haven't parted brass rags, have you?"

"No, but I decided his attentions were becoming a little too insistent. I didn't wish him to become too fond of me when I couldn't possibly return his affections. I made my feelings perfectly clear to him when last we chanced to meet, and I haven't"—there was a little break in her voice—"I haven't clapped eyes on him since."

144

Her aunt frowned and put down the sewing completely. "This seems so odd to me. I thought he had become fond of you, and you did return his affection."

"You are mistaken, Aunt," she replied almost in a whisper, just as Gavin Stanbury's curricle drew up outside the house. Immediately the girl's manner brightened. "This is a pleasant surprise. What a pity Flavia isn't here."

"A pity indeed," Mrs. Bowman echoed as she swiftly abandoned the sewing and patted her gray curls just as Mr. Stanbury was shown into the parlor by the maidservant.

"Lynette was only just saying what a lovely surprise this is," Mrs. Bowman enthused.

"You do me a great honor in saying so, ma'am. I called in on the merest chance that your nieces would enjoy a drive to Rottingdean."

"Flavia has gone into town," Lynette explained, her manner turning shy. "A sudden errand."

"She had a harness to collect from Mr. Arthur's Saddlery on New Street," Mrs. Bowman explained. "If we had more servants . . ."

"I was looking forward to the drive," Gavin told her. "Is it possible you'll allow Miss Lynette to join me?"

"Aunt, may I?" the girl asked, her good spirits entirely restored. "Rottingdean is such a lovely village. I do so enjoy visiting it whenever the opportunity arises."

"It would be churlish of me to deny you the pleasure after such an eloquent request, my dear. Go and fetch your bonnet and shawl as quickly as you please. You mustn't keep Mr. Stanbury kicking his heels."

When she had gone, Mrs. Bowman invited him to sit down, as his presence seemed to fill the room, but he declined.

"I trust that Miss Flavia is in good health at present?"

"Yes, yes, indeed, apart from being a trifle blue-deviled as she always is before a race meeting. You know how it is, sir, I'm sure. So much depends upon Beau's winning on Thursday."

"I know I'm always in a terrible fidge when I only place a wager on a horse. It must be considerably more nerve-racking for Miss Allenbrooke to contemplate."

"Truth to tell, sir, a lady of her tender years shouldn't be obliged to shoulder such burdens as she has taken upon herself since my brother died."

"I believe you concern yourself unduly, ma'am. Miss Allenbrooke is fully competent in all she does."

Her aunt smiled. "You are kind to say so, sir, but I cannot help but feel Flavia would ring a peal over me if she heard me fretting so."

"Then our conversation will remain a secret between us."

"You are too kind. I do hope Lady Stanbury and Miss Emmeline are both in good health and enjoying their stay in Brighton."

"Very much so."

"We do hope to return Lady Stanbury's call as soon as the race day is over."

"My mother will be delighted to receive you, ma'am, and Emmy will be pleased to renew her acquaintanceship with Miss Lynette."

It was at that moment the girl returned, wearing a poke-brimmed bonnet tied under her chin with a

146

large satin bow, and both her aunt and her would-be escort considered her to look exquisite. Although plainer girls might wear more fashionable clothes, Lynette possessed the knack of always looking fresh and pretty. The late Mr. Allenbrooke had possessed the good sense to leave his property in the capable hands of his elder daughter, probably aware, Gavin thought, that the younger one would soon make a good marriage.

Mrs. Bowman saw them off at the door, and as Mr. Stanbury drove away in his stylish curricle, she frowned slightly before returning indoors.

Lynette sat composed on the box next to him, but inwardly she was experiencing a good deal of excitement, for she had never thought to be asked to ride in such a fine curricle by so elevated a gentleman. The recent attention she and her family had been receiving from so many toplofty people had left her feeling somewhat dizzy. She thought Mr. Stanbury quite amiable, although he could not compare with Lieutenant Spendlow in any respect, in her opinion. However, as they drove away from Marston House, Lynette was uncomfortably aware that this gentleman was precisely the type she should set her cap at for the future well-being of her family, if only she knew how to go about casting out lures.

When he glanced at her, she forced a smile to her lips and ventured, "This is the most unexpected surprise, sir. It was fortuitous I decided to stay at home rather than ride into town with Flavia, for this is a good deal more comfortable than our old trap."

They had come to the narrow coast road that linked Brighton with the village of Rottingdean to the east. The Downs were to one side of them and the sea, sparkling in the sunlight, on the other. Today a faint breeze was whipping up the water into small white caps of foam as it surged into the shore.

"Your aunt tells me your sister is anxious about the results of next week's race," Gavin ventured.

"She is always anxious at such times," Lynette replied, somewhat morosely. "The prize money means so much more to us than the prestige, I'm afraid. I'm aware that His Royal Highness wants Beau only for prestige, but a win makes a good deal of difference to our finances, although I daresay I shouldn't speak of it to you."

"Be sure I shan't repeat to anyone a word of anything you say to me."

"You are too kind, sir," she murmured as she looked at him. Her blue eyes were wide, and he understood the effect they had on gentlemen.

"There are times when I wish my sister would sell Beau," Lynette went on a moment later, much to his surprise. She was toying idly with her gloves when he glanced at her curiously. "At least we should be full of juice for once, and not be obliged to hang in the hedge waiting for race day to make us plump in the pocket again, but, of course, she won't," she added with a sigh. "She loves him too much. Even if he stopped winning, it would make no difference."

"Sentimentality is not a good partner in business." There was a momentary silence before Gavin told her, "I encountered Lieutenant Spendlow at Ragget's yesterday evening. He was playing casino when I joined his table."

148

"I had no notion he was a deep gamester," she retorted huffily.

"He wagers no more than he can afford to lose, which is more than can be said of most gentlemen. He informed me he'd been out of town for several days on maneuvers with his regiment."

Lynette half turned toward him, her entire manner brightening considerably. "Out of town! Did you say he'd been out of town?"

"Yes, ma'am."

"But I thought . . ."

She averted her face from him and he cast her an innocent look. "Yes, Miss Allenbrooke?"

"It's nothing." On noting his continuing interest she added in a muted tone, "I haven't seen very much of him of late, that is all."

"I am most surprised to hear you say so. I understood you two were as thick as inkle weavers."

"You are mistaken, sir," she replied, having gone suddenly pale. "We were merely friends, and still are, as far as I am aware."

"You surprise me anew, Miss Allenbrooke. I had gained quite a different impression of your relationship."

After appearing to struggle with her thoughts for a moment or two, she asked, "It is difficult for ladies and gentlemen to be just friends, is it not, Mr. Stanbury?"

She posed the question with such a sense of maturity and experience, he was tempted to laugh, but when he replied, he was entirely serious. "I must agree with you on that point, ma'am, but if I am to be honest with you, I do not believe you and he wished to be mere friends. Two young people of marriageable age and so well suited rarely enjoy a friendship that is platonic."

"Oh, do not, I beg of you, say so, sir, for you make me feel totally wretched. I have used him disgracefully, I fear."

"I don't wish to distress you further, so we'll not talk about it anymore. You must be looking forward to going up to London for your debut. I know Emmy is quite excited at the prospect."

Lynette looked less than enthusiastic as she replied, "I am fortunate to be able to have a Season, although it will be a burden on my family."

"Your sister is sensible enough to know it can be afforded, so you need feel no qualms."

"No doubt, but I'm very much afraid we'll be obliged to take a house in Bloomsbury, which is most unfashionable. However, it will have to suffice."

"Bloomsbury is a very pleasant sort of place, I assure you. Several acquaintances of mine reside there. It's entirely possible your residence will elevate the place to being *quite* fashionable."

She cast him a grateful smile, although she couldn't help but continue to look woebegone. However, her companion was not sure if that was because of the awful prospect of taking up residence in Bloomsbury or her rift with Lieutenant Spendlow.

"I feel more confident about my debut now that I have made the friendship of Miss Stanbury, which I value greatly, and I have also made the acquaintance of Lady Allerton as well as Lady Jersey, who is a mite toplofty but quite condescending in her manner."

"You can only make a great many more friends when you arrive in London," he told her truthfully.

She flushed with pleasure. "It is so kind of you to say so. Naturally," she added shyly, "if I am able to make a suitable match *before* I leave Brighton, it will be even better. I am not in the least tonnish, although Flavia says I will become accustomed to life in the beau monde soon enough. You see, if I were to marry well, it would mean so much to my family."

"If that is all that troubles your head, I assure you there is no need to harbor any fears in that direction, my dear. I'm persuaded you will make a perfectly delightful match to the satisfaction of all concerned."

She gazed at him wide-eyed as they entered the village. Gavin brought the curricle to a standstill at the side of the road as they approached the green when he espied a column of riders coming toward them. Lynette transferred her attention to the column, the horse's hooves becoming ever louder on the road as it approached.

She gave a little gasp when she noticed that the riders were all soldiers of the Tenth Hussars, resplendent as always in their colorful uniform. Gavin sat back on the box waiting for them to pass, in total control of his team of chestnut horses, which displayed only the slightest restlessness as the others came closer.

Suddenly Lynette emitted a louder gasp when she recognized the officer leading the column. Lieutenant Spendlow nodded briefly in their direction as he passed by, and Gavin raised his whip to his hat in acknowledgment. Lynette turned almost completely round on the box to catch the very last

151

sight of the young soldier, and when he was no longer to be seen, she faced forward again. Gavin noted that the color had returned to her cheeks and her eyes had grown bright again.

"How handsome they look! I declare there is no finer regiment in the country than the Tenth Hussars!"

"The sight of a military uniform is always a moving one," he agreed.

As he started the team into motion again, Lynette said in a rather morose tone, "When I was at Lewes races, I had my palm read by a gypsy who said I would meet a gentleman who had a fortune and would offer me a brilliant future."

He reached out to take her hand in his and turned it over so that the palm was uppermost. "Why, Miss Allenbrooke, the gypsy was correct in every detail. I see it clearly, too."

She laughed in protest as she withdrew her hand from his. "Mr. Stanbury! I fear you are funning, sir! You're making a May game of me."

"I vow I do not."

"You couldn't possibly read my palm because you are not a gypsy."

"It is evident you're not acquainted with my family history. You don't know that one of my ancestors was a gypsy woman. It's rumored she had the sight, and I am coming to believe I have inherited her gift for seeing the future. Now, you must have no more qualms, for I can see quite clearly that you'll achieve your heart's desire, and in a very short time, too."

The girl averted her eyes shyly. "Sir, I believe you're roasting me."

"Miss Allenbrooke, I assure you I do not."

Despite her doubts about the veracity of what he had told her, she chuckled happily and turned her face forward as he set the team in motion again.

In the meantime, Flavia still felt disconsolate as she made her way along North Street toward her pony and trap, having made the purchase required by her sister, and one or two for herself, including a new pot of lip rouge, an impulse buy she felt sure she would regret.

She was just passing Mr. Choat's Emporium of Literature when the door opened and Lady Stanbury, accompanied by her daughter, stepped out. They were conversing, but they fell silent when their gaze alighted on Flavia.

"Miss Allenbrooke, this is an unexpected pleasure," Lady Stanbury declared a moment later. "We didn't look to see you here this afternoon."

For some reason she couldn't identify, Flavia felt discomforted by the encounter, and she bobbed a brief curtsy in the hope they wouldn't discern her confusion.

"At breakfast this morning my son indicated he intended to tool over to Marston to invite you and your sister to ride out with him. That is why we're so astonished to see you *here*."

Flavia was momentarily taken aback by the revelation and then, recovering herself somewhat, replied, "I must have missed him by only a short while." Aware that Miss Stanbury had been regarding her in the oddest manner, she asked, "Have you extended your stay in Brighton?"

"Only until after the race meeting," Emmeline replied. "Gav persuaded us to stay to see your colt win the main event."

Flavia couldn't help but laugh. "I am obliged to him for his confidence."

Lady Stanbury smiled and touched Flavia's hand lightly. "Whatever the outcome, be certain we will be there to cheer him on." She turned then to her daughter, saying more briskly, "Come, Emmy, let us not detain Miss Allenbrooke any longer. Until Thursday, my dear."

Flavia raised her hand to wave them farewell as the carriage drew away from the curb, and then her smile faded. Lady Stanbury had given her very good news indeed. She was certain Mr. Stanbury would at that moment be driving somewhere along the coast road with Lynette beside him. It couldn't be better. Yet she experienced only dismay as she conjured up a mental picture of them together, laughing and conversing easily. Lynette was no doubt responding in her naive and unselfconscious manner to all his witticisms.

All at once, as the mental picture danced in her mind, she was plunged into a feeling of the most utter despair.

FIFTEEN

During the next couple of days Gavin allowed himself time to consider thoroughly the matters that teased him, and then, when he had pondered sufficiently, he resolved to call upon Flavia with no further delay. In his opinion she wasn't sufficiently clever or calculating to succeed in making a suitable match for her sister, and it was past the time her little scheme was exposed for what it was—a sham. Although her patent transparency in trying to organize an advantageous marriage for Lynette had become quite endearing.

He rode on his hack across the Downs toward Marston rather than along the road, which would have been the quicker route. For once in his life he was uncertain of himself and his reception. Never before had the happiness of others been in his gift.

Finally, when he knew he could delay no longer, he pointed his horse in the direction of the Allenbrooke property and rode him hard. He was within a few hundred yards of the property when he saw a lone horseman riding away in the opposite direction. Gavin reined in his horse, which protested slightly at the sudden constraint put upon him, and he sat back in the saddle watching Sir Percy Cavander, unmistakable on his coal black stallion, riding away from Marston House at great speed.

After he had disappeared from sight beyond a fold in the hills, Gavin remained thoughtful for a moment or two before he spurred his horse into movement and rode on. A stable boy came to take the horse when he dismounted and, after tipping him a shilling for his trouble, Gavin walked purposefully toward the house.

He found Flavia alone, as he had hoped she would be, in the parlor, poring over the household accounts. However, when he was shown into the parlor by the housemaid, she immediately jumped to her feet, smoothing down the skirt of her shabby chintz gown in an uncharacteristically self-conscious manner.

"Mr. Stanbury, how kind of you to call," she greeted him in a breathless manner that was oddly reminiscent of her sister, for he had rarely seen her other than totally composed. "If you had hoped to discover Lynette at home, Lady Stanbury and your sister were good enough to call and take her and my aunt in their carriage."

"I know."

She half turned away from him. "You must know you're too late to ride out with the horses. In any event, in the last few days before a race, only Tommy is allowed to ride Brighton Beau."

From the first moment he had entered the room he had kept her under close scrutiny, noting her uneasy manner, and he wondered what might have occurred to cause her such discomfort.

"I didn't come to ride Beau. I would like, if you can spare me the time, to have a few words with you."

After subjecting him to a strange look for a moment or two, Flavia indicated a bergère chair, its cover showing decided signs of wear, and then she sat down on the edge of the sofa, facing him. Almost as soon as she was seated, she jumped to her feet again.

"How rag-mannered you must consider me, sir. May I offer you some refreshment after your ride? A glass of ratafia or porter, perhaps?"

He smiled faintly. "No, I thank you. Be pleased to sit down, Flavia."

She started slightly at the use of her name but then sank down onto the cushion again. Pleating her skirt between her fingers, she said, "You have about you the air of a gentleman who means business, so I am bound to suppose you have come to make a further offer for my horse."

"When will you believe me when I say I do not want to buy your horse, either for my own use of that of anyone else!" She looked up on hearing such a sharp tone from his lips, but he was immediately abashed and added, "Forgive me. I just regret my brief involvement in the matter, although it did have the advantage of bringing me the acquaintance of you and your family, and that I most certainly do not regret."

She flushed slightly and replied, "I am too ready to fly up into the boughs at present, so I must solicit your forgiveness. I have much to preoccupy me."

Gavin laughed shortly as he brought out his snuffbox. "I doubt that your recent visit from Sir Percy Cavander has done anything to soothe your nerves."

"Sir Percy?" Flavia echoed, looking up again. "I haven't set eyes on him for several days."

For a long moment he gazed at her steadily before he took a pinch of snuff from the box and snapped the lid down again. "My mistake, ma'am. The reason for my intrusion on your time is that I wish to speak to you about Miss Allenbrooke. . . ."

Flavia's eyes grew wide. "Lynette?"

"You might regard me as being impertinent to mention the matter, but during my delightful ride with her the other day I fancied she had the look of a mooncalf about her."

At that moment Flavia experienced a feeling of intense dread, despite suspecting she was about to have her dearest wish achieved. He could have contrived this meeting for only the one reason. She knew she should be feeling joyful, except that in settling her sister's future so satisfactorily, she would bruise her own heart.

"My sister has often proclaimed her admiration for you, Mr. Stanbury," she told him, and her voice had become rather high-pitched in her attempt to appear composed.

"I am greatly pleased to hear you say so, but I didn't fancy that her interest was aimed in my direction."

"You are mis—"

"Flavia, you must surely be aware that your sister is head over heels in love with Lieutenant Spendlow, and he with her."

Her heart was beating fast, and unconsciously she clasped her hands together hoping that would steady her quaking, but it did not.

"Lynette is very young, sir, and up until recently unused to all the flattery and attention she has been receiving. In those circumstances it is understandable if her head is turned a little. A handsome young gentleman in a uniform is sufficient to cause a green girl to believe herself in love. Why, I recall being quite taken by the soldiers when I was a girl, so if you wish to offer for her, I'm sure—"

"I haven't the least intention of offering for her, and wouldn't even if she fancied herself in love with *me*. Lieutenant Spendlow wishes to offer for her, but he is too afraid of rejection—by you, not your sister, although I'm certain she will do that if she believes it would please you. I have come to tell you Lieutenant Spendlow is a fine young man, and they make a handsome couple."

Flavia jumped to her feet, unable to hide her agitation any longer. She turned her back on him as she moved across the room. "Sir, I take exception to this unwarranted interference in my family's personal affairs. This matter cannot possibly concern you."

He got to his feet to stand behind her. "It seems I have a softer heart than anyone has previously given me credit for, and I cannot bear to see a young couple's hopes thwarted by blind ambition—and it is blind, Flavia, for I'm sure you want your sister's happiness above all things."

"This is a foolish conversation, sir. She is so young and has met only the one gentleman so far, two, if you are included. I believe Lynette can do better than a country squire's son."

"The Spendlows are the largest landowners in Yorkshire, and Sir Lionel Spendlow is the lord lieutenant of the county. Lieutenant Spendlow is heir not only to a baronetcy but also to one of the largest fortunes in the north of England."

She turned sharply on her heel to face him then, and her eyes were narrowed with suspicion. "You are roasting me, are you not?"

"I vow I am speaking the truth. They own the house and estate at Granton End as well as a house in Cavendish Square, and yet another in Scarborough, which is a pleasant enough, if unfashionable, watering place. Lynette has fixed the interest of a very eligible young man."

"Why on earth didn't he say something?" she demanded in outraged tones. "What is he trying to hide?"

"Like many young men in his position he has encountered all too many fortune hunters." She had the grace to blush, but he affected not to notice as he went on. "He wished Lynette to love him for what he is, and she does. She is willing to marry him even if it does mean living solely on the pay of an officer."

"You must think me a monster indeed," she murmured as she averted her eyes.

He raised her chin with one finger until she was looking at him again. "I think you are a devoted and loving sister, wanting only the best for Lynette. If you were as hard-bitten as you'd have me believe, you'd have sold Beau to the highest bidder long ago."

"I may have to if he doesn't win on Thursday."

He withdrew his finger, saying, "I didn't doubt Lynette and Lieutenant Spendlow would eventually bring you round to their side, but I hope you'll forgive me for settling the matter before any more anguish ensued. The other day your sister looked like a dying duck in a thunderstorm!"

Flavia laughed a mite uncomfortably before asking, "How may I put matters right between them with no further ado?"

"You needn't trouble your head over that, I assure you."

Realization dawned on her then, and she smiled at him knowingly. "I suppose at some point during her ride with Lady Stanbury, my sister will accidentally encounter Lieutenant Spendlow."

"I shouldn't be in the least surprised," he agreed, and then, moving toward her again, he took her hands in his. "You really shouldn't have doubted their compatibility; a gypsy at Lewes race course told Lynette she would make a brilliant match with a handsome gentleman. It was all preordained. I wonder what she would have told you had you consulted her."

"No doubt that I would also meet handsome and eligible gentlemen. The gypsy wouldn't know, of course, that they sought my racehorse, not my heart."

His eyes sparkled with amusement. "You can't be certain of that."

Suddenly, as her heart took a leap, the door burst open and the maidservant rushed in with one of the stable boys close on her heels.

They checked on seeing their mistress's visitor but pressed on into the room nevertheless. "Beggin' your pardon, ma'am, but you've got to come to the stables," the lad said in a breathless whisper. "There's been an accident."

Flavia grew pale. "Not Beau? Surely not Beau?"

"No, ma'am. It's Tommy. Tommy's 'ad the accident!"

Her hands flew to her lips. "Oh, my goodness. How badly is he hurt?"

"Don't rightly know yet, ma'am, but knocked cold, 'e was."

When Flavia cast Gavin a fearful glance, he said in as reassuring a tone as he could contrive, "Let's go and see for ourselves." He turned to the stable boy as Flavia drew her shawl closer about her and started for the door. "You, boy, go and fetch the family physician. Do you know where to find him?"

"I think so, sir."

"Doctor Parker," Flavia supplied. "He resides in one of the new houses in Regency Square." She paused in the doorway, looking both impatient and distressed. "I do hope he'll be at home just now."

"Don't delay," Gavin urged as the lad started to leave. "Impress upon him it's a matter of great urgency."

The stable boy tugged at his cap. "Yes, sir, you can rely upon me. I'll be there in a brace of snaps."

He ran off as Gavin and Flavia started to follow. "I do hope it isn't anything serious," she murmured.

"We shall soon find out, and very like it isn't."

She cast him a grateful smile while neither lessened their pace. "I'm so glad you are here."

"I'm sure you've been obliged to deal with crises before, and contrived very handsomely to do so."

"This could be particularly inopportune. The Brighton meeting is the day after tomorrow."

The reminder made Gavin look all the more grim. "I haven't forgotten."

When they reached the stable block, the boy galloped past them on one of Flavia's horses. They found Tommy laid out unconscious still in one of the stalls, surrounded by his colleagues, who were staring down at him worriedly.

"Has he regained his senses yet?" Gavin asked as he pushed his way through the grim-faced crowd.

"There's no sign of it," Munnings answered, looking particularly somber.

"What on earth happened?" Flavia asked as she knelt down at Tommy's side and took his small hand in hers.

"Don't rightly know, ma'am," Munnings answered. "Tommy came in 'ere to see to Flighty, as he usually does, and the next thing I knows is 'e cries out, and when I came in 'e was like this, hug to the ground, totally out of his senses."

Gavin went down on one knee at the stricken jockey's side, feeling for his pulse. Flavia watched him anxiously in the few seconds before he was able to proclaim, "He appears to be all right, Flavia." He brushed back a lank lock of hair from the boy's brow to reveal an ugly gash.

"How on earth . . . ?" she gasped before she looked up at Gavin again.

"Flighty can be a bit of a terror, ma'am," one of the grooms ventured to say. " 'Appens she jostled Tommy and he lost his footing. She might even 'ave kicked 'im."

Flavia drew a deep sigh and sat back on her heels. Tears sparkled in her eyes and she looked at Gavin, who smiled faintly and assured her, "He's in no danger of his life."

"That is a great relief to me."

At just that moment the boy began to stir, and Flavia became more anxious, squeezing his hand and saying, "Tommy, Tommy, can you hear me?" in an urgent tone.

The boy began to open his eyes, and when they

focused at last upon all those gazing down at him, he asked, "Lor', what 'appened?"

"You've had an accident," Gavin told him. "You were knocked senseless. Do you remember what happened?"

He began to shake his head but then winced. "Steady on, young man," Gavin cautioned. "You'd best keep still until Doctor Parker's had a chance to look at you. Now, try to recall the last thing you remember."

The jockey frowned in concentration. "I remember going in to check Flighty's left hock, sir. I'd been a bit concerned for it and wanted to check before I told Miss Allenbrooke when she came back down this afternoon. I bent down to look at it, and that's all I remember. She must 'ave given me a real mandozy."

While Gavin frowned, Munnings bent down to ask, "Do you think she kicked you, lad?"

"May 'ave done. Don't rightly know. I wish I could remember."

"You're going to be fine in no time," Gavin assured him as he got to his feet, brushing off the straw that was adhering to his pantaloons.

"I've got to be, sir. I'm riding Beau at the race meeting on Thursday."

Gavin looked only more grim at the reminder, but then he turned to the head groom and asked softly, "Could you organize a hurdle, Munnings? The boy will be more comfortable in bed, and he's in no state to walk to his quarters from here."

The fellow nodded in his surly manner and immediately went off to find a suitable implement to bear the stable boy to his quarters. Gavin watched him go, his lips compressed into a grim line. Flavia spoke in a comforting manner to the stricken boy while Gavin wandered around the stall looking for clues to the cause of the accident, but even to his searching look there seemed nothing likely to cause such an injury, unless the mare had kicked him.

"It was an odd thing to happen to someone as experienced with horses as Tommy," he murmured.

Flavia drew her attention away from the boy briefly to cast Gavin a faint smile. "You must know that all animals act by instinct and are not always reliable in their behavior."

He flashed her a reassuring smile in response. "Nor are humans."

She held his gaze as she replied, "That is not my experience. Human beings invariably stay true to character."

Immediately she returned her attention to the stricken jockey, and a short time later the others returned with a small gate, on which they put the injured boy.

"Shall we take him to his quarters over the stable block, ma'am?" Munnings asked in a deferential tone that Gavin thought a mite insincere. It was certainly out of character, but perhaps, he thought generously a moment later, he was chastened by the accident.

"Yes, of course, as quickly as you please. No, no," she added a moment later. "Take him up to the house instead. No doubt he'll require nursing until he's back on his feet."

A sad little procession made its way up to the house, with Flavia all the while urging the men to be as gentle as possible so as not to jolt the boy. The physician arrived soon after Tommy had been settled into the box room, and all the while the boy drifted in and out of consciousness. Gavin remained in the room while Doctor Parker made his examination.

Finally he declared, "No broken bones, young man, and in that you are most fortunate. I've seen far worse injuries caused in a similar manner."

"Then in your opinion the injury was caused by the filly?" Gavin asked, something that made the doctor look surprised.

"What else could have caused it?" When Gavin made no reply, the doctor turned back to his patient. "A few days' rest and you'll be as right as ninepence, I promise you."

Tommy attempted to raise himself from the pillows but sank back with a sigh. "None of that either," the doctor scolded. "The blow to your head needs resting. You wouldn't want to contract a brain fever, now, would you?"

"I've got to ride a race the day after tomorrow, sir, so I'd best bestir myself now."

Doctor Parker laughed. "Absolutely out of the question, boy. If you did, you'd do your health great harm. Moreover, you'd experience such dire discomfort that, I'm persuaded, would insure you had little chance of riding successfully against others who are in the peak of health."

Tommy groaned loudly. "Mr. Stanbury, what am I to do? Miss Allenbrooke is relying on me to ride Beau!"

"Don't concern yourself about it now, Tommy," Gavin assured him. "Miss Allenbrooke wouldn't want you to risk your health any further."

When they came out of the room, Doctor Parker told Gavin, "He needs only complete rest. I'm sure no permanent damage has been done."

"That, at least, is reassuring," Gavin replied, although he was preoccupied in his thoughts.

"Treacherous creatures, fillies," Doctor Parker said with a laugh as they came down the stairs. "I don't trust the female of any species, if the truth be told."

The young man smiled faintly, observing, "The boy has a rare affinity for cattle, sir. I cannot conceive of his being in the least careless."

"Don't need to be if a filly's turning testy."

Flavia was in the hall, looking anxious, when they came down the stairs. "How is my jockey, Doctor Parker?" she asked immediately.

"He'll live. Better still, he'll recover, but needs must rest quietly for at least the next se'nnight." She gasped at the implication of his words. "I have given him a small dose of laudanum, so he is bound to rest whether he wishes it or not. You may give him a few drops whenever his head hurts, and I will call in daily until he is recovered. With head injuries one must take the utmost care. I'm sure you will appreciate that, Miss Allenbrooke." He bowed, saying, "Until the morrow, ma'am. Mr. Stanbury."

When he had gone, Flavia turned to Gavin in evident anguish to say, "Of all times for Tommy to have an accident . . ."

"Yes, I grant you it is most inopportune, and no one is more grieved about it than the boy himself."

She turned away from him to hide her despair. When he followed her into the parlor, he realized her shoulders were shaking with emotion. He put his hands out to touch her, and she turned to face him as tears began to roll down her cheeks, unchecked at last.

"Don't distress yourself, I beg of you, Flavia. All is surely not lost."

"No, indeed," she sniffed, hating herself for her lack of control. "I am relieved and delighted that Tommy isn't badly hurt, and the news you brought me means that Lynette's future is assured, but this accident could not have come at a worse time for us."

He drew her into his arms, and she laid her head against his chest quite unselfconsciously and began to weep without restraint.

"You must consider me a complete peagoose," she sniffed some minutes later when she raised her head once again, and he handed her his cambric handkerchief to dab at her cheeks.

"Don't think that for even a minute. It would be a rare creature who took such a reversal with equanimity."

She smiled through her tears and continued to dab at her cheeks with his handkerchief, trying to put from her mind the feel of being held close to him. "We have not always enjoyed an easy accord, sir, but I'm obliged to you for your assistance today."

He still had his hands on her shoulders, and all at once the cozy camaraderie between them changed to something charged with emotion. Flavia's eyes, luminous with tears, gazed back at him questioningly as he looked down at her.

All at once she was anxious to be kissed by him. The blood coursing through her veins had turned considerably warmer at his touch. His lips were close to hers, and she trembled in anticipation of what was to come. Just at that moment, though, there came the sound of carriage wheels and horse's hooves on the gravel outside. The young couple sprang apart on hearing Mrs. Bowman bidding farewell to Lady Stanbury and Emmeline.

A moment later, when Lynette and her aunt came into the room, the two were standing yards apart, Flavia composing herself but unable to disguise her tearstained face. She wasn't in the least sure whether her discomposure was due to the accident that had befallen Tommy or to her alarming response to being held in Gavin Stanbury's arms.

"We have had the most delightful afternoon," Lynette was saying as she took off her bonnet. "You cannot venture to guess who we encountered on the road to Patcham. Lieutenant Spendlow! I was never more surprised in my life! Miss Stanbury says . . ."

Her inconsequential prattle died away when she began to realize something was wrong, but it was Mrs. Bowman who asked, "What is amiss, Flavia?"

The facts of Tommy's accident were quickly explained to them, and the pleasure the two ladies had exhibited after their delightful afternoon turned to consternation.

"What a terrible thing," Mrs. Bowman declared, while Flavia studiously avoided any eye contact with Gavin. "And all the while Lynette and I were enjoying ourselves so much."

"Had you remained, there was nothing either of you could have done," Gavin explained, glancing worriedly at Flavia. "I appreciate Tommy has a rare affinity with Beau *and* is a fine jockey, but you'll just have to allow one of the other boys to ride him on Thursday. You may not have as good a chance of winning, but with a horse the caliber of Beau it is still possible with another rider."

"Mr. Stanbury is, of course, quite correct, dear," her aunt agreed.

"No," Flavia said, turning toward him. "It's far too late for that."

His eyes narrowed as he replied, "I don't understand why."

"None of the others have ridden Beau. Only you and I have ridden him. I don't consider anyone else remotely competent to handle him."

Gavin looked astonished. "My dear girl, in these circumstances why on earth did you allow me of all people to ride him? No wonder Munnings was so sullen about it."

Flavia waved one hand in the air in a dismissive gesture. "Munnings is not so bad deep down. He just doesn't like strangers. He reckons they unsettle the horses, but you, at least, had ridden a horse in a major race. In any event," she added, her voice no more than a whisper, "I was disposed to oblige you. I hoped you would continue to call."

Lynette looked away in embarrassment, and Gavin drew a sigh. He began to move toward the door, something that alarmed Flavia. "You can expect me here first thing in the morning. *I'm* taking Beau out on the gallops tomorrow. I shall be riding him in the Brighton Premier Plate on Thursday," he declared.

All three ladies started, and it was Flavia who said, "It's good of you to offer, but I cannot possibly accept."

He paused to glance at her, his eyes narrowed. "I see. I daresay I have done little to engage your trust since our first meeting. If you don't wish me to ride Beau on Thursday, I can't blame it in you."

Flavia's eyes flashed angrily. "That is nonsense,

sir! This has nothing to do with your connection to the prince. The fact is you're far too heavy to ride him in a race."

"I know that as well as you, but even with a handicap of that nature I believe he can win. If he stays in his stall on Thursday, there is *no* chance at all of his winning!"

SIXTEEN

The Allenbrooke landau was standing quite close to the winning post at the Brighton race course as the perimeter began to fill with altogether smarter equipages. The Stanbury barouche was positioned nearby. Lynette had been allowed to accept an invitation for her and Lieutenant Spendlow to join Lady Stanbury and her daughter in their carriage for the event.

Flavia was at last delighted for her sister's sake that she was making both a suitable marriage and an excellent connection in what was a love match. In addition, at this particular event, where so much was at stake, she was also glad to be spared Lynette's inane chattering, for her already overstretched nerves seemed at breaking point.

Mrs. Bowman leaned forward to touch her hand. "Come, my dear, why be so blue-deviled about it? Even if Beau doesn't win for us today, you can be easy in your mind because you won't be obliged to finance Lynette's Season in London. There is no point in launching her now that you have accepted she will marry Lieutenant Spendlow."

It was then that Flavia contrived to smile at last. "I'm so glad my foolish ambition for her didn't result in Lynette's losing him to another. Even if he had been as poor as I supposed, I had no right to be so manipulative."

"You didn't exactly conspire against them in too obvious a way, and in any event true love is not so trifling it can easily be discouraged."

"It's just as well, and they do make a handsome couple, do they not?"

Both ladies glanced in the direction of the Stanbury barouche, and when Lynette noted their interest, she paused in her happy chattering to wave to them. At her side, resplendent in his uniform, Lieutenant Spendlow nodded to them affably, causing Mrs. Bowman to sigh with pleasure.

"Now, if only I could see *you* so well settled," she murmured, and then, on noting her niece's flushed cheeks, she added quickly, "It's good news that Lieutenant Spendlow intends to resign his commission and return to manage the family estates now that Sir Lionel is ailing. Lynette won't be obliged to be an army wife, after all."

"If Beau wins today, it will mean we can afford the most fitting wedding for them," Flavia enthused, having recovered her composure.

Just then Lady Allerton could be seen strolling in their direction, on the arm of Lord Cambourn, and Flavia looked uncertain once again.

"Mrs. Bowman. Miss Allenbrooke. I have just paused by Lady Stanbury's carriage to exchange a few words, and I am delighted to learn that your sister is about to be married."

It was Mrs. Bowman who replied, while her niece gazed in awe at the beautiful countess. "No announcement has been made as yet, but we thank you, ma'am, for your kind felicitation."

Lady Allerton then transferred her attention to

the unusually mute Flavia and said, her voice taking on an entirely harsher tone, "I hear that Mr. Stanbury is riding your colt in the big race today."

"Yes," Flavia answered. "He was kind enough to offer when my jockey became indisposed."

"There are few matters of endeavor that he does not attempt at some time. One can only admire him for it. I just hope he is successful and you have more than the one reason to celebrate today."

"Thank you, my lady," Flavia murmured as, with a brief nod of her head, she moved on to greet yet another acquaintance.

Flavia watched her go, seemingly fascinated by the woman who had entranced Gavin for so long. Only the sound of her aunt's voice attracted her attention.

"You mustn't concern yourself with Lady Allerton," Mrs. Bowman told her, eyeing her shrewdly.

Flavia affected to ignore her aunt's meaning, which was very clear to her. "Mr. Stanbury has neglected Lady Allerton to tender us his help and attention. I sometimes wonder why. . . ."

"Do you, dear?" Mrs. Bowman responded in an artless way.

Angrily Flavia looked away from her aunt's knowing smile. "He came to us purporting to buy Beau, which seems to me to be the sole object of every buck in Brighton. He declares he isn't interested in acquiring Beau for himself and he is no longer acting for the Prince Regent, but how can we be certain he has no underhand motive for what he does, Aunt?"

Mrs. Bowman's smile faded abruptly. "Are you asserting that Mr. Stanbury might try to *pull* Beau today?"

The first race had begun, to the great cheers of the huge crowd. For once Flavia didn't even notice it, let alone place a wager. She just drew a profound sigh.

"I truly don't know what to think. I have no experience with bucks of the ton, save for some alarming on-dits that circulate around the town every summer. All I know for certain is that Tommy had an accident at a most inopportune moment, and no doubt there are those who believe if I don't have a win today, I might be forced to sell, *and* at a reduced price."

"I believe I understood that Mr. Stanbury was with you when Tommy had his accident."

"He was." Her cheeks grew pink at the memory of how she had thoughts only for him at that very time. She dare not even contemplate what might have ensued if her aunt and Lynette hadn't arrived.

When the winning horse streaked past the post, to the great cheers of the crowd, Flavia began to get down from the landau, saying, "I must go to the saddling enclosure and have a few words with Mr. Stanbury before the race begins."

"Wish him good luck from me, dear. I have the utmost faith in him even if you do not."

Flavia had only just begun to make her way to the saddling enclosure when she spotted Sir Percy Cavender strolling toward her. She smiled slightly at what she considered an innocuous fashion sported by some of the more outrageous dandies. Sir Percy was carrying a parasol in striped silk to shade himself from the sun.

"What is this I have heard about *Stanbury* riding Brighton Beau in the plate this afternoon? It sounds like a whisker to me. In fact, I wagered Ponsonby a monkey he was mistaken."

"It's true, sir, I assure you."

"My stars! What possessed you, a lady of such commendable good sense, to allow such a thing?"

She felt uncomfortable at having her judgment brought into doubt, for she was so unsure herself, she didn't need any further undermining of her confidence.

"It wasn't a question of allowing, Sir Percy. My jockey was the victim of an unfortunate accident the other day, and in the absence of any other, Mr. Stanbury was kind enough to offer to stand in for him."

Sir Percy laughed. "How very strange!"

"What do you mean by that, sir?"

"Just that, Miss Allenbrooke, nothing more. I wish you had confided in me. I could have recommended a good jockey, one who is far more suited to the task."

"Mr. Stanbury happens to be well acquainted with Beau," she informed him, a coldness creeping into her manner.

"I don't doubt for one moment Stanbury believes himself up to all the rigs, but this . . ."

She cast him a challenging look. It was all very well that she doubted Gavin, but she would not allow Sir Percy to do so.

"Tell me, sir, do you believe he cannot succeed in winning for me?"

"I have no notion. I have never considered Stanbury to be as superior as he believes himself to be, but for your sake, ma'am, I trust he is, and to keep faith with you I fully intend to place a small wager on Brighton Beau."

"You may find yourself even plumper in the pocket as a result."

"I certainly hope I do, ma'am, but if not, and you find yourself in the suds as a consequence, my offer to buy still stands. I will not hold one loss against him, naturally. However, if the colt has a consistent losing streak from now on, his value might not be so great. You would do very well to think on the matter most carefully, Miss Allenbrooke."

"I have," she told him sweetly, and then, bobbing a curtsy, she hurried away, knowing he continued to watch her.

When she reached the saddling enclosure, she found Gavin properly booted and spurred, already in the saddle walking Beau around the paddock. When she first caught sight of him, she stopped where she stood, her heart skipping a beat before it commenced to race. Brighton Beau might well be the finest racehorse in England, but Gavin must surely be the handsomest rider. When he caught sight of her, he smiled, something to which she couldn't help but respond, and then he trotted the colt in her direction.

"Is everything in order?" she asked, forcing herself to be distant with him when all she could think about was how close to kissing her he had come before Lynette and Aunt Bella had interrupted them. It wouldn't do for her warmth toward him to become too effusive, for she had no wish to allow this notorious rake to know how much he affected her senses.

"As much as they can be. Beau's in fine form, as you can see, never better, I believe. Have you made a wager yet?"

She laughed then. "No! I have seen too many lose their everything for a horse."

"You possess too much good sense ever to risk that, I fancy, but the odds, I'm told, are lengthening. I'm not considered a good bet, so if you place a wager now, you could benefit considerably."

"I shall in any event if you win. If you don't, at least I won't have lost my purse, too."

His eyes sparkled with amusement. "You cannot always play safe in life, you know, Miss Allenbrooke."

"Yesterday you called me Flavia," she told him in a husky voice, ignoring the obvious hidden meaning in his words.

She only hoped it referred to flirtation and not her gamble in allowing him to ride her colt.

"Today you are the owner. I am the jockey. More decorum is in order, I think."

She glanced around the paddock, asking, "Have you noticed? There seem to be a great number of hussars present today, many of them in this particular area of the course."

"Courtesy of Lieutenant Spendlow."

She frowned. "Are they here for a purpose?"

"Only in the event anyone feels aggrieved about losing on a previous race, or indeed that Beau is running in this one."

She stiffened with tension then. "You don't really believe Tommy was the victim of an accident, do you?"

He shrugged his broad shoulders. "It's impossible to know for sure. The lad certainly does not. Suffice to say a great deal of money is wagered on races such as this. We shouldn't take any chances, but you shouldn't worry your head on the matter." He straightened up in the saddle as the last of the jockeys mounted his horse. "The weather is in our favor. Beau likes the going to be hard."

"You know him almost as well as Tommy does," she told him. "You have a good affinity with him."

"As Tom will tell you, it's essential. Today Beau and I are partners." He reached for her hand and raised it to his lips. "Wish us luck."

"Good luck," she whispered, her voice husky again.

Munnings stepped forward to check the girths, but Gavin snapped, "I've already done that, Munnings. You may stand back."

The groom scowled at him, saying, "As you wish, sir, but just you remember Beau's got energy to spare. Let 'im 'ave 'is 'ead all the way along. Don't 'old 'im back from the start."

Gavin nodded and, casting Flavia an encouraging smile, he rode off with the other entrants, and after watching him for a minute or two, she went back to join her aunt in the landau.

"Whatever else," Mrs. Bowman told her as she lowered her telescope after reviewing the field, "they appear to be the finest horse and rider in the race."

Flavia smiled her acknowledgment of the fact before raising the telescope to her eye to watch Gavin ride the colt to the starting line. Then she looked away, doubts and fears crowding into her mind again.

"Winning this race has nothing to do with Beau, or the prize money, has it, Flavia?" Mrs. Bowman asked as she watched her niece.

"We do need the money, Aunt."

"I'm as aware of that as you. I know what really

179

troubles you, though. If Beau doesn't win this race, you'll be afraid you'll never know if Mr. Stanbury is trustworthy or not, and that, at present, is the most important thing to you."

"I do so want to trust him."

"I believe he is an honorable man, and if he doesn't win this race, it won't be because he hasn't tried."

A great roar issued from the crowd as the horses started off on the most valuable race of the Brighton season. The Allenbrooke groom and coachman standing at the side of the course were shouting as loud as anyone, urging the colt on.

When Flavia raised the telescope to follow the field, the Prince Regent in his barouche, resplendent in the uniform of a field marshal—a rank he had accorded himself—came into sight. He was following the field of horses as avidly as anyone else.

"Cor!" the groom exclaimed. "What's the cove about, Billy? Just look at 'im. 'E's making no 'eadway at all. Beau should be streaking ahead by now."

Flavia swung the telescope round from the Prince Regent to the pounding mass of horseflesh at the far end of the course. Her heart sank like a stone when she saw Beau near the back of the field. To have any chance of winning he needed to be near the front at this point, especially as the second half of the Brighton course was slightly inclined uphill, making the final few furlongs hard going for the tired horses.

"We'll whistle for a win now," Billy replied. "I'd be flummergasted if 'e ends up anywhere but last. Chelsea College to a sentry box I'd 'ave done better."

Flavia put down the telescope and sank back into the squabs, fighting back her tears of dismay. In the face of Gavin's famous charm she'd behaved no better than a totty-headed schoolgirl, and that might well result in her ruination.

"My stars!" the groom cried a moment later. "That colt's a real thruster. Just look at him coming through on the outside. That Stanbury cove must be a real out-and-outer. The others are flagging and Beau's got all his wind left!" The fellow turned to his mistress and said, "Miss Allenbrooke, just look at Beau now! He's raking past them all."

Raising herself out of the depths of her despair, she lifted her head in time to see Gavin ride Brighton Beau across the finishing line by a clear head. She jumped to her feet, cheering as wildly as everyone else.

"He's won, Aunt Bella! He's actually won. I can scarce believe it!"

"I felt sure he would." Mrs. Bowman chuckled, not in the least dismayed.

Billy and the coachman were throwing their hats in the air. The occupants of the Stanbury barouche were waving in delight. Lieutenant Spendlow was throwing his shako in the air, and Flavia couldn't contain her own joy as she waved back to them.

"You had best make your way to claim the prize," Mrs. Bowman suggested as the landau became besieged by well-wishers.

All at once Flavia's eyes grew wide. "Aunt Bella! The Prince Regent is presenting the plate! How can I possibly face him?"

"With pride, my dear. Seriously, though, if Mr. Stanbury can bear to face him, you will also contrive handsomely to do so."

The groom tried to clear a way for her to pass, but she and her aunt were accosted at every step. Flavia had never enjoyed a win more, and it had nothing whatsoever to do with the value of the prize. Finally they reached the winners' enclosure just as Gavin rode in on the triumphant colt. Flavia went and flung her arms around the horse's neck, wishing she could embrace Gavin so easily. The colt whinnied appreciatively.

"You were both absolutely splendid," she cried. "I'm so proud of my horse and," more shyly now, "my jockey."

"It was my pleasure," he responded, sweeping off his hat.

She couldn't look directly at him, so ashamed was she of her earlier doubts. He dismounted, and Munnings and his stable boys moved forward to take the reins, remove the saddle, and cover the colt with his blanket, made up of the Allenbrooke racing colors of blue, green, and yellow.

"That was the most exciting race I have ever witnessed," Mrs. Bowman declared, addressing herself to Gavin. "Do you know I have won a full twelve months' pin money this afternoon?"

Flavia laughed at her aunt's confession, and Gavin answered, "Your faith is remarkable, ma'am."

Although she was aware of the irony in his voice, Flavia's eyes were nevertheless shining when she looked at him at last. "How can I ever thank you?"

"I believe I will think of some method," he replied, and his eyes were brimming with silent laughter, but that did not trouble her in the least at her moment of triumph.

She looked away from him only when she became aware of a great deal of consternation around her.

The Prince Regent was coming toward them, a look of definite displeasure on his face. The steward handed the prince the plate and a packet containing the prize money. Rather self-consciously Flavia stepped forward to receive her winnings.

The Prince Regent smiled then but displayed no pleasure when he did so. His eyes, she noted, were quite cold, something that made her shiver slightly and dampened her pleasure at the triumph.

"Quite a remarkable win," he commented as she disguised her disquiet in a low curtsy. "An amazing race, in fact. You are fully deserving of this, my dear," he added as he handed her both the plate and the packet.

"Thank you, sir," she murmured, stepping back a pace and drawing a deep breath of sheer relief.

Then the prince turned his displeasure upon the erstwhile jockey, who affected an inscrutable expression. "You are a package of surprises, Stanbury. Truly you are."

Gavin bowed low as the prince, the course steward, and several aides and equerries walked away. Flavia let out a long breath, and Mrs. Bowman said gently, "I must go and collect my winnings. Why don't you walk back to the jockeys' tent with Mr. Stanbury? You must have a good deal to talk about."

"You are full of good sense, ma'am," Gavin told her.

"I shall meet you back at the landau," Flavia murmured, feeling slightly embarrassed at being propelled so obviously into his company.

However, she was certainly not averse to being with him and wanted to enjoy that for as long as she was able. Once the summer season at Brighton was over, he would go back to the giddy social whirl in London and not return until next year. It was possible she might never see him again, which was, if only she would admit it, a painful prospect to contemplate.

She gave Mrs. Bowman the plate and the package for safekeeping and then walked along with Gavin, thrusting such a miserable thought to the back of her mind. There would be plenty of time for heartache. Today was her finest triumph. No other win would ever be as good.

"Does this win mean you are now out of favor with the prince?" she asked.

"I imagine so, but I'm in good company, I'm told. Brummel has returned to London after falling foul of the prince's pleasure."

"How has he contrived to do that?" she asked in astonishment. "I understood they were the greatest of friends."

"I'm given to understand the Beau made some slighting reference to the prince's girth."

She looked, for a moment, incredulous, and then she couldn't help but laugh. However, it was difficult for them to continue with any kind of conversation, for they were accosted by well-wishers at every step.

Lynette, accompanied by Lieutenant Spendlow and Miss Stanbury, hugged her sister as she expressed her delight. "Now that this race is won, you may have that gown," Flavia reminded her.

"Tush! That is of no consequence to me now. I have all I want. I fancy that we both do."

Emmeline told her brother, "You are so adept at riding racehorses, Gav, you should take up jockeying on a regular basis."

He laughed good-naturedly. "This is absolutely the last time. Nothing could be as good as today's win, for I'll never have a better horse than Beau to ride."

"The secret of your success was your own skill in waiting until the others flagged that insured the win," Lieutenant Spendlow pointed out.

"Your help has been most appreciated, sir," Flavia told him.

He smiled fondly at Lynette before answering, "It was my pleasure to assist, ma'am. After all, it is almost a family matter."

Lynette blushed, and Emmeline informed them in her irrepressible manner, "Lynette is trying to locate the gypsy who foretold her future with such accuracy so she may read my palm!"

The others laughed, and Gavin told her, "Don't let us keep you from so important a task."

When they moved off, laughing and chattering among themselves, Gavin looked at Flavia, and she was all at once shy again. "Do you not wish to join them?" he asked.

Suddenly she appeared wistful. "I have no need to consult a fortune-teller, sir. I have known my fate for a long time."

"You don't, I believe, possess the sight, so you couldn't possibly know."

"The gypsy had only to look at Lynette to know she would meet a man who would provide her with a brilliant future. There is nothing in the least remarkable about it."

"You are, I'm afraid, a cynic. It's as well you didn't apply that attitude to me today."

She cast him a sharp look. "You must know that I did."

"Then I must add bravery to the list of your admirable qualities. You do not, after all, play safe."

She bit her lip, hating herself for her transparency. They walked a little farther on without speaking, and just as she was about to take her leave of him, he drew her toward the back of the jockeys' tent.

Her eyes filled with a look of alarm. "Mr. Stanbury?"

"Miss Allenbrooke, I believe I have earned the right to do this."

Before she could question his meaning, he drew her into his arms and kissed her, gently at first and then with a growing passion that communicated itself to her with surprising ease. Startled for only a moment, Flavia threw her arms about him as his lips began to caress the soft skin at the base of her throat, and she succumbed gladly to his embrace, in which they remained locked until a footstep and the laughter of a passerby some considerable time later interrupted the idyll.

SEVENTEEN

When Mr. Stanbury had finally folded his neck cloth to his satisfaction, he turned to his valet for his opinion of it.

"Exceptional, sir," the fellow told him admiringly. "I admit to not liking in the least the way some young gentlemen have taken to wearing their neck cloths nowadays. Towering monstrosities, that is what they are. Some cannot turn their heads even slightly."

"They evidently believe that more is better."

The valet held out his master's forest green coat with mother-of-pearl buttons, but Gavin eyed it doubtfully for a moment before saying, "The midnight blue Bath coating, I think today, Tredeagar."

"As you wish, sir."

As the valet went to exchange the garment, Gavin asked, "Did you send for the curricle as I asked?"

"I did indeed, sir." He glanced out of the window briefly before returning with the midnight blue coat with gilt buttons. "Benton has it waiting outside now."

"Excellent, Tredeagar." The valet held out the coat and then smoothed it over his master's broad shoulders.

When Gavin went down the stairs, it was with a light step. He accepted his hat and gloves from the house steward, who commented to Cook a little later that he had never seen the master in such high gig.

When Gavin stepped outside the house, Benton came forward to hand him his whip. The young man paused on the curb to glance around at strollers and peddlers alike before he took a deep breath of sea air. Just as he was about to climb up on the box, he paused, catching sight of a pony and trap that came around the corner from the direction of the Steine at an unusually fast speed for a carriage in town. He stiffened with alarm when he recognized the driver as Flavia with Munnings at her side, and she was evidently in a state of considerable agitation.

He strode toward the trap as she brought it neatly to a halt just behind his curricle. Munnings leapt out and handed her down.

"Flavia, my dear," Gavin greeted her, looking a little concerned as he scrutinized her anguished face. "I was just about to call upon *you*."

"To gloat, no doubt," she accused.

"I beg your pardon?" was his bewildered response to her spleen.

"Judas," she hissed.

"Flavia!"

"You monster. I could kill you for this!"

"By Jupiter, for what?"

"How could I allow myself to be taken in by your moonshine when you plotted and planned to steal Beau from me all the while!"

The young man's face grew somewhat red. "What on earth are you babbling about?"

"Beau! He's gone. Gone! As if you didn't know where! I'll never, never see him again and all because I was cork-brained enough to believe in you!"

When she paused to choke back a sob, Gavin glanced at Munning's impassive features. "When? When did he go missing?"

"I don't know! You tell me."

"How could I?"

"Don't lie to me," she sobbed. "You insinuated your way into my life, earning my trust, only to rob me of Beau. I hate you!"

As Gavin briefly turned his face away, wondering how best to assure her of his innocence and, more importantly, think where he could find the colt, out of the corner of his eyes he saw her raising her whip, and in a flash he had gripped her wrist so tightly, she cried out, whether in frustration or pain he couldn't tell.

Her eyes filled with tears as she told him in a husky voice, "Yesterday was the happiest day of my life. How could you betray me so?"

Keeping her wrist tightly clamped in his hand, he removed the whip and then drew her back toward her trap. "Benton," he instructed the tiger, "drive Miss Allenbrooke back to Marston and make certain she stays there until I arrive."

"Yes, sir," the boy replied, sprinting to the trap.

"How dare you take so much upon yourself?" Flavia demanded, her eyes blazing with anger. "*I* shall decide when and how I return home, and I don't choose to do so now!"

"Oblige me in this," he said.

"You can't dismiss me so easily," she warned him, and the stubborn look that came onto her face made him sigh.

"I don't intend to," he told her, wiping her damp cheeks very gently with the tips of his gloved fingers. "Just go home and wait quietly if you want Beau back."

Flavia snapped her head away form his solicitousness, and she also resisted him as he forced her into the trap.

"Munnings," she called, and Gavin told her, "Munnings will stay and assist me."

"Now I see it all clearly," she gasped. "The two of you are in league in this business."

"Miss Allenbrooke!" Munnings exclaimed. "I never did nothing! Honest I didn't."

Before Flavia could climb down from the trap and berate them further, Gavin signaled his tiger to go and the boy whipped up the horse, leaving her looking furious as she gripped the side of the trap with no option except to do as she was told. As Benton maneuvered the trap into the road, Gavin strode back to the curricle and wasted no more time in indicating that Munnings should climb up beside him.

The groom hesitated, and Gavin snapped, "If you please, Mr. Munnings," and the man, recognizing the voice of authority, obeyed at last.

"Don't know what assistance I can give," he muttered as Gavin drove around the corner of Marine Parade to the mews where his horses and carriages were kept.

A groom came forward to hold the horses' heads, looking a little surprised at seeing the curricle return so soon after it had been taken out.

"Saddle Rocket for me," Gavin told another of the grooms, "one for yourself and one for Mr. Munnings." Then he turned to Flavia's head groom and said, "While the horses are being made ready for us, be pleased to tell me all you know about Beau's abduction."

Munnings feigned astonishment. "Me, sir? I don't know any more than Miss Allenbrooke told you. Young Walt went into 'is stall this mornin' and found 'im gone. Me steal Beau, sir? You've got me fair betwattled."

Gavin fingered his whip thoughtfully as the grooms brought out three glossy-coated horses and began to saddle them. "I think I should warn you I mean to know without any further delay whom you assisted in stealing the colt. I'm a very impatient man, and you should also be told that I have taken lessons in pugilism from Gentleman Jackson himself in his Bond Street saloon, of which you've no doubt heard."

The groom began to look uncomfortable as his eyes darted around the yard for a means of escape. There was none. Gavin stood foursquare in the way of the only exit.

"Well, Munnings?" he said, pushing open the door to an empty stall and slapping his riding whip against the palm of his hand. "Do you tell me now what I wish to know, or do you tell me in a very short time?"

"Give 'im a facer, sir," Gavin's groom called out as he tightened the girths of the saddle he'd put on one of the horses.

Munnings fingered his hat nervously and averted his eyes. "It was Sir Percy Cavander, sir."

"You don't surprise me in the least," the young man replied. "I thought this business bore his imprint. Such deviousness is beyond the prince. And you, sir, are a total disgrace to your calling."

"Now, just 'old 'ard there, sir. It's all very well you saying so, but Miss Allenbrooke don't pay much. Sir Percy's offer was too tempting to resist and not like to come my way again in an 'urry."

Gavin prodded him with his whip toward the horses that were now made ready for them, and the man moved nervously in their direction.

"You should have sought a better-paid post rather than betray Miss Allenbrooke in such a despicable manner. Lack of the ready can't explain your dastardly attack on one of your own colleagues."

"Didn't intend to 'arm 'im, sir, only keep the lad out of the race."

"You were successful. You may ride the gray."

Gavin watched as Munnings climbed up onto the horse. "Where are you taking me?"

"We are all going to pay a call upon Sir Percy at his house in Hopedean. Don't think to evade me either, Munnings. I think you're aware by now that I can outride you if the need arises, and I shan't be so indulgent of you if I'm obliged to go to that trouble."

All three rode in silence until they reached Sir Percy's house just outside the town on the edge of the Downs. There appeared to be a look of satisfaction on his face as he walked away from the stable yard, but it faded abruptly when he saw Gavin and his companions ride into it. He exhibited some alarm, too, when his gaze came to rest on the groom.

"Stanbury, to what do I owe this visit?" he asked as the three visitors dismounted and faced him.

"I believe you know, Cavander. I'm looking for a piece of stolen property."

192

Sir Percy had recovered his alarm, and he smiled now. "I scarce think this is the place to look." His eyes narrowed then. "Are you, by any chance, foxed, sir?"

"You must be to believe you can get away with such a monstrous robbery." He nodded to his groom. "Berry, be so good as to search the stalls."

"Search all you like," Sir Percy invited. "I don't know what you seek, but whatever it is you won't find it here."

"If I don't, you will tell me exactly where I can find Brighton Beau."

"Brighton Beau!" the other man exclaimed. "So that is the matter. How shocking!" Then he laughed. "I assure you, sir, I take it amiss that you seek him here. If the notion were not so ludicrous, I'd call you out for your temerity."

Just then Berry came across the stable yard, shaking his head. "There, you see," Sir Percy said, pulling at his coat in indignation. "What did I tell you?"

"Be certain I shan't leave until you tell me where you've hidden him, Cavander, and if it takes time, it will be all the worse for you for prolonging Miss Allenbrooke's pain."

Sir Percy made to go past him. "Stay as long as you please, Stanbury. It's all the same to me."

"There's some loose boxes around the other side of the stable yard," Munnings murmured.

Sir Percy turned on him furiously. "Hell and damnation! What a fool you are! I'll have your hide for this, Munnings." He began to wave his arms around like the sails of a windmill. "Get off my property, all of you!"

"When I have retrieved Miss Allenbrooke's property," Gavin insisted, and he appeared to be more relaxed now.

"There is nothing here that does not belong to me."

"Then you have nothing whatsoever to fear."

Berry had run off to search for the additional stabling, and as Sir Percy fumed helplessly in the yard, a few moments later he returned, smiling broadly and leading Beau out by his harness.

" 'E's come to no 'arm, sir. Bright as ever, that's Beau. Greeted me like an old friend, 'e did."

Looking satisfied, Gavin asked, "What did you say about calling me out, Cavander?"

"That is my horse," the man declared, but he looked considerably discomforted. "Velvet Star. Be pleased to return him to his stall immediately."

The colt whinnied happily and nuzzled Gavin when he saw him. The young man stroked him as he told Sir Percy, "If that's true, you can produce the documentation while my man saddles him."

Sir Percy just continued to glower angrily as the groom took the saddle off Rocket and put it on the racehorse. "You'll regret this, Stanbury," he warned.

"On the contrary, it's you who'll regret this despicable piece of trickery when His Royal Highness comes to hear of it. I doubt that you'll be received at the Pavilion or Carlton House, or indeed in any drawing room in the future."

Berry checked the girths and Gavin climbed into the saddle, looking down on Sir Percy and Munnings. "You can consider yourself fortunate that social ostracism is the only punishment you'll receive. I doubt that Miss Allenbrooke will have the law on you, although I cannot guarantee that. She

194

was in a towering rage this morning, as you might imagine."

Berry mounted his horse and took the harness of the one Munnings had ridden while Gavin took hold of Rocket's harness. Seeing they were about to depart, Munnings started forward and asked, "What about me, sir? How will I get back to Marston?"

"You don't," Gavin told him as he dug in his spurs. "Miss Allenbrooke has just dismissed you from her service!"

While the drama unfolded at Sir Percy Cavander's stables, Flavia prowled restlessly around the parlor, twisting her damp handkerchief in her fingers, while being watched worriedly by her aunt and sister.

After giving Mrs. Bowman an imploring look, Lynette ventured to suggest, "Shall I request Timothy to dispatch some of his men to search for Beau? He cannot be far away, I fancy."

Flavia laughed mirthlessly. "What a fine spectacle that would make. The Prince Regent's Own Royal Hussars searching his stables for a stolen horse. I wonder what measure of success they would be like to achieve."

"We cannot be certain Beau is in the royal stables," Mrs. Bowman ventured. "There have been so many others who've been interested in acquiring him. Engaging a Bow Street Runner might be an option."

"That would sap our slender resources long before he was found," Flavia told her.

Mrs. Bowman looked equally distraught. "You mustn't be too disheartened. Beau may be valuable to others as a racehorse, but he can't be raced by anyone else. He is too recognizable."

"It won't be too difficult to disguise him for someone determined enough," Flavia answered. "We ladies have a number of ways to alter our coloring and features. Whoever masterminded the theft would be able to disguise him adequately."

There was a momentary silence before Mrs. Bowman cleared her throat and ventured, "You shouldn't have rattled off to Brighton this morning, dear. We cannot be certain Mr. Stanbury is involved in the theft."

"Aunt Bella, I don't want you ever to mention that gentleman's name again in my presence."

"I think you're being most unfair," Lynette accused. "You were wrong about Tim. You could certainly be wrong about Mr. Stanbury, who has been only obliging to us."

"For good reason," Flavia retorted, "as we have now been unfortunate enough to discover."

When Lynette came across the room toward her sister, she was uncharacteristically agitated. "You know everything about horses, Flavia, but, I regret to say, nothing about gentlemen."

Flavia's head drooped and her aunt cast her a shrewd look. "I'm persuaded your sister isn't merely grieving for the loss of Beau. She has become fond of Mr. Stanbury."

"I feared as much was true," Lynette acknowledged, "even though it isn't easy to tell with Flavia. It pains me to think your heart is broken, dearest. I know how I would feel in such circumstances."

"I was so wary of him," her sister admitted. "I knew very well he might use his charm to persuade me to part with Beau. Oh, yes, I was aware of the danger and I felt sure I could outwit him, but he still contrived to steal my heart. How could I have been such a chucklehead?"

"When one falls in love, reason flies away," Mrs. Bowman acknowledged sagely, "so don't, I beg of you, be so hard on yourself."

"What is worse, I behaved with such a want of delicacy. That is what grieves me most of all."

"Flavia dearest," Lynette begged, "you mustn't torment yourself in this manner."

"I've made such a cake of myself, it's not to be borne, and now I've lost Beau, too."

"Don't give up. . . ." Lynette begged.

Flavia turned to look at her sister. "How could I have acted such a goose-cap to believe he preferred my company to that of Lady Allerton?"

Before either of the other two ladies could find some comfort to offer her, the sound of hoofbeats could be heard approaching the house.

As Flavia peered out of the window gloomily, Mrs. Bowman asked, almost fearfully, "Who is it, dearest?"

Her niece didn't reply. She just turned on her heel and ran out of the room, leaving Mrs. Bowman to glance out of the window herself. "Why, it's Mr. Stanbury, and he's riding Beau! Oh, my goodness . . ."

Just as Gavin rode the colt to a standstill outside the house, his own horse drawn along behind, Flavia came running out of the house. As she became suddenly aware of her unbecoming behavior, she checked herself in the doorway before walking toward them with more decorum. When she was at last certain her racehorse was truly restored to her, she paused on the gravel, staring at him in astonishment before she went to put her arms around the colt's neck.

"I'm so glad to see you," she murmured, fighting back her tears.

"If only you would say that to me," Gavin told her wryly as he dismounted, and she turned to him at last.

"Truly, I don't know what to say to you."

"You might ask me where he's been." When she merely bit her lip, he told her where he had found the colt.

"So he was not at the Pavilion after all?"

"Whatever his faults, Flavia, His Royal Highness would not sanction dishonest dealings."

She clenched her fists and struck out in the air with them. "Sir Percy! The muckworm!" So great was her emotion, she turned away in order to compose herself. "I am more indebted to you than I can say, and more ashamed than ever in my life before." Then she covered her face with her hands. "How can you ever forgive me for all I said to you this morning?"

"I shall have to give that matter some thought," he told her, and then he gently pried her hands away from her face and forced her to look at him. "Actually it's easy. All it takes is for you to do me the honor of becoming my wife."

Her eyes opened wide. "You're asking me to ... marry you?"

"Yes," he answered with a laugh. "So to be sure of my forgiveness for being falsely accused of *theft*, don't refuse me."

"You can't be serious. I mean ... there's Lady Allerton. . . ."

He kept her hands tightly clasped in his own.

198

"There is no one but you, my dear heart, the only woman I love. *Will* you marry me?"

Her face was suddenly transformed by a smile that lit up her entire countenance with joy. "Yes. Oh, yes, I will! I love you. What a goose-cap I've been."

"The most delightful goose-cap I've ever encountered."

He held her tightly against him, smiling at Mrs. Bowman and Lynette, who had been watching from the top step of the house. It was then that Mrs. Bowman turned and ushered Lynette inside the house, closing the door behind them and leaving the two lovers alone together, except for Brighton Beau and Rocket, who nuzzled each other in apparent approval of their owners' coming nuptials.